# Neo-Anarchist's The Guide to NORTH AMERICA™

1981 10th Anniversary 1991

FASA CORPORATION

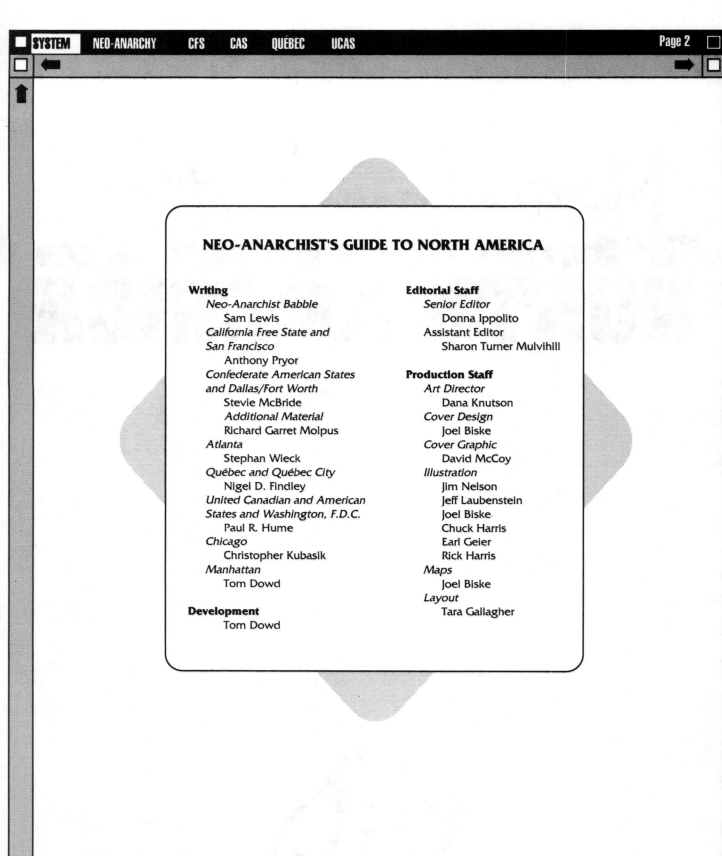

# NEO-ANARCHIST'S GUIDE TO NORTH AMERICA

**Writing**

*Neo-Anarchist Babble*
   Sam Lewis
*California Free State and San Francisco*
   Anthony Pryor
*Confederate American States and Dallas/Fort Worth*
   Stevie McBride
   *Additional Material*
   Richard Garret Molpus
*Atlanta*
   Stephan Wieck
*Québec and Québec City*
   Nigel D. Findley
*United Canadian and American States and Washington, F.D.C.*
   Paul R. Hume
*Chicago*
   Christopher Kubasik
*Manhattan*
   Tom Dowd

**Development**
   Tom Dowd

**Editorial Staff**

*Senior Editor*
   Donna Ippolito
Assistant Editor
   Sharon Turner Mulvihill

**Production Staff**

*Art Director*
   Dana Knutson
*Cover Design*
   Joel Biske
*Cover Graphic*
   David McCoy
*Illustration*
   Jim Nelson
   Jeff Laubenstein
   Joel Biske
   Chuck Harris
   Earl Geier
   Rick Harris
*Maps*
   Joel Biske
*Layout*
   Tara Gallagher

Published by
FASA Corporation
P.O. Box 6930
Chicago, IL 60680

# TABLE OF CONTENTS

## INTRODUCTION

The **Neo-Anarchists Guide to North America** is a supplement for the **Shadowrun** game system. It is a guide to the major nations of North America: California Free State, the Confederated American States, Quebéc, and the United Canadian and American States circa the year 2050. Much of the information is in the form of **shadow** information: opinions and evaluations of individuals who may be biased in their point of view. The gamemaster may decide whether to treat comments, observations, and information as valid. It is for the gamemaster to decide (and his players to discover) the accuracy of the information.

WELCOME TO...

## SHADOWLAND

> "I have taken all knowledge to be my province."
> — Francis Bacon, 1592

**CATEGORY**                                                    **GO TO:**

Message Base/Mail System                                         ( OK )

Special Categories/ Topics (SIGS)                                ( OK )

Library Archive                                                  ( OK )

Information Base — SPECIAL FEATURES! (Limited Duration Posting)

    ARES Winter Catalog 2052-53 (Annotated)            ( OK )

    Rigger Black Book 2053 (NEW!)                       ( OK )

    North American Compilation (A MUST!)                **( OK )**

    Paterson's Paranormal Creatures of North America (Annotated)   ( OK )

    Paterson's Paranormal Creatures of Europe (Annotated)          ( OK )

    Seattle Travel Guide (Shadow Edition—Current 09/52)            ( OK )

    United Kingdom/ Western Europe Compilation (En Route)   ( NOT AVAILABLE )

    UCAS Data Systems File Dump (HOT! Matrix/VR data!)             ( OK )

Problem? Drop CONTROL a line!

## NEO-ANARCHIST GUIDE TO NORTH AMERICA

California Free State                                            ( OK )

    San Francisco, CFS                                   ( OK )

Confederated States of America                                   ( OK )

    Atlanta, CAS (Capital)                               ( OK )

    Dallas/Fort Worth, CAS                               ( OK )

Denver National Cooperative                                      ( FILES CORRUPTED )

Native American Nations                                          ( FILES CORRUPTED )

Tir Tairngire                                                    ( FILES CORRUPTED )

    Portland, TT                                         ( FILES CORRUPTED )

United Canadian & American States                                ( OK )

    Chicago, UCAS                                        ( OK )

    New York, UCAS                                       ( OK )

    Washington FDC, UCAS

**DOWNLOAD ALL?**   **OK**

**NOTE FROM CONTROL—**
**Anyone with any knowledge regarding sabotage to this
system should contact me ASAP. Censorship will not be tolerated!**

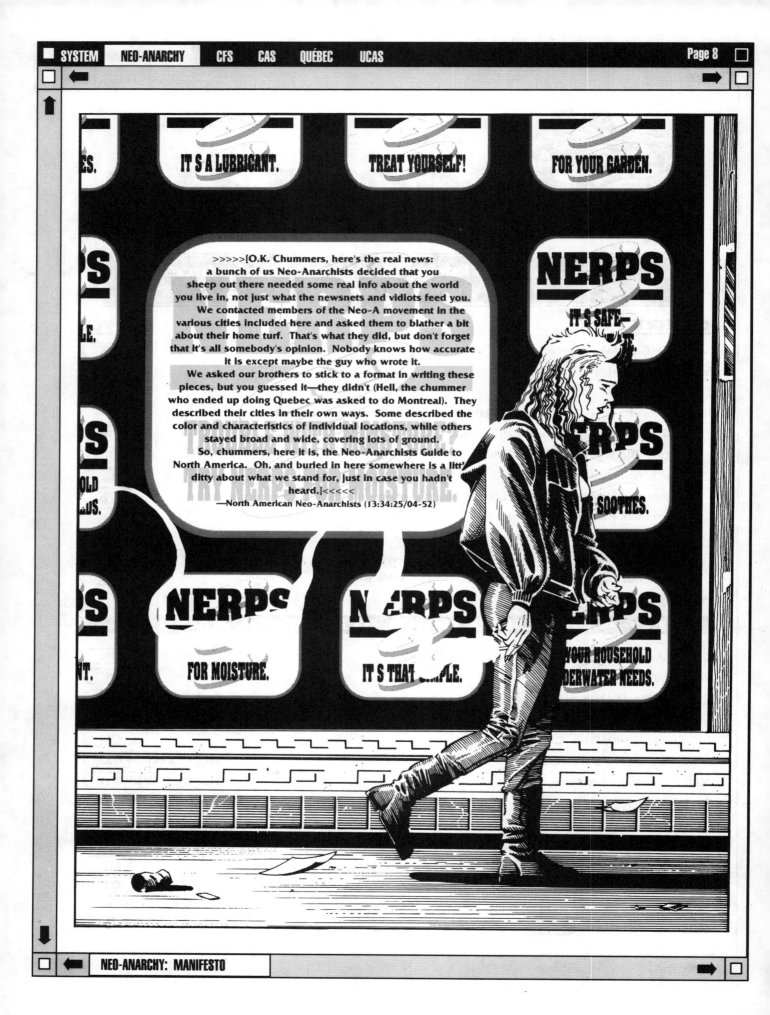

>>>>>[O.K. Chummers, here's the real news:
a bunch of us Neo-Anarchists decided that you
sheep out there needed some real info about the world
you live in, not just what the newsnets and vidiots feed you.
We contacted members of the Neo-A movement in the
various cities included here and asked them to blather a bit
about their home turf. That's what they did, but don't forget
that it's all somebody's opinion. Nobody knows how accurate
it is except maybe the guy who wrote it.
We asked our brothers to stick to a format in writing these
pieces, but you guessed it—they didn't (Hell, the chummer
who ended up doing Quebec was asked to do Montreal). They
described their cities in their own ways. Some described the
color and characteristics of individual locations, while others
stayed broad and wide, covering lots of ground.
So, chummers, here it is, the Neo-Anarchists Guide to
North America. Oh, and buried in here somewhere is a litt'
ditty about what we stand for, just in case you hadn't
heard.]<<<<<
—North American Neo-Anarchists (13:34:25/04-52)

# A Social, Economic, and Political Manifesto for the Fifties and Beyond

*Little Bunny Frou Frou hopping through the forest,*
*Scooping up the field mice and bopping them on the head*

*Along came the Good Fairy and this is what she said...*

*Little Bunny Frou Frou I don't want to see you*
*Scooping up the field mice and bopping them on the head*

*I'll give you three chances, and if you don't stop, I'll turn you into a goon.*
                                                    —Late 20th century nursery rhyme

Nice little nursery rhyme, isn't it? You hear it, or something like it, every time you run into a group of kids playing on the street. Nothing too much to the story. Just a rabbit beating up on some poor little mice who gets threatened with punishment by a metahuman mage. In the end, the errant rabbit does not change his ways and must take his licks.

But this childish song zeroes in on what is wrong with the society we live in...coercion. Corporate coercion, economic coercion, governmental coercion, majority coercion, minority coercion—this is what constrains and enslaves humanity. No one can escape it, not the squatters, not the sararimen, not the corporate executives, not even the vaunted shadowrunners. Coercion dooms SINners and SINless alike to sterile and empty lives, years of no hope, no goals, and no end.

Neo-anarchism is the means by which we humans can throw off our chains and live rich, fulfilling lives. Only through neo-anarchism can humanity transcend its current, degenerated state and rise up from the mire.

Neo-Anarchists are not the crazed bomb-throwers that simsense productions about pre-revolutionary Russia like to portray. Nor are they neo-Ludites or eco-terrorists. Neo-Anarchists believe in one overriding principle: that no individual has the right to coerce another to yield to his desires. Neo-Anarchists believe that unanimous consent, freely and willingly given, is the only just way to govern any society or group of individuals.

## ECONOMICS OF NEO-ANARCHISM

Economics have driven society since humans first began to trade with one another. To control its economic activity, mankind has developed feudalism, capitalism, socialism, communism, and now corporate feudalism. To control its economic system, man has invented kingdoms, republics, dictatorships, bureaucracies, and megacorp boards. Just as these economic and political structures all began with one goal in mind, so it is with Neo-Anarchism. The goal of any Neo-Anarchist economic structure is to maximize social welfare.

In economics, social welfare is measured by *utility*. Utility is a term coined in the 18th century as a unit measuring the satisfaction an individual receives from consuming goods and services. The more goods and services an individual consumes, the higher the satisfaction or utility. The study of how an individual derives satisfaction from the consumption of goods and services is known as utility theory.

One important precept of utility theory is that an individual can gain the same level of satisfaction from consuming a variety of goods and services. For example, an individual experiences the same level of utility from consuming 6 units of Goods A and 4 units of Goods B, or consuming 7 units of Goods A and 3 units of Goods B. The individual would not differentiate between the two mixtures of goods (see Figure 1). The graph represents mixtures of the two goods that would supply the same level of utility to the individual. The higher-numbered curves represent higher levels of utility to the individual, because he is consuming more of both goods.

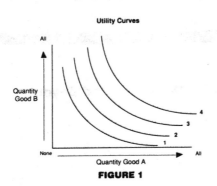

**FIGURE 1**

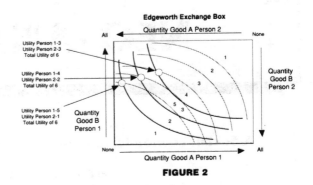

**FIGURE 2**

A second precept states that social welfare cannot be at a maximum if, through some reallocation of the society's goods and services, one person can enjoy an advantage over another. When reallocation of goods and services is possible without disadvantaging some members of society, the system has reached what is known as a Pareto optimal point. All economic systems claim to seek to achieve Pareto optimality.

Achieving Pareto optimality is the driving force behind neo-anarchist economic systems. However, the economic system cannot be coercive. The only non-coercive economic system is one of pure competition. This is not the competition of the megacorps, with their collusions and hostile takeovers. Such trade between individuals and business has no losers, only winners, and therefore will be entered into freely by all participants.

The belief that any bargain or trade must have a winner or a loser has been perpetrated on the masses for centuries. It is simply false. Trades, freely entered into and agreed to, result in both sides gaining increased utility. Thus both parties win, and the society attains Pareto optimality.

This system is easy to grasp in the model of a simple, two-person, two-good economy. Each individual gains various levels of utility by consuming various mixes of the two goods. Because this is a closed economy, however, if one individual consumes all of Good A, the second individual cannot consume any of Good A, and the same holds true for Good B. The graph below shows utility charts drawn to reflect this situation; this is known as an Edgeworth Exchange Box. Note that the utility curves of the two individuals intersect. As one set of curves increases in value, the other set gets smaller. It is at this point that most individuals conclude that trades must have a winner and a loser, for one individual cannot increase his utility without decreasing the utility of another. Thus, according to the argument, trade and competitive economic systems cannot achieve Pareto optimality.

This is only true if one individual coerces the other, forcing the latter to give up so much of his goods that he moves to a lower utility curve. This will not happen if no coercion is allowed. Trading will still occur. Any mix of goods between the two individuals lies on a utility curve for both individuals. Therefore, these curves must either intersect or lie on a tangent to one another. If the curves intersect, then a "trading zone" exists, in which both individuals will gain an advantage (be on a higher utility curve) if they exchange goods. In addition, the total utility for the society has been increased to its maximum (Pareto optimal) point.

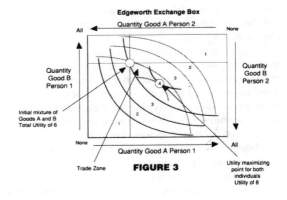

**FIGURE 3**

From this conclusion, two centuries of economic theory goes on to prove mathematically and empirically that an economic system based on pure competition, or free markets, will always arrive at a Pareto optimal point. Additionally, such a system produces its goods and services in an economically efficient manner, resulting in the highest possible utility for society as a whole. For a Neo-Anarchist, a pure-competition economy has a major advantage, as it is by nature non-coercive. However, an economy based on pure competition can only be achieved by meeting the following four conditions.

## NUMEROUS PARTICIPANTS

Many buyers and sellers must exist for the goods and services offered. Only one or two buyers or sellers in the market results in collusion and monopolistic practices, both of which are coercive and economically inefficient.

## HOMOGENEITY OF PRODUCT

The buyer does not differentiate between the goods or services offered. Each seller's product is of equal quality and worth to the buyer.

## FREEDOM OF ENTRY AND EXIT

New firms can enter into the market to sell a good or drop out of the market without any special impediments.

## PERFECT INFORMATION

All buyers and sellers are well-informed about the available products and their prices.

## ACHIEVING PARETO OPTIMALITY

The fact that pure competition achieves both Pareto optimality and efficiently uses the resources available to the population is widely accepted. The problem has always been achieving the four necessary conditions. These conditions have always been viewed as impossible to achieve in the real world. It has also been assumed that perfect competition could not provide Pareto optimal solutions in the face of natural monopolies and public services. These objections provided justification for the creation and maintenance of the democratic and communist governmental systems of the 20th century.

The advent of cheap computer and robotic manufacturing technology, easily accessible information-processing, and instantaneous worldwide telecommunications have made it technologically possible to meet each of the four conditions. This was accepted as early as 2009 and disposes of the first objection to Neo-Anarchism. The fall of communism in 1989 and the steady erosion of governmental power prove that pure competition is a workable and natural state for humanity.

The second argument cited against an economic system of pure competition is that of natural monopolies. Effectively, natural monopolies use technologies that have a continuously declining marginal cost. The more produced, the lower the cost per unit. Thus, any producer able to get a jump on another will be able to outproduce its competitors and drive them out of business. The surviving company can then charge monopolistic prices—a coercive and non-Pareto optimal state.

Big government was supposed to be the instrument that would prevent the formation of such monopolies. In the 19th and 20th centuries, governments controlled power utilities, airlines, telephone companies, television networks, taxicabs, and a host of other so-called natural monopolies, all in the name of preserving Pareto optimality. But Pareto optimality was not achieved through government regulation; by the end of the 20th century, many of these natural monopolies were deregulated. The doomsayers denounced this development, but their fears never materialized. The advanced manufacturing techniques currently available prevent any industry or business from achieving a natural monopoly.

The final argument in favor of governmental control of business is public goods and the free-rider problem. Public goods are goods or services whose consumption cannot be limited only to those individuals who pay for them. Providing the good to one individual means providing it to all individuals. Roads, street lighting, sanitation systems, and national defense all fall under public goods. The problem with public goods is that no one wants to pay for them; they want to get a free ride, letting others pay for the service. This is the justification for taxes. Taxes force people to pay for public services at levels that do not reflect the utility received from the service.

But taxes are not necessary. Many so-called public goods can be provided on a user-fee basis. Other public goods, such as education, can be financed by a simple system in which an individual pays according to how valuable he considers the service. After people vote on the need for a project, the cost of the project is determined. The people then decide how much they are willing to donate to the project. The total amount pledged is posted. A second round of voting is held, and the voters are asked to pledge again. If, by the end of the third round of voting, the pledged amount does not equal the cost of the project, the project is abandoned. An interesting phenomenon occurs when using this system. The first round pledges are usually low, as each individual attempts to get a free ride. By the second and third rounds, people recognize that the project may have to be abandoned if the funds do not become available and so they will pledge an amount reflecting what the program is really worth to them. Allowing for negative pledges (i.e., an individual wishes to be compensated if the project succeeds because it will harm him in some way), then any public work can succeed. In this way, coercive taxation can be eliminated in any Neo-Anarchist society.

## CALL TO ACTION

Over the last 200 years, mankind has moved inexorably toward a decentralized and Neo-Anarchist society, a society in which no member is ever coerced, a society in which the individual, not a government or corporation, is free to decide what is in his best interest. The economic and social rationale for coercive governmental or corporate control of an individual's life is no longer valid. As technological advances drove mankind's economic and political systems from feudalism to capitalism to today's corporate feudalism, so will they naturally drive mankind to neo-anarchism.

A Neo-Anarchist society has one overriding principle: no rational, adult being can be coerced into performing actions to which he has not acquiesced freely and willingly. With that principle in mind, the individual will be free to follow his goals and dreams.

The current megacorporations will never wish to give up their power, their hold on society. Though they embrace technologies that reinforce their monopolistic hold on society, they suppress the technology that could break their hold. With state-of-the-art technology, no industry in this world requires megacorporations to efficiently produce and sell goods. Dismantling the megafactories would mean dismantling the corporations' power base, and so they must resist the change.

Neo-Anarchists must break this hold that the corporations have on humanity. Once we do so, a Neo-Anarchist society will naturally arise. But in breaking this hold, we must not destroy the very technology that will give us the Neo-Anarchistic state for which we long. Rather than bombs and bullets, Neo-Anarchists must use the more subtle yet powerful tool of information. By exposing the lies and corruption of the corporations to the masses, we will show that the social contract between the governed and governors is invalid. When the masses are fully informed, when the current feudal capitalistic society has ground to a halt, then will a Neo-Anarchist paradise surely arise.

# CALIFORNIA FREE STATE

So long isolated from the old United States and torn by internal strife, the people of California declared their independence in 2037, hoping at last to become masters of their destiny. Whether this dream will ever be realized is doubtful, for much of the California Free State is currently under foreign occupation and the central government lacks any real authority. Only the people of California, men and women of unquestioned courage and perseverance, will determine whether this new state can survive and prosper.

## HISTORY

Once the most populous, prosperous, and heavily urbanized state in the United States, California was hard-hit by the upheavals of the early 21st century. First came the Anti-Indian Riots of 2009, followed the next year by the outbreak of the devastating VITAS plague. In 2011, the first elves and dwarfs were born, signalling the start of Unexplained Genetic Syndrome (UGE). The people struggled to recover from these crises over the next ten years, only to stagger again when UGE suddenly began to metamorphose humans into orks and trolls. In California, as elsewhere, thousands of normal humans underwent a change of physical form so drastic that their fellow humans considered them to be twisted caricatures of humanity. It was in this climate of bewilderment and unrest that the California governor overreacted. Declaring martial law, he ordered a state-wide roundup of the changed humans, now known as metahumans. Many fled, but many others fought and died rather than surrender their freedom.

Metahumans were the victims of widespread violence, especially in outlying communities. Many elves and dwarfs, those metahumans most resembling normal humans, banded together into protective societies, or formed their own communities, but most orks and trolls fled into the wilderness. There, they formed the basis of the warrior tribes that still inhabit the California wilds.

At the height of the anti-metahuman hysteria, VITAS struck again, further shattering the social order. The disease spared no one—rich, poor, human and Awakened perished by the millions.

As in other parts of the world, the shared suffering of the plague made California's xenophobia subside. Numerous incidents of mutual cooperation and kindness helped improve relations between the subspecies. In one such instance, an ork-troll go-gang assaulted the stronghold of a local biotech corp that was holding back VITAS vaccine in order to sell it at inflated prices. The metas scattered the defending corp troops, seized the vaccine, and distributed it to the people free of charge.

The U.S. government soon became the target of Californians' anger. The excesses of martial law and the bureaucratic mishandling of distribution of the VITAS vaccine combined to create a deep, steadily growing resentment. The Treaty of Denver had physically isolated the state from the rest of the country, a separation that now took on political and social ramifications. To many, California was a tinder box just waiting to spark.

Those sparks began to fly in 2030, when almost every local election included a referendum calling for secession from the United States. Support for secession grew quickly, as did the federal government's protests against it. Californians became even more enraged when the Act of Union of 2030 merged the United States of America with the Dominion of Canada to form the Union of Canadian and American States. Californians saw themselves becoming ever more isolated as the contiguous size of the rest of the country grew.

Lacking power in the Senate, the California representatives to the U.S. House of Representatives showed their anger by working diligently to make President Andrew MacAlister's term in office pure hell. They also incurred the wrath of most other members of the UCAS government, who thought they were behaving like spoiled children.

Another threat of secession occurred in 2036. Displeased with what they perceived as MacAlister's preferential treatment of the midwestern and northeastern sprawl zones, the southern states of the UCAS threatened to withdraw from the union. MacAlister, in his oft-quoted "Eat My Shorts" speech, responded that if the southern states walked, there would be hell to pay. A few days later, ten southern states seceded from the UCAS.

His bluff called, MacAlister eventually agreed to and signed the Treaty of Richmond with the rebel states, establishing peaceful boundaries and a working political and economic relationship between the two countries.

Seeing MacAlister give in to pressure from the ten states that came to form the Confederated American States, California state legislators decided to play the same game. "Unofficially" supporting the new secession

Proposition 129 on the ballet, California's representatives in Washington began to push for heavy economic and political concessions. MacAlister, bruised from the CAS debacle, called the Governor of California, Nelson Treacle, and told him that if the state voted to secede he would hang them out to dry.

Proposition 129, which would require ratification by the state legislators and Governor Treacle, passed the popular vote a few days later. The following day, the state lawmakers approved the legislation dissolving California's political bond to the UCAS. Secession from the union lacked only the governor's signature, but Treacle was in Africa at the time.

MacAlister moved swiftly. Upon hearing the news from California, he went before Congress and declared, under a skewed interpretation of Article IV, Section 3 of the UCAS Constitution, that California no longer qualified as a member of the UCAS.

The reaction was intense and immediate. Lieutenant Governor Marshall called a press conference to announce that Proposition 129 would not be signed into law, and that the governor was cutting short his photo-safari to handle the crisis. In the meantime, MacAlister's cronies distributed clichéd sound-bites about California wanting to play with the big boys and then complaining about the rules. They also stated that secession, based on the vote for Proposition 129, was the popular choice and that such a mandate could not be ignored.

Federal resources were immediately withdrawn from California, beginning with military forces based in the state. Naval forces were redeployed to either Seattle or Hawaii, while air and land assets were transferred to other UCAS bases. It is of some note that certain of those "assets" vanished during the transfer, perhaps deliberately misplaced so that California would not be left defenseless. However it happened, the errors were fortuitous.

Government services, such as the FBI, FTC, FAA, and IRS were suspended in California. Though the people rejoiced to see the IRS disappear, they were not happy to learn that California residents no longer qualified for Social Security benefits because they were not UCAS citizen. The UCAS maintained veteran's benefits, however, no doubt to ensure the continued support of the UCAS military.

In the midst of this turmoil, the elven nation of Tir Tairngire seceded from the Native American Nations. Incorporating most of Washington State, Tir Tairngire claimed land extending down into California to approximately Redding. The newly declared High Prince and the Council Lords of Tir Tairngire ordered all non-elves to leave their new domain within 30 days. Though the migration of non-elves was massive, it was tempered by the fact that many of California's elven community had already migrated north from the vast southern sprawls. A long-planned conspiracy? Perhaps.

Governor Treacle immediately mobilized what was left of the National Guard and moved north. Though frightened by the prospect of Tir Tairngire wielding even a fraction of the power of the Ghost Dance, Treacle wanted to show that California, even without UCAS, was a force to be reckoned with. He, of course, had forgotten Aztlan.

At the time of California's Proposition 129, many people in Southern California cities, especially San Diego, were voicing their own differences with the local government. This was especially true of San Diego's Latino population whose deep desire was to become part of Aztlan.

As California forces moved north to staging areas along the Trinity and Little Cow Rivers, an Aztlan light armor division rolled into San Diego, annexing it and the surrounding area. Seeing his state trapped in a kind of giant pincer, Treacle appealed to President MacAlister for his state's readmission to the UCAS. MacAlister promised to place the matter before Congress the following Monday, but advised Treacle that the Technocratic Party was conducting a filibuster over the price of plastic. In all likelihood, the matter of California's readmission might not come up until much later that week.

Fearful that Aztlan would perceive its easy occupation of San Diego as a sign of California's weakness, Treacle made semi-covert overtures to Japan, many of whose megacorporations had divisions and assets in California. An Aztlan takeover would jeopardize those assets, given Aztlan's penchant for nationalizing corporations. It was Treacle's intent that news of his discussion reach both Washington and Atlanta in hopes that one or the other would offer assistance. His plan almost worked.

Troubled at the prospect of increased Japanese presence on the North American continent, both the CAS and UCAS governments began to formalize responses to the Aztlan threat. Earlier in 2035, the CAS had nearly come to blows with Aztlan over Texas, but the CAS had not ultimately dared Aztlan for fear that NAN would take sides against them. Because Aztlan was obviously the aggressor this time, the leaders of the CAS hoped NAN would stay out of the fight. The Japanese, however, moved faster than anyone anticipated.

While the CAS and UCAS governments deliberated their states of preparedness and the level of opposition to be expected from Aztlan, Japanese troops arrived in California.

In the early morning hours of February 7, 2037, two Japanese Imperial Marine light divisions arrived by air at San Francisco's International Airport and the Alameda Naval Air Station, all but abandoned since the UCAS pullout. It is possible that one of the two light divisions was destined for Los Angeles, but the presence of a UCAS carrier battlegroup clustered around the aging *Theodore Roosevelt*, conducting air training operations nearby, may have persuaded them to change their plans.

Whatever the original plan, Japanese troops were now in San Francisco.

Aztlan did not attack, but neither did they give up San Diego. Meanwhile, the Japanese refused to assist California's attempts to regain it. The leaders of the Tir seemed content with their current border, even making diplomatic gestures to begin restricted trade relations with their southern neighbor.

The CAS and UCAS governments looked at each other, cursed a lot, but ultimately did nothing.

Years passed. The occupation continued, and was eventually accepted as a distasteful, but inevitable fact of life. The government in Sacramento exercised less and less control over outlying counties and towns, leaving most of them responsible for their own defense. Though free, California remained a rough, dangerous place, with civil authority extending only to the urbanized areas of the coast and central valley.

## CURRENT SITUATION

California Free State is a bizarre amalgam of big-city sophistication and small-town independence. Surrounded by neighbors who are, at best, indifferent to their existence, most Californians are fiercely independent, ready to defend themselves at an instant's notice.

Cities remain at the center of California culture. Los Angeles, despite severe depopulation by VITAS, is still the media capital of previous years, being the leading producer of simsense recordings and trideo programs. Any aspiring actor, writer, or director must "do time" in L.A. if he wishes to succeed. Los Angeles society is as permissive and decadent as ever, with massive abuse of dreamchips, rampant debauchery, and excessive alcohol abuse the rule for most of the upper class.

Beyond L.A.'s urban core, the go-gangs rule, fighting turf wars of ever-increasing severity, with the legions of the poor and homeless caught in the middle. Chipped-out misfits who long ago forgot why they were fighting have reduced many outlying regions, such as Griffith Park and Chavez Ravine, to wastelands of burned tenements, broken roadway, and abandoned shopping malls.

Los Angeles' cops are the best-trained and equipped in California. They make extensive use of automatic weapons, cybernetics, armored vehicles, and combat magic. Despite this and the huge number of ganger arrests each day, many Angelinos believe that the go-gangs are slowly winning the war.

After CFS lost San Diego, Los Angeles became a major naval facility. Today it is the base for the small, efficient CFS navy as well as for CFS armor and infantry, striking an aggressive pose against the southern powerhouse, Aztlan. Of course, a handful of Japanese Navy vessels are usually present as well.

San Francisco, long the symbol of everything different and good about California, remains under occupation by the Japanese Marines. Though a cross-cultural nightmare of conflicting American and Japanese traditions, it remains one of the most beautiful cities in the world because the Japanese have taken pains to keep it so.

Sacramento is still the seat of California government. Here, the President and American-style Congress wrestle with issues of the day, blissfully ignoring the fact that their authority extends not much beyond the San Joaquin Valley. Members of the CFS Congress can remain in their districts but still participate in Congressional assemblies and functions via Matrix-simsense link. The computer network that makes this possible was created at enormous expense, but has proven vulnerable to electronic terrorists.

Much of California has reverted to the ways of the old 19th-century frontier. Many remote communities are a law unto themselves, responsible for their own defense and administration. The Sacramento government rarely bothers them because it already has more problems than it can handle. Northern California remains in a cold war with Tir Tairngire, while outlying towns in central and southern California Free State must contend with the threat of roving go-gangs, bands of hostile metahumans, and occasional acts of terrorism by groups from every band of the political spectrum. These cities and towns have large militias, and their well-armed citizenry do not hesitate to use violence to resolve even minor matters.

Outsiders and metahumans are usually not welcome in these towns. A higher tolerance exists for dwarfs, but other subspecies are disliked because of the depredations of wilderness-dwelling orks and trolls.

Intertown terrorism, even warfare, is not uncommon. A town with a grudge against neighboring settlements over water, highway taxes, and similar matters, often hires outside "talent" to help them fight. Deckers, mages, samurai and other independent contractors are often in demand, though are not usually welcome to stay around once the dirty work is done.

## ECONOMY

The economy of rural California is quite varied. Farming predominates in the northern and central areas, while cattle-raising is the basis of the economy in the arid southern portion of the state. As rural California is also a haven for shamanic magicians, magical supplies from the region are greatly prized.

California's cities, particularly San Francisco and Los Angeles, are major producers of high-tech equipment such as decks, entertainment electronics, cybertech, and security devices. Though most of San Francisco's production is destined for foreign markets, the Yakuza manages to steal enough of them to produce a thriving black-market business.

Though simsense and trideo form the great bulk of Los Angeles' economy, the city is also a major weapons production center. Go-gangs and their allies, the burgeoning criminal elements of Los Angeles, engage heavily in the smuggling of weapons, dreamchips, cybertech, and many other contraband items.

## COST OF LIVING

Prices in California's major cities and coastal settlements are equivalent to other urban areas, but the cost of some items is ten times normal in San Francisco because they are officially banned. In rural areas, however, prices differ, shown on the table below. If an item is not listed, assume it commands the normal price.

| RURAL COST OF LIVING | |
| --- | --- |
| ITEM | COST |
| **Weaponry** | |
| Ammunition | 150–200% |
| Armor | 150% |
| Explosives | 200% |
| Firearm Accessories | 150% |
| Firearms | 150–200% |
| **Surveillance and Security** | |
| Communications | 80% |
| Security | 150% |
| Surveillance Countermeasures | 200% |
| Surveillance Measures | 100% |
| Vision Enhancers | 100% |
| **Lifestyle** | |
| Lifestyle | 150–300% |
| **Electronics** | |
| Electronics | 75% |
| **Cybertech** | |
| Bodyware | 150% |
| Headware | 80–90% |
| Internals | 80–90% |
| **Cyberdecks and Programs** | |
| Cyberdecks | 90% |
| Programs | 150% |
| **Biotech** | |
| Biotech | 150–200%* |
| **Magical Equipment** | |
| Hermetic Library | |
|    Computer | 200% |
|    Hard Copy | 500% |
| Magic Weapons | 75% |
| Magical Supplies | 75% |
| Power Foci | 75% |
| Spell Foci | 75% |
| **Vehicles** | |
| Aircraft | 1000% (not normally available) |
| Boats | 150–200% |
| Ground Vehicles | 200–300% |
| Military Vehicles | 1000% (not normally available) |
| *(DocWagon™ is not available in rural areas) | |

## LAW AND ORDER

California Free State's North American heritage produced a legal code similar to that of the UCAS. Penalties are similar to those in such American cities as Seattle, though enforcement varies. In Los Angeles, high crime, limited jail space, and a generally more libertine culture make sentences lighter. In San Francisco, on the other hand, the conservative Japanese administration makes maximum sentences the rule. Rather than incarcerate criminals within the city, the San Francisco Japanese hand them over to central CFS authorities. The uneven nature of San Francisco's justice system (many judges are Japanese with only a limited grasp of American jurisprudence)

## WEAPON FINES AND PUNISHMENT TABLE

| Weapon Type | Offense and Fine | | | | |
| --- | --- | --- | --- | --- | --- |
| | 1 | 2 | 3 | 4 | 5 |
| Type | Possession | Transport | Threat | Use | Intent |
| (A) Small Bladed Weapon | — | — | 500¥ | 1,000¥/3 mo | 2,500¥/1 yr |
| (B) Large Bladed Weapon | 100¥ | 500¥ | 1,000¥ | 2,500¥/6 mo | 8,000¥/1 yr |
| (C) Blunt Weapon | 100¥ | — | 500¥/1 mo | 1,000¥/6 mo | 2,500¥/1 yr |
| (D) Projectile Weapon | — | — | 1,000¥/3 mo | 2,500¥/6 mo | 5,000¥/1 yr |
| (E) Pistol | 500¥ | 1,000¥ | 2,500¥/6 yrs | 5,000¥/1 yr | 10,000¥/3 yrs |
| (F) Rifle | 1,000¥ | 2,000¥ | 5,000¥/1 yr | 10,000¥/2 yrs | 25,000¥/3 yrs |
| (G) Automatic Weapon | 10,000¥ | 15,000¥/6 mo | 1 yr | 3 yrs | 5 yrs |
| (H) Heavy Weapon | 25,000¥/2 yrs | 50,000¥/3 yrs | 2 yrs | 5 yrs | 10 yrs |
| (I) Explosives | 2,000¥ | 5,000¥/1 yr | 2 yrs | 5 yrs | 10 yrs |
| (J) Military Weapon | 6 mo | 1 yr | 3 yrs | 7 yrs | 150 yrs |
| (K) Military Armor | 5,000¥ | — | — | — | — |
| (L) Ammunition | 2,000¥ | — | — | — | — |
| (M) Controlled Substances | 250¥ | 1,000¥/2 mo | — | — | — |
| (CA) Class A Cyberware | 5,000¥ | — | — | — | — |
| (CB) Class B Cyberware | — | — | — | — | — |
| (CC) Class C Cyberware | 10,000¥ | — | — | — | — |
| (CD) Unlicensed Cyberdecks and Matrix Software | 10,000¥ | 50,000¥/6 mo | | | |

leads to the reversal of many convictions on appeal, assuming one can somehow get the appeal addressed outside of San Francisco.

Rural areas are usually strict about enforcement of the law, but firearm rules are often suspended. Some border towns are attacked so often by go-gangs and marauding metahumans that gun ownership and training or membership in local militias may even be required of citizens.

## GOVERNMENT

The CFS government is a smaller version of the UCAS, with a President, a Supreme Court, and two houses of Congress. Each county has one senator, elected to a maximum of three 6-year terms. The number of representatives, elected for up to six 2-year terms, is based on its population. The Northern California counties, still considered part of California Free State, still have seats in the Congress, though they are never occupied.

The Congress meets once a year. Those rural congressmen unable to reach the capital because of poor travel conditions, go-gang attacks, or other unforeseeable circumstances, can attend a session through the Matrix. When the Matrix is down—which is fairly common in outlying areas—congressmen have proxies to serve in their place and vote for them.

The California Free State government is always busy debating issues of foreign relations, taxes, crime, dreamchip abuse, and other such issues, but their authority extends only to the central portion of the state and larger cities such as Los Angeles, Santa Barbara, and Monterey. Their decrees have no authority elsewhere.

# SAN FRANCISCO

San Francisco—the city by the bay, the jewel of the West Coast, a living symbol of American history—is today a city under foreign occupation.

When California Free State declared its independence in 2037, San Francisco was already in disarray. Disease, famine, and social upheaval had wracked the city as severely as any of its famous earthquakes. When the Japanese government recognized the California Free State, San Franciscans hoped that peace would mean an end to their troubles.

Instead, their troubles were just beginning. Japanese Imperial Marines were now present in strength and a naval task force always within striking distance "to protect Japanese lives and property." Of, course, then-Governor Treacle had asked for their protection from Tir Tairngire and Aztlan invasion.

In the intervening years, San Francisco has transformed into a city of clashing cultures. In addition to constructing soaring new corporate headquarters, the resurgent imperialist movement in Japan was determined to transform the new colony into the image of the homeland.

They were, however, only partially successful. Fully 40 percent of San Francisco's permanent residents are now Japanese, but the city continues to run on the labor of the hordes of day laborers who commute across the Bay and Butterfly Bridges each morning and evening. Tourists also bring outside cultural influences into the city, and the nuyen they spend is indispensable to the local economy. Japanese culture is strong, and in many ways permanent, but it is isolated from the formerly dominant culture it replaced. The arrogance of the occupation forces has created so much simmering resentment among most San Franciscans that the Underground movement against the Japanese, their I-Marines, and corporate feudalism, is growing.

## GEOGRAPHY AND CLIMATE

Compressed into a peninsula between San Francisco Bay and the vastness of the Pacific Ocean, San Francisco has always suffered from limited space. Today, more than 500,000 live in the city's cramped, hilly environs.

Ecological crises that have affected climate in other parts of the world have barely affected San Francisco, however. Temperature varies from 18 degrees Celsius in summer to 10 degrees Celsius in winter, and the ocean breeze keeps the air clean and fresh even in the warmer months. San Francisco's famous fogs are most common in summer, when they make the morning commute as picturesque as it is hazardous.

## POLITICS

San Francisco retains its mayor and city council. Though virtually powerless, the council can be a potent advocate in disputes with the local Japanese authorities. The city council also wields some authority in civil matters that do not overly concern the Japanese. It's anyone's guess to whom the various council members are loyal.

Real political power in San Francisco rests with the Imperial Governor, a military officer appointed by the Japanese government, with headquarters in the Presidio. The current governor, General Shiro Kawanaga, is a virtual dictator, so unquestioned is his power over the city and its inhabitants. In keeping with ancient Japanese tradition, however, a lord is responsible for the well-being of his vassals, and Kawanaga rarely imposes any truly draconian measures. All the same, anyone who violates the law suffers harsh punishment.

## LAW, ORDER, AND CRIME

The Japanese authorities insist that crime is non-existent in San Francisco, and the boast is largely true. Robbery, assault, murder, and other crimes meet with swift arrest and trial. Summary execution by the Imperial Marines usually follows. Today's San Franciscans are a law-abiding lot, and many non-Japanese citizens have come to appreciate the occupation government's get-tough approach. Sheep, all.

California Free State law is officially in force, but the Japanese in San Francisco will not permit criminals to remain within the city borders. Any one convicted of a crime is immediately deported to serve his sentence outside of the city. That means any chummer who hasn't gotten his noggin lobbed off for his crime has about an even chance to pull an appeal wherever they send him. Remember, though, ya rolls the dice, ya takes yer chances, chummer.

The San Francisco Police Department (SFPD) carries out most law enforcement. Numbering more than six thousand, the department's ordinary cops are Caucasian, with all officers and administrators being Japanese. Cops must live up to a high standard of conduct, but corruption is no stranger. The cops are just better at keeping it quiet.

None of this implies that crime does not exist in San Francisco. Shadowrunning and other forms of covert lawbreaking are surprisingly widespread, thriving despite the authorities' efforts to eliminate them.

Data steals, espionage, and acts of terrorism against the occupation forces occur regularly. Inter-corporate wars sometimes reach the shooting stage, with small armies of security guards, street samurai, and other mercenaries fighting it out in the steel-and-glass corporate towers. The Japanese corps bring in outside talent, though they are usually discreet in their recruitment. Last year's little scuffle between Elite and Fuchi was kept quiet, but my best estimate is that it cost nearly a hundred lives. Overt action on the streets of S.F. drives the Imperial Governor wild like nothing else can. He's had to roll out the Imperial Marines stationed at the Presidio to quell disturbances more than once in the last decade. So that rumble you hear may not be an earthquake, chummers.

Weapons, adult simsense recordings, BTLs, cigarettes, and liquor are all illegal or heavily taxed, making them popular with smugglers. Cautious smugglers carry these items in modified cars and trucks, while more adventurous types skim across the bay in hovercraft, high-speed boats, or light aircraft.

Vagrancy is a crime in San Francisco. Defined as anyone without a job or valid travel pass, a vagrant is subject to summary expulsion by the police or I-Marines. Every week, boatloads of "vagrant" foreigners are summarily dumped off at the Oakland Marina, where they are left to fend for themselves. Those naive and short-sighted individuals who praise the Japanese authorities for "eliminating poverty and homelessness in San Francisco" never seem to mention this particular aspect of civic policy. The homeless problem in Oakland and Berkeley may soon reach the flashpoint, however. Several riots and other incidents have already erupted, but the local authorities quickly hushed them up.

### THE UNDERGROUND

Sympathy for the Underground is widespread, but actual membership is, of necessity, limited. Most Underground activists favor reunification with CFS, though some favor Free City status or union with UCAS. Some even want to join the CAS—anything to get out.

Most Underground members are not terrorists and shun violence. Many are, in fact, Neo-Anarchists who revel in uncovering dirt on Japanese corporations and government officials. Many deckers and mages sympathize with the Underground and lend support. The movement also counts a few mercs and samurai in its ranks in the rare instances when muscle is needed. Disenchanted metahumans, tricked into immigration and stranded by the Japanese government, form yet another pool of support for the movement.

## TRAVEL PASSES

Non-Japanese citizens must register each year and pay a substantial "municipal surtax" for the right to continue living in San Francisco. Non-citizens have even greater hurdles to overcome.

Day-workers must obtain a day pass, which allows them to remain in the city between six in the morning and nine at night. Those who drive must also obtain a day-worker vehicle pass. A monthly pass costs 20¥ for an individual and 50¥ for a vehicle.

Corporate executives and others who spend extended time in the city may obtain a residential pass, which costs 1,000¥ initially, plus 250¥ per month. This includes a vehicle pass.

Forgery is a burgeoning industry. Prices start at 100¥ for a forged day pass and 20,000¥ for a residential pass forgery. A forger whose motivations are sufficiently political may charge substantially less, however.

Each pass contains a coded magstrip that S.F. police and Imperial Marines can decode with a special reader. Linked to the central police computer, the reader matches the magstrip information to a personal datafile, enabling the policeman to confirm the subject's identity. Normal forgeries are only surface-deep, relying on the fact that most police are content to simply look at a pass. Forgeries with pre-generated cover identities loaded into the central files cost up to ten times more.

## TRANSPORTATION

San Francisco's most famous public transportation, the cable cars, are maintained primarily as a tourist attraction; only the California Street and Powell-Hyde lines are still operational. Of these, the Powell-Hyde line provides the best view of the bay and the Golden Gate. Rides cost 2¥ per person.

Most San Franciscans rely on public transit, known as the Muni. Vehicles vary from antiquated wheeled buses to ultra-modern Chrysler-Nissan G10s. Fares vary from .5¥ for short trips to 2¥ for longer trips. All-day passes allow unlimited travel and cost 5¥ per day.

Taxis are popular, too. Fares range from 5¥ to 50¥ per hour, depending on the luxury of the vehicle and efficiency of travel.

Hydroplane ferries carry cars between San Francisco and the East Bay. Popular with more affluent commuters, these ferries travel under tight security and always carry at least a squad of police. Ferry trips cost 5¥ each or 75¥ for a monthly pass.

The old Bay Area Rapid Transit System, BART, once among the finest in the country, was eliminated by the occupation forces as too difficult to monitor. The BART underground tunnels, which stretch from San Francisco to the north and east across the bay, have been sealed up. Some claim that a thriving ork underground survives among those tunnels, while other rumors tell of less savory creatures roaming their depths.

## SNEAKING IN

Japanese Imperial Marines patrol the major approaches to San Francisco: the three bridges and the highways entering the city from the south. Official Japanese authority extends only to the San Mateo county line in the south, however. The network of streets between San Francisco and Daly City is impossible to patrol completely and offers the most common illicit entry.

Mission Street, Geneva Avenue, Bayshore Boulevard, and other major thoroughfares have I-Marine checkpoints. SFPD vehicles and occasional Marine armored cars patrol the rest. Each night, smugglers play a complex and deadly game of chicken with the authorities. Stealth and deception are the smugglers' best weapons; gunfire or other combat activity is a sign of failure. The occupation forces want to put an end to the smuggling, but they are outnumbered and stretched to the limit.

The sealed BART tunnels may also offer a means of illicit entry into San Francisco, but so far no one has investigated them. The rumors of wild ork tribes and dangerous animals keeps most of the curious away.

## IMPERIAL MARINES

The real authority in San Francisco lies with the Japanese Imperial Marines. Grim, silent, and heavily armed, the Marines man all checkpoints into and out of the city. They tend to check passes more thoroughly than the SFPD, so travelers, licit or otherwise, are advised to steer well clear of the I-Marines. Under no circumstances should the traveler offer bribes or back-talk.

## CORPORATE SECURITY

Corporate cops form still another level of San Francisco law enforcement. They have carte blanche to enforce security in buildings, vehicles, and other holdings of their employer. All major corporations have security units, which they outfit and equip in the most intimidating manner. Notable among these are the Renraku "Red Samurai." These infamous corp cops are all military veterans, chosen for their size and toughness and rumored to be cybernetically enhanced with a variety of top-secret ware.

## STATUS OF METAHUMANS

Metahumans encounter much prejudice in San Francisco. At the bottom of the ladder are orks and trolls, who do the menial work and are generally ignored. Elves and dwarfs fare a little better but still face many obstacles. In Japan, orks and trolls are promised good-paying jobs in San Francisco, shipped out, and then dumped into the same menial occupations they left behind. When metahumans are no longer useful, they are often put out on the street, where they must fend for themselves in the spreading slums of the East Bay.

Elves can sometimes rise to moderate levels in Japanese corporations, finding employment in a variety of positions. Dwarfs generally work at jobs such as maintenance supervisors, techs, and other manual labor tasks, but with better pay and conditions than orks and trolls receive. A typical labor crew consists of a dwarf foreman and a team of ork workers.

As a rule, metahumans do not officially exist for the average San Franciscan, who will treat them, at best, with polite indifference.

## ECONOMY

San Francisco serves as primary North American headquarters for a wide range of Japanese firms. These employ many so-called "foreigners," but mostly in low-level clerical and support jobs. Possessing only day passes, these individuals spend their working hours in San Francisco, crowding the Bay and Butterfly Bridges mornings and evenings.

## ENTERTAINMENT

Traditional Japanese art forms such as *kabuki* and *no* dramas are performed widely, though the city's North American inhabitants take little interest in them. Opera, however, often crosses the cultural barrier. The San Francisco Opera Company's *kabuki* production of *Aida* garnered critical acclaim last year, but high production costs forced the program to close after only a short run.

Sports remain a mainstay of San Francisco entertainment, though Urban Brawl is officially banned, surviving only in the more liberal East Bay. The Forty-niners and Giants still play at Candlestick Park, but most team members live outside the city limits.

The city continues to cling to its cultural traditions. Performance artists, dancers, musicians, comedians, and others can still make a name for themselves in San Francisco's nightclubs. Many rising rock bands first gain notice in San Francisco. San Francisco's hottest young singer last year was Axe Slayer, a neo-metal revivalist. He seemed destined for greatness until his exploding codpiece detonated prematurely. He lost his life, but the video of that fatal last appearance sold millions.

Simsense parlors are popular, but content is limited and often edited by blue-nosed occupation officials. Some parlors, patronized only by tourists, show more or less uncut productions, but these are still tame and inoffensive. Adult simsense is one of the most popular black-market items for smugglers.

## NEIGHBORHOODS

Modern San Francisco neighborhoods vary from virtual paradises of corporate wealth to low-class metahuman slums. Major neighborhoods, their standard of living, and security ratings, are listed below.

|  | Security Rating |
|---|---|
| **Balboa**: Middle Class | A-B |
| **Bay View**: Low Class (High percentage of ork and troll residents) | C-D |
| **Bernal Heights**: Middle Class | B |
| **Crocker Amazon**: Low Class | C |
| **Diamond Heights**: Upper Class | AA |
| **Duboce/Castro**: Middle Class | B |
| **Excelsior**: Middle Class | C-B |
| **Forest Hill**: Luxury | AAA |
| **Glen Park**: Upper Class | AA |
| **Haight-Ashbury**: Low Class | E |

(This area still retains much of its old reputation as home of the counter-culture. Low-cost housing is utilized by shadowrunners and similar dregs of society.)

| **Ingleside/Ocean View**: Middle Class | B |
|---|---|
| **Western Addition**: Middle Class | B |

(Formerly "Japan Town," Western Addition has been renamed and is home to many Japanese middle class workers and *sararimen*.)

| **Lake Merced**: Middle Class | B |
|---|---|
| **Marina**: Upper Class | AA |

(Exclusive and expensive, the Marina is owned mostly by corporate types)

| **Mission**: Middle Class | B-C |
|---|---|
| **Noe**: Middle Class | B-C |
| **Outer Mission**: Low Class | D-E |
| **Parkside**: Middle Class | B-C |
| **Potrero**: Low Class | D-E |
| **Presidio Heights**: Upper Class | AA |
| **Richmond**: Middle Class | B-C |
| **Sea Cliff**: Upper Class | AA |
| **South of Market**: Upper Class | AA-AAA |

(Many exclusive bayside homes are found here — small and unassuming, but very, very expensive, and very, very well guarded.)

| **Sunset**: Low Class | E |
|---|---|
| **Sunset Heights**: Middle Class | B–C |
| **St. Francis Wood**: Luxury | AAA |
| **Twin Peaks**: Upper Class | AA |
| **Visitation Valley**: Low Class | D-E |

## CHINATOWN (B)

The Japanese have allowed this picturesque and historic region to remain relatively unchanged due to its value as a tourist attraction. Densely populated and poor, Chinatown is at the same time a colorful, culturally rich environment, still harboring a large Sino-American community. Visitors may sample a wide variety of Chinese cuisines here, as well as purchase produce and far-eastern imports from the motley store-front shops. Tiny talisman shops dot Chinatown, selling magical equipment and supplies.

Chinatown is also the heart of the magical Underground, and is the site of serious confrontation between the Yakuza, various Seoulpa gangs, Tongs, and common street gangs. While the main avenues are relatively safe, the winding, chaotic, back streets contain many surprises, secrets and dangers. It is also heavily rumored that a series of tunnels and passageways radiate outward from under Chinatown and cover half the city. Some say that the conflicts that occur on the surface streets pale in comparison to the drek that goes down underground. I'll take their word for it.

## DOWNTOWN

The heart of Japanese corporate America, Downtown San Francisco is further divided into several neighborhoods.

|  | Security Rating |
| --- | --- |
| **The Embarcadero:** Middle Class | **B** |
| (A waterfront neighborhood with numerous warehouses and docks) | |
| **Financial District:** Upper Class | **AA** |
| **Lombard Street:** Upper Class | **AA** |
| **Nob Hill:** Upper Class | **AA** |
| **North Beach:** Middle Class | **A-B** |
| **Russian Hill:** Middle Class | **B** |
| **Tenderloin:** Middle Class | **B** |
| **Union Square:** Upper Class (A largely business district) | **AA** |

## OTHER BAY AREA COMMUNITIES

Numerous other communities surround San Francisco. The best known are described below.

### Alameda (AA, AAA in Yard)

Once a pleasant middle-class community, Alameda today exists under the shadow of the Japanese Imperial Navy, which has taken over the Alameda Naval Yards and garrisoned them with the grim, humorless Imperial Marines. Though Alameda itself is not under occupation, the locals resent the fences, razor wire, sandbags, and bunkers that surround the Yards. I-Marines man the Yards' defenses around the clock, and do not hesitate to open fire on any interlopers.

The Marines' zealousness is understandable, considering that the Yards are home to the Japanese aircraft carrier *Hiryu*, three squadrons of VTOL aircraft, and numerous military vehicles and supplies. Hovercraft and boat patrols sweep the bay daily for smugglers and unauthorized traffic. Contact with the outside world is strictly forbidden, and few non-Japanese know anything about what lies beyond the fences surrounding the Yards.

### Berkeley (A)

Once called the Athens of the West, Berkeley still boasts an avant-garde, vital culture. The University of California, Berkeley, is an important learning institution, and its Department of Magical Studies is acknowledged as one of the best in the world. Artists, poets, and writers still consider Berkeley a good place to live and work. Unfortunately, growing numbers of desperate metahuman refugees and a steadily increasing gang presence have made police beef up patrols and armament. College and city officials fear that Berkeley is starting down the same road as Oakland.

### Emeryville (B-C)

Located between Oakland and Berkeley, this small settlement shares problems and advantages with both. Gambling is legal in Emeryville, making it something of a Bay Area "Sin City." Housing laws have been relaxed to allow artists and writers to live in their own studios, and so the town is a haven for creative people. Deckers, computer artists, and shadowrunners also find Emeryville's housing laws useful. Gangs and other criminal trouble-makers from Oakland have sent Emeryville's city fathers to Berkeley to appeal for help, but the overburdened Berkeley police can do little.

### Marin County (A-AA)

Marin County, the area north of the Golden Gate, is a pleasant, multi-cultural region where humans and metahumans co-exist peacefully, relatively free of San Francisco's negative influence. A well-armed police force keeps go-gangs and other undesirables at bay, while local ordinances ban acceptance of shipments of metahuman outcasts from San Francisco. Though this policy has kept Marin reasonably secure, it has increased the pressure on Oakland and Berkeley. When the inevitable explosion comes, Marin may be dragged along in spite of itself.

### Oakland (D-E, sometimes Z)

As a result of the occupation government's short-sighted policies, Oakland has become the dumping ground for the human and metahuman refuse that the San Francisco overlords do not wish to keep. Civil authority has long since vanished in Oakland, swept away by the press of gangs, organized crime, metahuman refugees, un-employment, and other problems inherited from the sister-city across the bay. Much of Oakland, particularly the residential neighborhoods south of Lake Merritt, has been converted into a metahuman ghetto. Reduced to a state of grim hopelessness by crushing poverty, unem-ployed orks and trolls fight, rob, and kill one another. By night, go-gangs rule the city's streets, and the sound of automatic weapons fire is ever-present.

Most Oaklanders live in constant fear, and those who have jobs commute at a terrified pace. A few simsense theaters still exist by paying protection money, but Oakland's once-great sports teams, the Raiders and the Athletics, are no more than a memory. The San Francisco Terminators Urban Brawl team plays its games at Oakland Stadium, giving the city its only major professional fran-chise.

Through all this, Oakland maintains a government and police department of sorts, which keep most sections of downtown reasonably safe, if not crime-free, during the day. Pay is low for police, and equipment outdated or nonexistent, so corruption is rampant. The mayor and city council are not much better, but a handful of activists still struggles to make Oakland the peaceful, liveable city it once was.

### Tiburon (AAA)

A small, elite community north of the Golden Gate, most of Tiburon lies on a peninsula and is accessible along a narrow strip of land that is fortified and constantly patrolled. The Japanese and American corporate execu-tives whose homes are here also maintain heavy security, both electronic and magical.

## LOCATIONS

### AIRPORTS

#### San Francisco International Airport (not on map, south of Downtown)

Highway 101, south of San Francisco/Yoei Doekasu, Airport Manager/LTG# 12415 (76-0800)

Located outside of San Francisco city limits, the airport is nonetheless administered by the occupation authority. Twenty-four airlines serve this four-terminal, tri-level facility. Extensively remodeled in the early 2000s, San Francisco International was the early 21st century's major connecting point between the United States and the Pacific Rim. The Bufano statue titled "Peace," which once graced the median on the entrance roadway, was destroyed in the anti-metahuman riots of the 2020s. The airport remained in a state of disrepair until the Japanese occupation of 2037.

Rebuilt and refurbished, the airport is today a model of efficiency, though most of its traffic is to and from the Far East. Boarding areas E and F are reserved for metahuman contract laborers, whose passports are all one-way. Contact between Asian passengers and others, especially metahumans, is scrupulously prevented, with polite but well-armed Imperial Marines ready to enforce any infraction of the rule. Non-Asians are strongly advised not to leave areas posted for their use.

Most metahumans shipped to S.F. are promised good pay and told they will be allowed to return home if they do a good job. This is an outright lie, for those of us who go to San Francisco as contract laborers never see our homes or families again.

### MEDICAL FACILITIES

#### Fuchi Tech Medical Center (1)

Hospital Archetype/900 Hyde/Bias Against Non-Japanese/LTG# 1415 (33-1178)

Formerly St. Francis Memorial, Fuchi Tech Medical now serves only company employees. The care provided is superb, most of it covered by employee health insurance. Lesser known is Fuchi Tech's cybernetics wing, where employees are modified into high-tech spies or warriors. It is heavily rumored that Fuchi Tech will also service non-corporate "clients" if the price is right. Something else to remember is that DocWagon does not service this facility because of a contract dispute.

### MediMark Cyberware (2)

Body Shop Archetype/150 Third/No Racial Bias/ LTG# 1415 (64-8428)

The only legal bodyshop in San Francisco is popular with wealthy corp types, police, corporate agents, freelancers, and bored young Japanese with money burning a hole in their pockets.

### Nick's Bodyshop (not on map, south-southwest of Downtown)

Body Shop Archetype/3306 – 21st/No Racial Bias/ LTG# 3415 (31-1900)

Offering economy bodywork at its worst, Nick's is still around mainly because it is one of the few black market bodyshops in SF. Though the work is sub-par and often little more than butchery, "Nick" (real name unknown) has a constant stream of customers.

### San Francisco General Hospital (not on map, just south of Downtown)

Hospital Archetype/1001 Potrero/No Racial Bias/ LTG# 2415 (64-5455)

The largest hospital still open to the general public, San Francisco General is usually overcrowded and the quality of care provided is marginal. This is the usual destination for injured orks, trolls, dwarfs, and other metahumans, as well as those injured in gang scuffles or shadowrunning. The staff, frustrated by the occupation government's limited support or outright ignorance, usually looks the other way when there is no real evidence that a patient was injured during possible criminal activity. The occupation authorities do not approve this lax attitude, but they know the injured undesirables have nowhere else to go.

## HOTELS

S.F. remains famous for its hotels, but obtaining good accommodations is distinctly difficult for anyone not Japanese. The more luxurious hotels are the scenes of high-level power brokering, secret data wars, and the sybaritic pleasures of the ultra-rich and -powerful.

### The Dandelion (not on map, just south of Downtown)

Cheap Hotel Archetype/650 Potrero/Laura Delaney, Manager/No Racial Bias/LTG# 6415 (35-6712)

Another cube-hotel, the Dandelion is notorious as a haven for prostitution, BTL dealing, and other underworld activities. The SFPD raid the place regularly, but rarely make any big arrests. Word is that local smuggling operations are also run out of the Dandelion.

### Downtown Cube (7)

Cheap Hotel Archetype/364 Ninth Street/Masado Kawanaga, Manager/No Racial Bias/LTG# 1415 (46-1020)

A typical coffin hotel, the Cube's guests are primarily contract workers, lower-class Japanese travelers, and foreign students. Someone can stay here, no questions asked, for quite an extended period. The only problem is that non-Asians might attract too much attention in a place like this because their ilk usually stay in luxury hotels. A cover identity as a student or contract worker might be a good idea.

### The Drake (5)

Luxury Hotel Archetype/432 Powell/Edward Kohl, Manager/Bias Against Metahumans, Especially Trolls/ LTG# 1415 (42-9955)

Originally built in the 1920s, the Drake suffered from neglect in the early 2000s. It has since been sold to a syndicate of American and NAN investors. Now extensively restored, the Drake's vintage decor makes it popular with non-Japanese.

### Mamoro-Hyatt-Regency (3)

Luxury Hotel Archetype/5 Embarcadero Center/ Hasado Koechi, Manager/Bias Against Metahumans/LTG# 1415 (27-1420)

One of the best-known luxury hotels in San Francisco, the Hyatt is famous for its vast interior atrium. With its high security and attention to service, the hotel was a favorite of Fuchi Tech for having special guests and visiting corporate officers, and for high-level meetings. Fuchi recently switched its business to the Four Seasons, however, because the Mamoro-Hyatt's so-called "high security" is alleged to be a load of drek. According to rumor, a shielded micro-cam was hidden in the ventilation system during a Fuchi "business seminar," which just happened to involve the services of under-age elven joygirls. Income from sales of that tape to Mitsuhama will keep the perpetrator in silks for some time to come.

### Plaza (6)

Family Style Hotel Archetype/465 Grant Avenue/ Ralph Turmee, Manager/Bias Against humans and elves/ LTG# 1415 (22-7812)

Popular with ork and troll contract workers, this plain, inexpensive hotel sometimes serves as a "safe house" for orks or trolls on the run. The SFPD raided the Plaza last year, looking for some ork supposed to be carrying important corporate datafiles. They found nothing of the sort, but some *zaibatsu* were said to be plenty embarrassed by what did turn up.

### The Shogun (4)

Luxury Hotel Archetype/222 Sansome/Kuo Morimoto, Manager/Bias Against Metahumans and Non-Japanese/LTG# 1415 (46-3300)

Formerly the Mandarin Oriental, this hotel was sold to the Otsu Hotel conglomerate in 2038 and converted to its present state. The Shogun caters exclusively to Japanese clientele, and its decor is typically restrained Asian elegance. Meals are as expensive as they are lavish. Virtually every luxury—legal or otherwise—is available for a price. The scuttlebutt is that several high-ranking Yakuza actually live here, with the entire top two floors reserved for their exclusive use.

## RESTAURANTS AND BARS

### The Barghest (not on map, southwest of Downtown)

Bar Archetype/2154 24th/Michael Dreyfuss, Manager/No Racial Bias/LTG# 3415 (79-1471)

The Barghest is a hangout for gang members, mercenaries, orks, trolls, and young Japanese who want to look tough. Prices are minimal, quality is non-existent, and decor is early-American dive at its best. The Barghest is useful primarily as a place to make contacts with society's less-reputable members. The SFPD raid regularly, but never do more than make a few arrests for minor weapons and BTL violations.

### Bubba's Sports Bar (12)

Bar Archetype/2306 Larkin/Jack Lee, Manager/No Racial Bias/LTG# 2415 (49-1168)

Run by "Bubba" Lee, former 49ers linebacker and one of the best trolls ever to play the game, the bar caters to athletes, tourists, and Japanese sports fans. The array of trideo sets show sports contests from all over the world while patrons sip suds and chow down on soyburgers. Though gambling is officially illegal, a fair amount of betting goes on at the bar. So far, though, Bubba hasn't butted heads with the authorities.

### The Chiphead (not on map, west of Downtown)

Bar Archetype/4637 Geary/Morgan Silver Moon, Manager/Racial Bias/LTG# 6415 (23-0178)

As the name implies, the Chiphead is a decker hangout. It is also frequented by tourists, wealthy Japanese, and thrill-seekers hoping to catch one of the promising bands that perform here on Friday and Saturday nights. The Chiphead was the scene of the unfortunate exploding codpiece incident, which everyone thought was part of the show.

### The Chrome Stallion (not on map, west-southwest of Downtown)

Night Club Archetype/1725 Haight/Adam Greenway, Manager/No Racial Bias/LTG# 8415 (75-3756)

The Stallion is a schizophrenic bar whose booths are dark and intimate while the dance floor is flashy and open. Frequented by tourists and young Japanese, it is also a good place to catch promising bands. The bands usually ignore local indecency laws, but the authorities rarely make any trouble.

### The Count's (18)

Bar Archetype/473 Broadway/Victor DeLann, Manager/No Racial Bias/LTG# 2415 (27-6633)

A novelty bar decorated in the style of an old flatscreen vampire movie, The Count's has stone walls, crumbling columns, chains on the wall, stained glass windows, and so on. The effect would have worn thin long ago if not for the fact that the manager, Victor DeLann, is actually a vampire. Duly registered with the occupation forces, DeLann subsists mostly on whole blood purchased from San Francisco General and on the occasional willing victim. Tourists who come here expecting a Bela Lugosi look-alike will be disappointed.

### The Dragon's Claw (15)

Large Restaurant Archetype/240 California Street/Tadeo Yorimoto, Manager/Bias Against Non-Japanese/LTG# 1415 (54-1385)

High-class, expensive, lushly decorated, the Claw is a favorite of powerful corp executives, as well as Japanese mercenaries and fixers. Corps in the market for high-level war talent use the Claw for recruitment.

### House of Swords (8)

Bar Archetype/39 New Montgomery Street/Tomoe Miasaki, Manager/Bias Against Metahumans and Non-Japanese/LTG# 1415 (44-1663)

Probably the oldest continuously operated establishment in the city, the House of Swords was built in 1912 and retains much of its Edwardian charm. The House is very expensive and caters almost exclusively to Asian patrons. Those lacking Japanese surnames can rarely make a reasonable reservation. The House is also popular with the Yakuza, occasionally making it the scene of some violent encounter.

### JJ's (11)

Bar Archetype/1312 Polk/Miyaki Ishido, Manager/ No Racial Bias/LTG# 1415 (87-4017)

An island of "American" culture in the ever-rising tide of orientalism, JJ's maintains the old tavern traditions of serving beer, wine, and mixed drinks as well as soyburgers, fries, sandwiches, and so on. Though Ishido is Japanese, he has a soft spot in his heart for American food and drink. This is a good post-run rendezvous. Ishido doesn't like the cops or the I-Marines, and gets off on the excitement of shadowrunners hanging out in his place.

### The Katana (not on map, just southwest of the Presidio)

Large Restaurant Archetype/2909 Webster Street/ Obi Kiasawa, Manager/Bias against Non-Japanese/LTG# 2415 (79-8156)

The traditional Japanese decor makes the Katana popular with conservative Japanese businessmen and Marines on leave. Reservations are not required, but non-Japanese will be informed that all tables are full.

### Kijutsu (17)

Bar Archetype/566 Columbus/Hoto Asakichi, Man- ager/No Racial Bias/LTG# 2415 (87-3841)

The Kijutsu is popular with sararimen, low-level executives, and other wage-slave types. Non-Japanese and even metahumans can expect reasonable service. As a working-class bar, the 'Jutsu is usually alive with con- versation, complaints, and discussions of the day's work. Alert patrons may sometimes overhear useful gossip and insider information.

### The Neon Lotus (9)

Large Restaurant Archetype/777 Sutter Street/ Morimoto Hasegawa, Manager/Bias Against Metahumans/ LTG# 2415 (26-1750)

An elegant restaurant, the Neon Lotus is especially popular with corporate executives. Prices are high and portions are small, but the food, mostly Japanese and Szechwan cuisine, is exquisite. The quiet bar is also high- priced. Many corporate wheeler-dealers use this bar to keep their negotiations away from prying eyes. Several corps and runner groups have been notably unsuccessful at bugging the place.

Hasegawa has a couple of tame mages working for him, and they have detected all attempts at surveillance. He also hires ork leg-breakers to convey his displeasure to anyone who gets caught.

### The Nighthawk (14)

Bar Archetype/1098 Howard/Alicia Brubaker, Man- ager/No Racial Bias/LTG# 1415 (42-8329)

Street samurai, mercenaries, and other talent-for- hire frequent this run-down but private establishment. Its value as a hiring hall for muscle to back up corporate squabbles may explain why the Nighthawk still exists and is rarely raided by police.

### The Officer's Club (16)

Bar Archetype/2330 Filbert/Jiro Shinawa, Manager/ Bias Against Non-Military/LTG# 2415 (74-9437)

A hold-over from the pre-occupation days, the Officer's Club retains a military atmosphere, with its antique weapons, martial prints, and photos of past heroes. Clientele consists primarily of soldiers and mer- cenary types. The I-Marines also like to come here, but usually insist that non-Marines be cleared out before they arrive. Any who are reluctant to leave are dealt with harshly.

### Rick's Place (13)

Large Restaurant Archetype/56 Gold Street/Simon Cohan, Manager/No Racial Bias/LTG# 1415 (44-1314)

Based on an old flat-screen flick, Rick's features slowly rotating ceiling fans, artificial potted palms, and a piano player named Sam (whose actual identity changes regularly). Service is bad and drinks are watered, but all the same, Rick's is the major hangout for shadowrunners, particularly those anachronistic types who collect old movies.

### Yoshi's (10)

Mid-Sized Restaurant Archetype/1582 Folsom Street/ Hua Chon Pak, Manager/Bias Against Metahumans/LTG# 2415 (26-8654)

Moderate prices and good food highlight this Japa- nese/Korean restaurant, which is quite popular with tourists. Most of the food is soy-substitute, but that rarely presents problems. Yochi's is said to be a hang palace for some Seoulpa Ring members.

## GOVERNMENT AREAS

### City Hall (20)

300 Polk/LTG# 1415 (21-1765)

Rebuilt to replace the City Hall that burned down in 2011, the new Hall is a starkly modern building of black and white marble, sweeping staircases, cramped, un- comfortable offices, and an unreliable ventilation system. The mayor and the city council meet here each day, doing whatever a city council does during enemy occupation. Much debate goes on, but little real decision-making. The Japanese governor deals with all important matters.

Council meetings are broadcast on trideo. Particularly spirited sessions make popular viewing, and it seems that the pettier the issue, the more vituperative the confron- tation. One of the most entertaining in recent memory occurred when City Councilman Dan Tuber tried to thrash Mayor Paul Morgan with his cane in a dispute over the color tile to be used in city public restrooms.

### The Presidio (19 and Main area west-northwest of Downtown)

LTG# 80001 RESTRICTED

Formerly an American military base, the Presidio is now the domain of the Japanese Imperial APCs who patrol the perimeter, and do not hesitate to use their weapons if anyone ignores their orders. The Presidio is home to Imperial Governor Shiro Kawanaga, a tough but fair ruler who descends from an ancient Japanese noble family.

## CORPORATE BUILDINGS

### Aztechnology Pyramid (21)

Corporate Office Archetype/600 Montgomery Street/ LTG# 1415 (79-3289)

Sold to its current owners in 2035, the Pyramid has undergone considerable renovation, having been converted into what the Azzies call a "pseudo-arcology" for Aztechnology employees. The interior includes spacious offices, recreation areas, living quarters, and medical facilities for employees and their families. Restricted by the company, and wary of anti-Aztlan sentiments, those who live and work in the Pyramid rarely venture outside. Most of Aztechnology's Pacific and West Coast operations are coordinated here, making this location second only to the corporation's massive Seattle installation.

Allegedly, Seretech has managed to infiltrate about a dozen employees into the Pyramid. Aztech suspects something, but has no idea how to locate any plants. The Aztechs will richly reward anyone with info on the identities of the sleepers.

### Federated Boeing (25)

Corporate Office Archetype/225 Bush/LTG# 1415 (88-0990)

The aerospace giant maintains offices in San Francisco, but the building is so ugly that many Japanese consider it an eyesore. The Federated Boeing logo, a massive stainless steel affair, is placed specifically to reflect late afternoon sunlight directly into the eyes of occupants of nearby buildings.

### Fuchi Industrial Electronics (27)

Corporate Office Archetype/110 Sutter/LTG #1415 (29-0416)

North American headquarters of the powerful cybertech corporation, the Fuchi building is a masterpiece of understated neo-classical design, its interior an intimidating warren of dark wood, marble, and indirect lighting. The heavily guarded workshops and labs are hidden behind multiple electronic interlocks and are under constant observation. Fuchi makes extensive use of wage mages, who make periodic sweeps of the building. This extensive security makes corporate espionage against Fuchi almost an exercise in futility.

### Kenshi Electronics (23)

Corporate Office Archetype/464 California Street/ LTG# 2415 (44-2867)

As heavily guarded as any Japanese corp headquarters, Kenshi's differs from the others in employing many non-Asians as clerical workers and even low-level executives. Metahumans find work as janitorial staff, but must pass a rigorous security check when they arrive and leave.

### Nippon United (26)

Corporate Office Archetype/1 Sansome/LTG# 1415 (45-4312)

A new company with plenty of capital, Nippon United purchased this building, former headquarters of the bankrupt Hiowaru Data Systems, and rapidly converted it into one of the most modern facilities in the city. NU's aggressive corporate tactics have made enemies of both Renraku and Fuchi, and rumors of a new corporate war are flying thick and fast.

### Renraku Corporation (22)

Corporate Office Archetype/555 Montgomery Street/ LTG# 1415 (39-3633)

This towering glass, steel, and chrome edifice is an eyesore to some and a monument to others. Renraku specializes in the "golden handcuff" treatment, providing its employees with every comfort, from luxurious offices and accommodations to recreation, lounges, enclosed gardens, and so on. Expected to spend long periods of time in their offices, employees are less reluctant to do so in such posh surroundings. Renraku's private security keeps watch over the building, maintaining tight security.

### Tokugawa Technologies (24)

Corporate Office Archetype/580 California Street/ LTG# 1415 (29-4791)

Few in San Francisco objected when this lot's previous occupant, a department store whose decor reflected the worst and most self-indulgent of the so-called "postmodern" movement, was demolished and replaced by Tokugawa Tech. The current high-rise is surfaced with refractive material that makes it appear to change color through a spectrum of cool blues and greens as the day progresses. Tokugawa's offices are small, but comfortable, and its range of luxuries (cafeteria, gym, and sauna) is limited compared to the other corporate headquarters in the area. Seeking to remedy this, Tokugawa is now taking bids from contractors on expansion of its employee facilities.

## BRIDGES

### Bay Bridge (28)

Once an ugly industrial span, the Bay Bridge has been extensively rebuilt and buttressed since the Japanese occupation. The major artery between Oakland and San Francisco, the bridge is jammed daily with rush-hour workers. By day, members of the SFPD are on guard, and they can be lax in enforcement of travel pass regulations. When the bridges close down for the night, however, heavily armed Imperial Marines man the toll booths and approaches to the bridge, opening fire on any vehicle that approaches too closely.

Midway along the bridge is Treasure Island, a former American military installation that now serves as barracks for the I-Marines. A tunnel, also heavily guarded, goes through the island.

### Foran Bridge (29)

First designed in the 1950s by the famous architect Frank Lloyd Wright, the Foran bridge languished in obscurity until traffic pressure brought the public's attention back to it. Renovation was begun in 2000, but social upheavals delayed completion until 2016. Some claim the bridge has dramatically improved traffic congestion in the Bay area, while others say that it has simply created another highway to gridlock.

Whatever its value, the Foran Bridge, better known as the Butterfly Bridge, is a beautiful structure, with its soaring twin lanes diverging near the middle of the bay to create a man-made island. The island, originally parkland, provides yet another base for the Imperial Marines and bay-patrol vessels. Both ends of the Butterfly Bridge are guarded in the same fashion as the Bay Bridge.

**Golden Gate Bridge (not on map, near Presidio)**

As one emerges from the Marin Tunnel, the Golden Gate Bridge is the first sight that greets a visitor to San Francisco. The enduring symbol of San Francisco has retained its bright orange color and its characteristic double-span architecture. The newer features are a second deck and on-ramps to allow for increased traffic, both added in the late 1900s. The I-Marines guard all approaches to the bridge, showing no mercy to anyone without a valid travel pass.

## TOURIST ATTRACTIONS

Following are some great places for those still into that secret agent/company man kinda stuff.

**Alcatraz Prison (not on map, northeast of Downtown, in Bay)**

No Racial Bias

Still crouching in mid-Bay as an ugly reminder of bygone days, the buildings of Alcatraz are in such hazardous condition that the Japanese occupation government has declared them off limits. Occasional boat patrols inspect the island, but authorities do not enforce regulations too harshly. The former home of such colorful figures as Machine Gun Kelly and Al Capone is a powerful enough lure that a small but steady stream of illegal visitors still treks to the prison. It is possible that the restrictions on visits reflect more than concern for public safety. No statistics exist on how many illegal visitors get to Alcatraz each year, so no one knows how many disappear mysteriously. I have heard stories of small parties vanishing in the night, leaving behind only a few tattered shreds of bloody clothing. I also knew a street shaman a few years back who was so sure that an evil force inhabited Alcatraz that he ended up migrating to Seattle. Since then, I've run into other shaman who say the same thing, claiming that something has been visiting them in their dreams.

**California Academy of Sciences (not on map, west of Downtown)**

Golden Gate Park/No Racial Bias/LTG# 4415 (23-4388)

This vast, sprawling complex of exhibits, offices, and labs sits in the middle of Golden Gate Park. The Academy includes a natural history museum, planetarium, library, gift shop, and the Steinhart Aquarium, still acclaimed as one of the best in the world. The Steinhart includes a fine collection of rare marine creatures, including the only family group of Merrows in captivity. As might be expected, it is the site of extensive metahuman rights protests.

**Candlestick Park (not on map, south of Downtown)**

Extensively damaged during the social unrest of the early 21st century, "The Stick," as it is affectionately known, was razed and completely rebuilt in 2024. The Giants and 49ers still play here, though the non-Japanese players live mostly in the suburbs. The San Francisco Whales of the Japanese besaboru league also play their own version of the great American pastime, and have amassed a respectable record against teams from the Japanese homeland. Urban Brawl has been banned, forcing the hometown San Francisco Terminators to play in Oakland.

**Coit Tower (30)**

Telegraph Hill/No Racial Bias/LTG# 2415 (65-6431)

Perched atop Telegraph Hill, Coit Tower is a symbol of San Francisco almost as widely known as the Golden Gate Bridge. The view of Fisherman's Wharf from the Tower is exceptional. The 70-meter-tall tower was built in 1933 with money from the estate of Lillie Hitchcock Coit, a San Francisco pioneer. The Japanese government has carefully restored the frescoes decorating the building's interior. Coit Tower is a popular tourist spot, but a pair of I-Marines stands guard to eject troublemakers.

**De Young Art Museum (not on map, west of Downtown)**

Golden Gate Park/Bias Against Geeks/LTG# 4415 (33-4025)

Opposite the Academy of Sciences, across the landscaped Music Concourse, is the De Young. The numerous treasures housed here range from an impressive collection of Mayan frescoes to the Crane collection of Modern elven masterpieces. The former, pilfered from their temples more than a century ago, are considered part of Mexico's stolen cultural heritage by Aztlan, which is demanding their return. The De Young so far refuses to part with them.

**Fisherman's Wharf (31)**

No Racial Bias

Among the least-restricted areas of San Francisco, the Wharf normally teems with tourists, who are observed but rarely bothered by SFPD officers and occasional I-Marines. Here, one may purchase fresh fish (or a soyfish substitute for the less affluent), crab cocktails, chowder, abalone, squid, and other seafood delicacies. Numerous restaurants line the wharf, many with spectacular views of the Bay. Souvenir shops are also abundant.

Moored here are several vintage sailing ships that may be toured for a small fee. The ships include the square-rigger *Balclutha*, the schooner *C.A. Thayer*, and the submarine *U.S.S. Pampanito*. This last is an irritant to the Japanese government, for the *Pampanito*'s crew sank five Japanese ships during World War II. The ship remains here, however, because she is such a popular attraction.

Many other attractions crowd the Wharf, including the Cannery, the National Maritime Museum, Ghirardelli Square, and the Cable Car Turnaround. Though some noises have been made about converting the cable cars to a maglev system and eliminating the turnaround altogether, no one takes the idea seriously.

### Golden Gate Park (not on map, west of Downtown)

Over 400 hectares in area, Golden Gate Park dates back to the 1860s. Since the occupation, much of the park has been transformed to a more Japanese style, but many traditional landmarks remain. These include the Conservatory of Flowers, a huge, ornate greenhouse filled with palm trees, orchids, and other exotic greenery; the California Academy of Sciences (see above); the De Young art museum (see above); the Japanese Tea Gardens (expanded and renovated by the occupation forces), numerous lakes, playing fields, trails, and kilometers of winding roadway. Still one of the most peaceful and inspiring places in San Francisco, the park is heavily patrolled by the SFPD and I-Marines.

### The New Ginza (32)

Kearny Street, between Bush and Columbus, was purchased, in its entirety, by a consortium of Japanese corps after the occupation, then converted into a smaller version of the famous Ginza district of Tokyo.

At night, New Ginza's neon signs flash garishly in all colors as Japanese businessmen and hostesses crowd its streets. The cacophony produced by taxis, bicycles, pushcarts, and street peddlers is deafening. Police and marine patrols are lax, and virtually anything is for sale if one has the proper price. The occupation authorities do not crack down on the New Ginza, realizing that it is an important safety valve for San Francisco's overworked Japanese population.

## MISCELLANEOUS

### Captain Whizbang's (not on map, far west of Downtown)

Small Store Archetype/5759 Geary/No Racial Bias/Thomas Albert, Manager/LTG# 4415 (23-0432)

Though small, this shop is a haven for San Francisco musicians and the small but active counter-culture. Ostensibly a music store, where one may buy virtually any imaginable rock or jazz instrument (no one knows where Albert finds room for all his stock), Whizbang's doubles as a free forum and coffee shop. Saturday night jam sessions often lead to spirited political discussions, as well as much mutual griping about the Japanese occupation and the inherent weaknesses of corporate neo-feudalism.

### Joe's Shadowtech

No fixed address or LTG/Joe Knight, Manager

In a city where shadowrunning is virtually a capital crime, those who supply the needs of runners are few and far between. Joe Knight, an itinerant technofreak, has taken it upon himself to provide various illegal gear, as well as the odd weapon, to those in need. Finding Joe's current location is never easy; he and his friends are ever-vigilant against discovery by the occupation authorities.

### Norwood Simsense Theater (34)

609 Sutter/No Racial Bias/LTG# 1415 (75-9500)

Tourists and non-Japanese patronize the Norwood, which shows first-run, largely unedited simsense productions. It also offers idyllic documentaries of life in Japan, which, true to form, gloss over the growing problems of the imperial-corporate feudal state.

# CONFEDERATED AMERICAN STATES

## HISTORY

### 2032

Led by senators from Alabama and Georgia, a major walkout of legislators from the southern bloc threatens to derail the merging of the United States and Canada. As the rest of the U.S. Senate argues over new tax structures and fund allocation, the delegates from ten southern states meet to discuss secession.

### 2034

Alabama, Arkansas, Florida, Georgia, Louisiana, Mississippi, North Carolina, South Carolina, Tennessee, and Texas vote to secede from UCAS. Though the UCAS is reluctant to lose the natural resources and tax revenues from the southern bloc, secession goes smoothly. National Guard units loyal to the seceding states are allowed to break away, reforming under a new name, yet retaining some of their old equipment. Aztlan, newly withdrawn from the Native American Nations, is the first to recognize the Confederated American States. The former governor of Alabama is voted pro tem president of the CAS until regular elections can be held.

### 2035

The CAS senate votes to make Atlanta the permanent capital. As the new government reels under demands for economic aid from its member states, Aztlan begins a military takeover of southern Texas. Despite the efforts of the Lone Star Militia and the Texas Rangers, Austin is lost before the invaders are stopped. The new Texas capital becomes the sprawling metroplex of Dallas/Fort Worth.

In the CAS fall assembly, Texas demands military backing to regain her lost lands. Though the pro tem government sympathizes with its largest state, disorganization keeps it from mobilizing any significant aid. Texas announces its withdrawal from the CAS, again becoming a Republic.

Aztlan forces remain in place as the Republic of Texas petitions for assistance from the UCAS. Fearing magical reprisals, the UCAS politely declines. Within the month, chagrined representatives from the Republic of Texas come before the CAS senate to apply for re-admission.

### 2036

Texas rejoins the CAS. The CAS government legis-

lates a new tax structure that meets with wide-spread disapproval. CAS elections are scheduled for the fall and campaigning focuses heavily on taxation.

Large portions of New Mexico and Oklahoma join the CAS, though the government intends to exclude residents from participation in the upcoming elections until a distinct border can be determined. Elections are sporadic and ill-run. Most pro tem officials are elected by default.

### 2039

Senate hearings begin in the CAS to investigate charges of racial prejudice against metahumans. The committee's shocking report verifies that conditions amount to slavery in most states. The Native American Nations impose heavy trade sanctions on CAS to speed up metahuman equality laws.

### 2040

Campaigning for CAS presidential elections heats up, with the Metahuman Protection Act as the most publicized issue. Coalitions of orks, trolls, and elves lobby for equality. The elections run more smoothly this time and the competition for all offices is fierce. South Carolina Senator Joseph Alexander is elected President, with Florida's former governor Jeanette Malory as Vice President. Several metahumans are named to key cabinet posts, which persuades NAN to lift some of its sanctions.

### 2044

The Confederated American States is accepted into the United Nations. President Alexander is re-elected. Mississippi Senator Timothy Newstrom is the new Vice President. Texas leads the CAS embargo on all Aztlan goods after the power-hungry nation annexes the remainder of Mexico.

### 2045

President Alexander dies in office. Though some believe he was assassinated, no conclusive evidence emerges. Vice President Newstrom assumes the presidency, becoming little more than a puppet for cabinet members. Secretary of State Gabriel McCoy fills the Vice President's post, and becomes the only force keeping the cabinet in check. Despite fierce mudslinging, McCoy is elected Vice President by popular vote.

**2048**

Edna Wallace, former governor of Louisiana, is elected President of CAS. Jeanette Malory returns to the Vice Presidency. Newstrom retreats to self-imposed exile in the Louisiana swamps. Anonymous death threats to the former president force Governor Ivory McCabe to declare martial law in the southern portion of the state.

Scandal rocks the CAS cabinet as Secretary of State Douglas Bennett is discovered dead with his elven mistress. Innuendos of policlub involvement fill the press. Headlines scream "Government Cover-Up!" as President Wallace approves a gag order on police and federal investigators assigned to the case. National Guard units are called to escort the suspect from the courthouse following the arraignment.

**2049**

The "Racial Revenge" trial of Bennett's accused murderer begins. The proceedings quickly turn into a media circus. Despite President Wallace's gag order, several facts important to the defense are aired on Atlanta's evening news. Hostile witnesses from both sides confuse the issue with dogma and political slogans. A mistrial is declared near year's end. The suspect is moved to Texas' new maximum-security facility to await a change of venue. Texas Ranger units replace the National Guardsmen outside the prison.

**2050**

Oklahoma City is named as the new trial site for the Bennett murder trial. Each side prepares new expert witnesses, cautioned that inflammatory remarks will be punished by stiff jail sentences. Evidence linking the defendant to a brutal policlub surfaces, further injuring the defense case.

In Atlanta, thousands of orks, trolls, elves, and dwarfs converge on the capital, calling for increased awareness of the metahuman's plight. Members of the militant Metahuman Organized Rebellion (MOR) accuse the Confederated American States of encouraging genocide by their inaction.

## GOVERNMENT

Notoriously conservative, the CAS government is structured to emphasize the importance of the popular vote. To ensure that a representative will more accurately reflect the wishes of his constituents, there is one congressman per 15,000 people. Each state must have at least two representatives present for all sessions. This level of public interaction has made passing any legislation a lengthy process.

>>>>>[What it's made is any attempts to pass real laws impossible. It takes weeks just to call the fraggin' roll.]<<<<<
—Beekeeper (12:31:24/09-12-51)

>>>>>[Hey! This is a non-annotated posting! What gives!]<<<<<
—Netsujo (17:51:49/09-19-51)

>>>>>[Oh well, gee wiz, I was wondering what that coding was in the file header, drek-head.]<<<<<
—Beekeeper (08:38:12/09-21-51)

Fights in the House, not limited to verbal volleys, are frequent and well-televised. The most recent bill passed by both the House and the Senate makes carrying firearms (and other explosive or projectile weapons) into a government building a capital crime, punishable by death.

>>>>>[Ignore the B-person. This sounds like a real law to me.]<<<<<
　　—Gator (16:47:19/10-13-51)

>>>>>[That one falls under "self-preservation." It ain't the wackos *outside* that they're worried about; it's the wackos *inside* that make them nervous. They're worried about one of their own packin' a Uzi and wasting one of his fellow esteemed colleagues who starts to blather.]<<<<<
　　—Beekeeper (06:51:38/10-16-51)

Each state, including the Confederate sections of Oklahoma and New Mexico, is required to provide three senators. This ensures that no stalemate can ever occur within a state's ranks—there will always be majority rule. With a two-thirds vote, the Senate can block any legislation that passes the House. In turn, a two-thirds House vote can block any bill passing the Senate.

>>>>>[Legislative ping-pong anyone?]<<<<<
　　—Wango (21:17:31/12-19-51)

The final power over any legislation lies in the President's hands, for he can veto any bill passed by the House and the Senate. Though the Confederated American States President is influential, his power is tempered by the House of Representatives and the Senate's power to remove the President from office.

CAS foreign policy is dedicated to non-interference and isolationism. Though the Confederated American States is strong financially, it is small. The Secretary of State makes every effort to deal evenly with all parties, but makes it clear that the CAS will not be compromised in any way. Nor will Confederate forces be used to intervene in another nation's politics. Foreigners are welcome within CAS borders as long as they obey the rules and do not jeopardize Confederate security. After that point, they are either expelled from the country or sentenced to the maximum prison term allowed by law.

>>>>>[Militarily, the only thing that the CAS has going for it is one Heavy Strike Carrier Battlegroup, based around the *Atlanta*, some light and intermediate Surface Action Groups, and a handful of subs. No boomers.
They do, however, have enough ground/air forces to strangle themselves fiscally. Having incorporated what air assets they had after secession into the Army command

structure, CAS may have the strongest standing army in North America. And most of it is aimed at Aztlan.]<<<<<
—Sgt. Pruit (06:14:45/01-13-52)

## ECONOMIC STRUCTURE

For hundreds of years, the states that today constitute the Confederated American States have been known for their fierce independence and respect for tradition. Much of this region's wealth came from cultivation of the land and exporting its natural resources. Thus, when the United States government tried to take control of all natural resources in 2002, the southerners felt that was going too far. Less than 30 years later, they became a separate nation.

>>>>>[One of the reasons the states broke away was the fact that the South had gained some hefty clout during the first quarter of the 21st century and they saw the industrially heavy and politically malleable Canadian provinces as a threat. That, coupled with President MacAlister's ill-concealed contempt for Southerners, made many people begin to wonder where their best interests lay.]<<<<<
—Beemer (08:15:21/11-18-51)

By the end of the 20th century, most industry in the North had relocated to the southern United States in search of cheaper labor, better tax breaks, and lower overhead. When the secession occurred, most of the businesses found it advantageous to also become independent. The CAS offered such attractive tax breaks to those industries remaining within CAS borders that old allegiances became superfluous. Many of these businesses are now international corporations, with their own standing armies and global influence.

>>>>>[Of course, those tax breaks and that same pro-corporate legislation eventually cut the CAS tax base by 40 percent. Talk about cuttin' off your foot while trimming your shoelaces.]<<<<<
—Longhorn (21:47:08/11-28-51)

The changing climate and high export fees forced most of the country's farmers out of business. Much of the land once used to grow fresh produce has been taken over by conglomerates marketing soy products. Huge, sprawling factories churn out vast quantities of this synthetic food, barely keeping pace with the demand. Large, corporate-owned farms still grow fresh vegetables, but the taxes on such items make these operations rare.

The Confederation's location also plays a role in its economic stability. Bordering Aztlan, the Native American Nations, the United Canadian and American States, as well as the Caribbean League, the CAS has become the northern hemisphere's shipping hub. With its huge, international airports and several key water ports, it is almost impossible to ship anything without crossing CAS borders. Fast, efficient truck lines make deliveries across the continent at reasonable fees. "All roads lead to CAS," according to a popular variation of an old saying.

>>>>>[And because of the high tariffs and such, the Confederated American States is the black-marketeer's Promised Land.]<<<<<
—Hangman (13:59:20/12-18-51)

>>>>>[For those so inclined, here's a comparison of what things cost in the CAS, compared to what they call standard. Prices, of course, subject to change without notice.]<<<<<
—Beekeeper (17:39:48/02-03-52)

| CAS COST OF LIVING | |
| --- | --- |
| **ITEM** | **COST** |
| **Weaponry** | |
| Ammunition | 60–70% |
| Explosives | 100% |
| Firearm Accessories | 75% |
| Firearms | 70–80% |
| **Clothing and Armor** | |
| Armor | 150% |
| **Surveillance and Security** | |
| Communications | 200% |
| Security | 300% |
| Surveillance Countermeasures | 300% |
| Surveillance Measures | 200% |
| Vision Enhancers | 100% |
| **Lifestyle** | |
| Lifestyle | 75% |
| **Electronics** | |
| Electronics | 200% |
| **Cybertech** | |
| Biotech | 100%* |
| Bodyware | 300% |
| Cyberdecks | 300–400% |
| Headware | 200–300% |
| Internals | 200% |
| Programs | 200–250% |
| **Magical Equipment** | |
| Foci 250% | |
| Hermetic Library | |
| Computer | 200% |
| Hard Copy | 125% |
| Magical Supplies | 250% |
| **Vehicles** | |
| Aircraft | 200% |
| Boats | 70–80% |
| Ground Vehicles | 70–80% |
| Military Vehicles | |
| Surplus, Ground | 125% |
| Other | Market Price |
| *(DocWagon™ is not available in rural areas) | |

## WEAPON FINES AND PUNISHMENT TABLE

| Weapon Type | | | Offense and Fine | | |
|---|---|---|---|---|---|
| | 1 | 2 | 3 | 4 | 5 |
| Type | Possession | Transport | Threat | Use | Intent |
| (A) Small Bladed Weapon | — | — | 500¥ | 1,000¥/3 mo | 2,500¥/1 yr |
| (B) Large Bladed Weapon | — | — | 1,000¥. | 2,500¥/6 mo | 8,000¥/1 yr |
| (C) Blunt Weapon | — | — | 500¥/3 mo | 1,000¥/4 mo | 2,500¥/1 yr |
| (D) Projectile Weapon | — | — | 1,000¥/3 mo | 2,500¥/6 mo | 5,000¥/1 yr |
| (E) Pistol | — | — | 3,000¥/1 yr | 6,500¥/2 yrs | 15,000¥/3 yrs |
| (F) Rifle | — | — | 5,000¥/1 yr | 10.000¥/2 yrs | 25,000¥/3 yrs |
| (G) Automatic Weapon | 1,000¥ | 5,000¥/1 mo | 7,500¥/1 yr | 15,000¥/3 yrs | 40,000¥/4 yrs |
| (H) Heavy Weapon | 15,000¥/3 yrs | 25,000¥/4 yrs | 5 yrs | 10 yrs | 15 yrs |
| (I) Explosives | 1,500¥ | 5,000¥/1 yr | 4 yrs | 15 yrs | 20 yrs |
| (J) Military Weapon | 50,000¥/2 yrs | 100,000¥/2 yrs | 5 yrs | 7 yrs | 10 yrs |
| (K) Military Armor | 10,000¥ | — | — | — | — |
| (L) Ammunition | 500¥ | — | — | — | — |
| (M) Controlled Substances | 750¥ | 2,000¥/6 mo | — | — | — |
| (CA) Class A Cyberware | 2,500¥ | — | — | — | — |
| (CB) Class B Cyberware | — | — | — | — | — |
| (CC) Class C Cyberware | 10,000¥ | — | — | — | — |
| (CD) Unlicensed Cyberdecks and Matrix Software | 5,000¥ | 15,000¥/6 mo | | | |

# ATLANTA

## FACTS AT YOUR FINGERTIPS

A century ago, Atlanta was considered a model city for the future, and it has lived up to some of those expectations. Indeed, with its current police policies and efficient transportation systems, Atlanta is at least a model city from the megacorp point of view. Not everyone is satisfied with the status quo in this modern sprawl. Among the slums and the shadows are those who dream of change and revolution.

The Atlanta sprawl has no real boundaries, but is part of the urbanspill stretching down the east coast of the North American continent. The region known as Atlanta begins roughly south of the Appalachian Mountains, east of Birmingham, and north of the southern Georgia wastelands.

Atlanta is the seat of government for the Confederated American States, the State of Georgia, and the City of Atlanta. It is also home base for several top-500 international megacorporations in the fields of communications, computers, insurance banking, textiles, and soft drinks.

## ATLANTA AT A GLANCE

**Population**: 6,000,000+
   Human: 68%
   Elf: 3%
   Dwarf: 2%
   Ork: 23%
   Troll: 3%
   Other: <1%
**Density in Populated Districts:** 450+ per square mile
**Per Capita Income:** 26,500¥ (roughly $125,000)
**Below Poverty Level:** 26%
**On Fortune's Active Traders List:** <1%
**Corporate Affiliation:** 56%
**Persons of Government Employ:** 5%
**Means of Commuting to Work:**
   Air Commuters: 2%
   Electric Vehicle: 24%
   Internal Combustion Vehicle: 8%
   Public Transportation: 49%
   On-Site Workers: 16%
   Other: 1%
**Education:**
   High School Equivalency: 41%
   College Equivalency: 20%
   Advanced Studies Certificates: 6%
**Hospitals:** 81
**Felonious Crime Rate (city police statistics):** 11 per 1,000 per annum
**LTG Access Number:** 1404

## GOVERNMENT

The government of Atlanta is headed by a democratically elected mayor and a city council who serve four-year terms. The current mayor is Drew Anderson, elected to his first term in 2048. The government of Atlanta, unlike that of most other sprawls, prefers to handle many of its civic responsibilities itself rather than contract out to corporations. Atlanta has its own police, sanitation, and transportation departments. Franklin Associates Incorporated provides fire control, the only service for which the city does contract.

Atlanta is also home to the Georgia state government, which is slowly becoming obsolete as the city of Atlanta spreads to envelop the state. Currently, the power of the state government is only marginally greater than the city's.

The state government consists of a one-chamber legislative house whose members are democratically elected to two-year terms. The head of the executive branch is the governor, who serves four-year terms. Donald Prester is currently serving his second term as governor. The mutual hate between Mayor Anderson and Governor Prester has also increased the tensions between state and city government.

The Atlanta sprawl is also the capital of the Confederated American States. The CAS government is based out of a huge complex of buildings and facilities called Freepark, located in the eastern portion of the sprawl around the Stone Mountain Monument.

## TRANSPORTATION

Getting to Atlanta is easy. The Hartsfield International Airport is constantly expanding to meet the increasing volume of traffic. As a hub for larger air-travel corporations, Hartsfield has suborbital flights to almost any destination worldwide. The airport also offers regular supersonic flights to other North American cities as well as to several Western European destinations.

Intercity travel and business commuting are reasonably efficient. Atlanta has an excellent public transportation system run by MARTA (Metro-Atlanta Rapid Transit Authority), which is contracted as a non-profit utility company. Though the use of electric grid cars never caught on in Atlanta, the sprawl's excellent road and expressway system compensate somewhat. Major expressways include I-75, I-85, and I-20, which cut through the sprawl and serve as arteries of traffic flow.

Two so-called perimeter expressways serve the sprawl. The oldest is 285, which is now buried in the heart of Atlanta because of the city's expansion. The outer perimeter is 985, but it too is becoming buried in urban expansion. There is talk of adding yet another perimeter expressway that would stretch into neighboring states.

The commute of choice for Atlanta's corporate elite is via helicopters and VTOL aircraft. Many corporate executives choose to live in the mountains of northern Georgia and commute to work by private or company aircraft.

Between commuters, media, emergency medical teams, police, and advertisement blimps, the Atlanta skyline buzzes with activity at all hours. Riggers are in high demand among the Atlanta corporations. The city government maintains a central control tower that attempts to monitor air traffic over the city, but accidents do happen.

## LAW ENFORCEMENT

Just as there are several levels of government in Atlanta, so too are there several levels of law enforcement. The CAS controls Dobbins Air Force Base located inside the sprawl, and the Fort Bennings infantry base just south of Atlanta.

In case of a city emergency or catastrophe, CAS troops could respond quickly. Additionally, the state of Georgia maintains a State Guard made up of volunteers who gather for training three times a year. The State Guard is little more than a formality these days, however. They are poorly trained, poorly coordinated, and lack real military hardware. In the event of a riot or similar occurrence, it would be largely up to CAS troops to keep law and order.

Actual day-to-day law enforcement in the Atlanta sprawl is handled by the city police department and the megacorporations. Atlanta's megacorps maintain sizable private armies of security personnel because the city government leaves so much law enforcement up to them. Any crime committed on corporate-owned grounds falls within the jurisdiction of that corp's security teams. Corporate security arrests the perpetrator and turns him over to the city police for prosecution. Over the past decade, corporate jurisdiction has expanded to encompass the residential areas of their employees and whole suburbs. The enforcement in these corporate sectors varies widely, but is usually much stiffer than city-patrolled areas.

Most of the city is patrolled by the Atlanta Police Force, or the APF. The city police maintain several forts throughout the sprawl and patrol the city with electric cars and helicopters.

As in most sprawls, some neighborhoods get more police protection than others. Crime runs rampant in many districts, and even the most violent ones warrant only casual investigation in districts such as Southtown.

The APF is an enormous organization, with branches for everything from homicide and computer theft to those for paranormal animals and astral invasion. The APF is considered seriously corrupt, despite the force's strong internal affairs division.

### ENTERTAINMENT AND TOURISM

Atlanta boasts several tourist attractions. These include those parts of Freepark open to tourists, several of the new CAS headquarters buildings remarkable for their sheer size and modern architecture, and also the Stone Mountain Monument at Freepark.

Another architectural attraction is the Cord Mutual Insurance building. This 500-story office building is one of the world's few skyrakers. Other Atlanta attractions include the Atlanta Zoo, the High Museum of Art, and any number of underground retail malls or nightclubs.

Atlanta also has a full complement of professional sports teams. These include the Falcons football team, the Hawks basketball team, the Braves baseball team, the Attack soccer team, and the Butchers, Atlanta's successful Urban Brawl squad. Next season, Atlanta will also welcome the Rebels combat-bike team who are relocating from Detroit. These teams play in either the old Peach Dome, the Omni Plaza, or the new Galaxy Dome.

### CRIME

Though Atlanta projects the image of a model city, its streets are just as dirty and its shadows just as dark as in other sprawls. Most of Atlanta's poor and homeless live in the Southtown district, which is also the source of most of Atlanta's organized illegal activities.

Seoulpa Rings have become the dominant form of organized crime, driving the Yakuza out of the extortion, gambling, and BTL chip rackets they so often dominate.

The Seoulpa Rings control large sections of the city, with territorial wars between Rings becoming commonplace. The Yakuza presence in Atlanta is mainly expressed through the sprawl's thriving black market, which they still control. Unlike the Seoulpa Rings, the Yakuza have no territorial claims, being a more nebulous entity bonded by black-market connections and individual loyalties.

Relations between the Yakuza and the Seoulpa Rings have improved recently. The Rings find it necessary to acquire hardware through the black market and the Yakuza recognize good business when they see it.

Youth gangs in Atlanta tend to be small and not particularly powerful. Seoulpa Rings usually recruit among older gang members, which keeps the average age of gang members low. Also, gang activities are largely controlled by the Ring whose territory includes the gang's turf. Gangs are often little more than pawns for the Seoulpa Rings' extortion and BTL-pushing rackets.

Pressure from the Seoulpa Rings have made go-gangs increasingly popular among the disillusioned youth of Atlanta. These gangs are not tied to one Ring's territory, which means they can often get away with more without exciting the ire of any one Ring. Go-gang members tend to be much tougher and older than turf gangs.

### LANGUAGE

City Speak in Atlanta is similar to the pidgin languages that have evolved in other major sprawls. The influx of corporate Japanese in the early part of the century has given the developing language a bias toward Japanese vocabulary.

Listed below are some slang words common to the Atlanta sprawl to help you get along in the streets any time you venture out of the corporate sectors.

**Dark Tower** or **The Tower** n. The Cord Mutual Insurance skyraker.

**Domers** n. People who live around the Fulton County Stadium.

**Fultons** n. Street slang for the APF. Stems from Fulton County Police before the city's consolidation.

**Killground** n. Refers to the old Fulton county stadium. Stay away from it.

**Mad Castle** n. Any of the APF fort stations throughout the sprawl, particularly the one near Southtown.

**The Park** or **The Rock** n. Short for Freepark, the CAS government complex. The Rock refers to Stone Mountain.

**Thrill Cave** n. Any of the underground night spots, especially one whose entrance is secret or restricted.

**'Town** n. Southtown

**Whiners** n. Electric patrol cars of the APF. So called for the highpitched whine they emit at high speeds.

>>>>>[Doctor Philip Tanner? Doctor? Who are you fooling? Listen, folks, I've read this Atlanta piece and it's the real story, but I also know the guy who wrote it and he's no doctor. He's just putting on the dog.]<<<<<
—Io (17:45:33/10-01-52)

>>>>>[Take Tanner's advice on the Killground, chummers. A lot of people go there to sneak a peek and become the main attraction.]<<<<<
—Doog (20:03:01/2-21-52)

>>>>>[Certainly the dominance of the Seoulpa Rings over their Yakuza enemies can be attributed to the group initiative common in small-group structures such as the Rings over the tradition-burdened decision-making process of the Yakuza clan. An example of how social evolution breeds anarchy. I laud Dr. Tanner's work.]<<<<<
—Omega (08:08:09/2-22-52)

>>>>>[Sure, the zoo's a great place to visit. Nice paranormal collection. Of course, you have to go through a couple blocks of the hell Atlanta calls Southtown before you get to the zoo. And some of the stuff you meet on the streets *outside* the zoo look more like they belong inside.]<<<<<
—P.O.M. (13:56:48/2-24-52)

>>>>>[Go Butchers!]<<<<<
—Kid (14:32:24/2-24-52)

>>>>>[Dr. Tanner neglected to mention a couple of things about security enforcement in Atlanta's corp sectors. The corp security boys will grab you and rough you up something good for so much as spitting on the sidewalk, unless you've got a valid corp ID. I don't recommend any ladies going into the corp sectors alone if they're young and not corp-affiliated. Nobody controls those security boys.

Also, that part about the corp teams turning you over to the city for prosecution is a bunch of drek. The corps forget that real quick if they catch you doing anything really illegal on their grounds. Then those security boys become judge, jury, and executioner. I know because I've been there.]<<<<<
—Icepick (20:43:28/2-26-52)

>>>>>[I'd agree with that. I heard about a guy who was wandering in a corp sector and got jumped by a gang of corp kids out for a few laughs. When security arrived, they sent the brats home, roughed up the guy a little more, and turned him over to the APF on charges of assault and resisting arrest.]<<<<<
—Doog (21:23:02/2-26-52)

## HISTORY

### EARLY 21ST CENTURY

The Summer Olympics of 1996 showcased Atlanta to the world community as a prosperous city, growing fast and strong as Americans moved south to work in warmer climates. Then, at the turn of the century, the city experienced a large influx of domestic and foreign business because the tax structure and climate made both life and doing business more pleasant. This influx included several Japanese corporations relocating their North American headquarters.

All through the early decades of the 21st century, Atlanta continued to grow at an alarming rate. Gradually the city lost the battle against overcrowding and the resulting lack of transportation and educational facilities. As taxes rose to alleviate these problems, the corporations no longer found the incentive to relocate here.

The effects of these early decades still exist today in the overcrowding in the northern suburbs and a lingering animosity toward the Japanese and other representatives of foreign corporations. Several policlubs based on warped ideals of national and racial purity still exist in Atlanta.

### SECESSION

Revolution was in the air throughout the start of the century, with Aztlan forming and the United States of America fragmenting. Everywhere, society was breaking down into smaller and smaller units of government in the slow process toward anarchy. The secession of ten states from the UCAS marked the beginning of rapid historical changes for the city of Atlanta.

During the restructuring of government following secession, the City of Atlanta government annexed large portions of the sprawl, causing several county governments to dissolve and some public agencies to consolidate. The Fulton County Police Department, which had served most of Atlanta, was combined with police forces of the annexed regions and renamed the Atlanta Police Force.

The city government divided Atlanta into several districts, each electing councilmen to the city's legislative body. This annexation was the beginning of the tension that has developed between state and city governments.

### BLACK MARKET

Atlanta's black market was born almost the same day the CAS government decided to adopt its own currency standard rather than basing the economy on the nuyen. At first, the market was run by independent businessmen (who called themselves Fixers), but gradually the Yakuza moved in and took over the illegal market.

The black market served as a great money-laundering machine, making its profits by laundering the new CAS bills for real nuyen. As inflation soared and the CAS bills became more and more worthless, the black marketeers became richer and richer. By the time CAS finally capitulated and returned to the nuyen standard, the black market had become a powerful permanent fixture in Atlanta.

When the market no longer had money to launder, the black marketeers had to find new sources of income. They accomplished this through more traditional black market operations. The market became the medium through which all manner of items were funneled into Atlanta. Smuggled goods entered without taxation, and illegal goods such as military weaponry, BTL chips, and vat organics found their niche in the market as well. The prosperous black market has become the trademark of the Atlanta Yakuza and also serves to employ a host of runners and street people.

### THE INSURANCE WAR

One of the darkest times in Atlanta's history was the so-called Insurance War that rocked the city in the year 2035. The war was between Cord Mutual Insurance and North American Eagle Life Insurance. The stake was the coveted insurance contract for all employees of the new CAS government.

Cord Mutual had just completed construction of their impressive skyraker and had relocated their home offices to the new Atlanta building. Meanwhile, North American

Eagle had a long-standing tradition of reliable service in Atlanta, which made them the candidate favored for the governmental contract.

The clandestine war of terrorism between the companies is thought to have started on June 8, 2035, with the simultaneous explosion of six Geas jets in flight from their Atlanta departure point. Geas Airline was insured by North American Eagle, which paid out enormous sums both for the jets and for civil suits by relatives of slain passengers. No connection with Cord Mutual was made at that time.

What followed was a sweep of assassinations of vidstars and entertainment personalities across the continent, and especially in Atlanta. The only connection between the victims was that they all held large policies with North American Eagle, which was beginning to have difficulty paying off its policies.

At some point, it is thought that North American Eagle's corporate investigators made a connection between a suspected assassin and Cord Mutual. Not much is known except that North American Eagle began funding a terrorist organization known as the Medusa Sisterhood to retaliate against Cord Mutual.

The Medusa Sisterhood made a series of vandalous attacks on Cord Mutual-insured corporations and individuals. Cord Mutual responded with attacks on the Sisterhood as well as on more North American Eagle targets. What began as a clandestine corporate power struggle became a bloody war, claiming the lives of hundreds of insured. The media finally broke the story, acting on rumors of the two corporations' involvement in the rash of violence sweeping the sprawl. The coverage caused the CAS government and the City of Atlanta government to come down hard on both corporations, ending the war.

In the aftermath, Cord Mutual was able to provide evidence of North American Eagle's funding of the Medusa Sisterhood, while no official connection was made between Cord Mutual and the independent operatives they used as soldiers in the Insurance War. North American Eagle was assessed fines and several top officials were arrested. Cord Mutual won the CAS insurance contract despite a storm of controversy.

Shortly after the fiasco, Cord Mutual went through a power struggle and several changes in upper management. There was also a supposedly unrelated accident in the company's skyraker, which led to the closing of the building's top 25 floors. Cord Mutual officials said only that it was declared structurally unsound.

## CURRENT TRENDS

In 2043, construction of Freepark was completed and the turbulent governmental transition came to an end. The tension between city and state only increased, however. If the two do not merge at some point, the State of Georgia will probably be ripped apart, only to be futher gobbled up by Atlanta.

In the aftermath of the Insurance War, corporations were given greater leeway to protect their own holdings because the APF had proved unable to protect the corps. Larger corporations were given law-enforcement juris-diction in their own corporate sectors, and corporate security continues to assume more prerogatives as we move into the fifties, with the government making no apparent effort to curb the trend. Most corporate citizens who are registered voters feel safer in their corporate sectors than in APF-patrolled city regions. Until this changes, the corporations will continue their strong-arm enforcement practices.

Mayor Drew Anderson promised Atlanta a great many things upon his election, but he's come through on few of his promises. Perhaps it is no longer possible for government to control the Atlanta sprawl. Few other sprawls have such a fine line between the have's of the corporate sectors and the have-not's of the streets.

>>>>>[I've dealt with the Atlanta black market, and I'm here to tell you that it infests the entire Atlanta business community. Most of the black marketeers have two or three connections, one of whom may be a Yak. Each contact has his own two or three connections, making a web of informants and traders. Deals for goods or infor-mation are arranged through a broad net of subtle con-nections, all of which involve nuyen, favors, and debts. Some blackmarket deals can involve as many as seven or eight middle men. The Atlanta Yakuza oyabuns are prob-ably the only ones who know all the connections and favors involved in the black market.

If you're an outsider, it's almost impossible to make good black-market connections. If you want some hard-ware, information, or shadowtech, and you don't have a Fixer or Yak friend in Atlanta, it's best to find a club owner or pimp. These are the guys who can point you in the right direction, though they probably only know just a non-Yak fringe dealer. I know because I've been there.]<<<<<
—Icepick (20:13:35/2-02-52)

>>>>>[Dr. Tanner's insightful look at the evolution of the world toward its eventual state of anarchy is refreshing. Of course, we must all continue to support the policlubs and organizations that agitate for peaceful social evolution. We must not let society stagnate in a quagmire of corporate control.]<<<<<
—Omega (09:01:11/2-11-52)

>>>>>[Who stuffed this Omega guy's shirt? Geez, fella, if ya wanna lose some hot air, go fill a McDonald's blimp, but don't fill the network with that drek. And…Go Butch-ers!]<<<<<
—Kid (14:56:34/2-11-52)

## NEIGHBORHOODS

### DOWNTOWN (A)

The heart of the Atlanta sprawl is the Downtown district, an area filled with blocks of skyscrapers rising into the sky and casting their shadows on the city streets far below. The sky is filled with buzzing commuter aircraft and video ad blimps shouting sales slogans. Once you leave the main highways, the streets are packed with traffic and the sidewalks are crowded with pedestrians.

Towering above all the downtown buildings is the Cord Mutual Insurance skyraker. This 500-story building vaults into the clouds like a great ebony pillar of metal and polymers. It is a tribute to modern civil engineering, though the top 25 stories are closed now because of structural instability.

The first 97 floors are occupied by Cord Mutual employees. The rest of the lower floors are leased to other corporations, who use the space predominantly as Atlanta regional offices.

Building security is very tight, with guards posted at every turbo lift. Tourists are normally allowed only on the 378th floor, though Cord Mutual will occasionally let VIPs and employee guests visit the 470th floor.

Cord Mutual is the largest insurance firm in the world, with policy-holders and regional offices around the globe. The current president is Heinrich Messer, who took control of the company shortly after the Insurance War. To many, Messer is a living icon of corporate greed. He climbed the corporate ladder using fear and violence and now rules Cord Mutual the same way. His office is on the 475th floor of the skyraker, the highest office in the city.

The only other top-500 international corporation that makes its home in downtown Atlanta is Hisato-Turner Broadcasting. This entertainment conglomerate controls the cable network for the Atlanta sprawl and the entire southeast. Besides their area subscribers, who receive the network through standard fiber-optic link, HTB broadcasts its signal to its orbital space platform, which distributes the programming around the world through satellite relays.

The HTB broadcasting antenna is the second-tallest structure in the sprawl, next to the Cord building. HTB maintains a 180-story office building next to its antenna. Almost every corporate function, from office work to studio production, is handled in the building. The only HTB employees not based in Atlanta are the space-platform personnel, those in the Osaka office, and the roving news crews who bring the world home in a nicely condensed 30-minute show. Hisato-Turner Broadcasting is remarkable among corporations for their support of environmental issues. The corp will not hesitate to bring its mass media clout to bear on any corporate peer who wantonly destroys the environment, especially those corps not advertising on HTB networks.

The State Capitol building is located at the south edge of the Downtown district. This building is famous for its gold-covered dome and historic architecture. Next to the Capitol building is the main APF fort, which services both the Downtown and the Southtown districts. The regular APF patrols from this fort are perhaps the only thing that keep Southtown inhabitants from bringing their crime and squalor Downtown.

Also situated in this cluster of public buildings is the Atlanta Intercity Air Control Tower. This city-sponsored control tower attempts to direct commercial air traffic over the city, with some success. Most accidents occur in foul weather and involve aircraft lacking modern Shortscan™ radar-imaging.

The Georgia Institute of Technology, also located Downtown, is one of the leading engineering universities in North America. In addition to turning out some of the world's most qualified technical personnel, its Bachelor's Degree in Hermetic Magic is also ranked as one of the top ten such programs in North America.

Though Georgia Tech is a state-sponsored school, most of the university's funding comes from corporate research grants, and most of the students attend on corporate scholarships. These students are already in-dentured to the megacorp, which is providing them with training. Georgia Tech also offers continuing education courses to keep older engineers up-to-date with the rapidly changing technical world.

Other places of interest in the Downtown district include the Omni Plaza, owned by Hisato-Turner Broadcasting. This combination of convention center, hotel, and entertainment arena takes up several city blocks. The Hawks play basketball in the Omni and the Butchers brawl here.

The downtown area also offers Atlanta's best in the arts. The ancient Fox Theatre is still Atlanta's equivalent of New York's Times Square for live performances. And the ever-expanding High Museum of Art offers fine collections of paintings and sculptures.

Finally, Atlanta's largest park, Piedmont Park, is in the downtown area. The park contains a small botanical garden and a man-made lake.

>>>>>[Take my advice, chummers. Never work for Mr. Messer and never work against him. All the rumors are true and then some. I know because I've been there.]<<<<<
—Icepick (14:56:22/2-19-52)

>>>>>[I heard that those top 25 stories of the Cord building are used for terrorist club and policlub meetings run by Messer himself. I also heard from a friend of a friend of a Cord Mutual wager that a lot of cargo goes up the turbolifts to those floors but not much ever comes down. Skyrakers make for expensive warehousing space. What do you think they're keeping up there?]<<<<<
—Doog (19:36:11/2-25-52)

>>>>>[Like I said before, all the rumors are true and then some. But it's better not to know or talk about it. I'm going to get these Shadowland network guys in trouble if I don't shut up.]<<<<<
—Icepick (16:03:50/2-26-52)

>>>>>[Go, Butchers!]<<<<<
—Kid (10:11:34/2-27-52)

>>>>>[Is it true that HTB hires mercenary types to combat environment-abusers?]<<<<<
—P.O.M. (15:21:34/2-27-52)

>>>>>[I knew a G.A. Tech wiz once. He knew his mumbo-jumbo pretty darn well. Those guys go through a hell of a curriculum there. I guess a lot of them are on corp scholarships, though, and become wage mages.]<<<<<
—He Xadeck (23:45:58/3-4-52)

## BUCKHEAD (AA)

If you're hip, cool, stylish, or just plain rich, Buckhead is the place to be in Atlanta. This section of the Downtown district offers every imaginable luxury and expensive vice. The elegant galleries and department stores are busy all day, and the night spots draw huge crowds every night.

Along with the nightclubs and retail showrooms that make Buckhead famous, there are several neighborhoods filled with expensive condominium buildings. Many corp executives live in company-owned condominiums in Buckhead during the work week, and then go home to suburbia on weekends. This saves them the hassle of commuting and lets them work longer hours every day. Many executives also take the opportunity to enjoy the nightlife away from home and family. Other residents of Buckhead's condominiums include the rich, young, and healthy who inherited their money or earned it through illegal means. These residents are the staple patrons of Buckhead's nightclubs and entertainment spots.

The retail stores in Buckhead are clustered in large shopping malls both above- and below-ground. Notable malls include the rustic Lenox-Phipps Gallery Mall and the more modern Futura Plaza. Several Buckhead malls, such as Futura Plaza, are located partially or completely underground, following a trend begun almost a century ago. These underground shopping malls (and the subterranean nightclubs) are now a trademark of Atlanta.

Stores in Buckhead include Atlanta's most fashionable clothing boutiques, run by famous designers such as Karl Grussberg and Nicole Tremont. These stores also sell the latest in home-entertainment technology and personal electronics. Futura Plaza even features a registered Body Enhancement Clinic, though the clinic does more cosmetic surgery for Buckhead's wealthy than cyber implants. Some of Atlanta's finest ethnic dining is also available in Buckhead. Most renowned are Raja's Indian cuisine and Hapsburg Castle's authentic German dishes.

No matter what the fad, cult, or trend, there's bound to be a Buckhead night spot to match it. These run the gamut from heavy rockers to restricted races to business privacy. Approximately ten large clubs dominate the Buckhead scene, constantly changing their names and images to match current trends in music and style. The owners, however, never change.

Dozens of underground clubs also exist. Some are large and open to the public, and some are accessible only via secret passwords and entrances. Known as "thrill caves," these spots cater to an elite clientele of regular customers and offer the utmost privacy. Becoming an accepted member of a thrill-cave crowd is a hard-won honor.

Thrill caves come in three varieties. Most of them are little more than meeting places for illegal connections or radical policlubs. Some are dance clubs that restrict their clientele to certain metahuman races or to individuals who have a taste for BTL-chipping or pornography. A few are simply simsense arcades combined with bars. These arcades are gambling dens, where the arcade players become something like professional athletes or racehorse jockeys. These arcade aces have their own code of ethics and ranking system, which does not welcome outsiders to play until they earn the right.

>>>>>[If you go to the club on Piedmont and East Paces Ferry, say hello to Vic the bartender for me and give him a good tip. I don't know what they call the place these days, but I'm sure Vic is still there.]<<<<<
—Doog (15:35:10/2-23-52)

>>>>>[The thrill cave arcades are really something. Those guys do some serious business. Most of the arcade jocks are just kids. Some sleazy agent will find one on the streets, get his reflexes boosted so high the kid can see raindrops in a hurricane, and then train him on the latest game. Almost none of those jocks lasts more than a year, and the few who do are considered old veterans. Most of the kids burn out when the cheap reflex-boost treatment dries up their synapses. Others just can't handle the pressure.]<<<<<
—Kid (16:42:46/2-30-52)

>>>>>[If you're planning to do some shopping at Futura Plaza or any place like it, you'd best have a gold credstick or they'll laugh you out of the store. And don't bother going to the designer boutiques unless you're pure human. They'll tell you the clothes aren't cut for metahuman physiques.]<<<<<
—Io (12:08:19/3-1-52)

>>>>>[Buckhead is one of the easiest places to make business contacts. Most corps have a Mr. Johnson who's a regular at some thrill cave unknown to the APF. I know because I've been there.]<<<<<
—Icepick (19:22:30/3-2-52)

>>>>>[Despite all this talk about illegal activities, I recommend you behave yourself in Buckhead. A lot of upper crust live there and the APF man the streets like watchdogs.]<<<<<
—Krieg (07:34:03/3-4-52)

## DECATUR (B)

Decatur is the district encompassing most of the eastern Atlanta sprawl. Within its boundaries are the CAS government headquarters, along with entire suburbs of housing for government employees. Decatur also includes the Emory University Campus and the new Galaxy Dome sports coliseum.

Freepark is without a doubt Decatur's main attraction. It was once a recreational park surrounding the Stone Mountain Monument, the largest rock in the world with the world's largest carving etched on it. Perhaps this carving, which depicts several great Confederate generals from the American Civil War, was the reason for selecting the park as the site of the new CAS government headquarters. Freepark is one of the most beautiful spots in Atlanta, with well-kept grounds that include woods and a small, clear lake. The huge CAS government buildings and new access roads dominate the area, but the scenic beauty of the setting remains.

The government complex includes more than a score of buildings. The president's Manor House sits atop Stone Mountain, with a view of Freepark and the sprawl. The largest building contains the legislature halls. Other buildings house various bureaucratic agencies and the still-developing CAS archives.

Most of Decatur consists of residential housing subdivisions for government employees, most of them modular clone housing projects for lower-middle income government workers. The neighborhoods where legislators and bureaucrats higher on the totem pole reside show a grander, old-South plantation style.

Emory University, founded in 1836, is on the western edge of the Decatur district. Emory has a long-standing reputation of fine education, and they have managed to keep pace with the rapidly changing world. Emory excels in business, law, and medicine, with a decline in liberal arts because corporate sponsorships now play such a major role in higher education. As a complement to a medical degree, Emory has recently begun to offer a two-year certificate in Medicinal Magic, and they also offer a minor in Shamanic Magic Studies.

Decatur's final attraction is the new, recently completed Galaxy Dome, the largest sports arena in the southeast and one of the few featuring trideo magnification of the playing field. The Falcons play football here in the fall, and the Rebels will take to the arena for combat bike events in the spring of '52.

>>>>>[Security at Freepark is a lot tougher than in the city, but so many people work there and so many tourists are always passing through that it's hard for them to keep secured areas secure. I've got a media friend who slipped in and bugged an army meeting, slick as you please. Actually, my friend is pretty good at that stuff, and actually I guess he did have a little problem with some guards. Well, never mind.]<<<<<
—Replicant (03:35:22/2-20-52)

>>>>>[I hear the magic studies at Emory are behind the times. They're afraid to teach anything that will cause too much backlash pain in the students.]<<<<<
—Io (19:06:28/2-27-52)

## DOUGLASVILLE (C)

The Douglasville district includes most of the western portion of the sprawl and stretches westward some distance along I-20. The annexation of this large western area was a major point of contention between state and city government during the restructuring of Atlanta. Douglasville is largely a residential area, with a fair amount of industry.

The Coca-Cola™ Company is the only top-500 international corporation that makes its home in Douglasville. The company recently relocated its home offices from the Downtown district to a new complex in Douglasville. Coca-Cola™ also operates an immense, completely automated production facility in Douglasville. Most Coca-Cola™ employees are either technicians who maintain and upgrade the machinery or else they are drivers who distribute the product to stores across the sprawl and to the area's more than 100,000 dispensing machines.

The residential areas are typical of suburbia. Wage slaves commute to work via MARTA or by electric car if they can afford it. For entertainment, Douglasville has some tame night clubs as well as the usual simsense and trid theaters.

On the westernmost edge of Douglasville, hovering on the edge of the sprawl, are whole zones filled with homeless people taking refuge wherever they can. These shantytowns are often nothing more than rows of crates and husks of abandoned automobiles. Some of the inhabitants are permanent fixtures, scrounging among the city's refuse to stay alive. Others are nomadic families who ride the lonely highways of the continent, stopping here and there in gypsy-fashion. Some say that these wandering families are key Yakuza instruments for smuggling black market goods into Atlanta. Perhaps that explains why these groups are usually so well-armed and potentially dangerous.

>>>>>[Tanner doesn't mention the old abandoned fun park along I-20. Not much is left now, but I hear that kids can still go there to have a good time. I guess they've stolen power and juiced up some of the old rides. They also say it's becoming a big hangout for the BTL pushers and gangs, but the corp kids haven't been scared away yet.]<<<<<
—Kid (16:14:25/2-4-52)

>>>>>[The go-gangs love to cruise out to the shantytowns and shoot up the place. The punks like to cruise around on the dirt roads, scaring people. But the laugh's on them if they run across a nomad family. Those people give new meaning to the word mean.]<<<<<
—Doog (02:03:49/2-12-52)

## MARIETTA (B, varies in corporate sector)

Once a suburb that grew up around I-75, the city of Marietta came to encompass the entire northwest section of the sprawl after Atlanta annexed other portions of the state. Most of the Japanese corporations that came to Atlanta at the turn of the century are located in Marietta. It also has heavily populated residential areas dominated by the influence of the many Japanese immigrants who followed the corps. Whole sections of Marietta are predominantly Japanese in culture, language, and food.

Oddly enough, the only top 500 corporation whose home base is in Marietta is an American firm, Shaw Textiles. The vast Shaw production facility spans the equivalent of 18 city blocks. It is here that Shaw produces the volumes of carpets, fabrics, and synthetic weaves that make it the number one textile firm in North America.

Shaw also controls several auxiliary plants in the northwestern corner of Georgia, outside the Atlanta sprawl. Shaw has been granted its own corporate sector for law-enforcement jurisdiction, which includes their production site as well as several nearby neighborhoods populated mainly by Shaw employees. Security enforcement in the Shaw sector is average at best.

Almost all the Japanese industries and office complexes in Marietta are regional branches of mother corporations based in Japan. The manufacturing industries include automotives, entertainment electronics, and electronic media production, and most of the service organizations are engineering-based. Several of the manufacturing plants have their own corporate sectors and maintain tight security.

Housing in Marietta comes in two basic forms. Anglo residents prefer house-style dwellings, which are more expensive, while the Japanese population seems to prefer high-rise condominium structures similar to housing projects in Tokyo. Housing corporations are building more and more of these condominiums as the cost of real estate continues to rise. The result is that the high rises are squeezing out the residential suburbs. Combined with the difference the two groups pay in property taxes, tensions between ethnic groups has built to a critical point. Hate-group policlubs are on the rise in Marietta, and the children mimic their parents by refusing to socialize with those outside their group. Some have taken it to the point of forming gangs, which fight it out on the street.

>>>>>[Just when you thought policlub members only hated metahumans. If you hear somebody say Little Chiba, they mean Marietta.]<<<<<
—P.O.M. (20:34:19/1-25-52)

>>>>>[Sony's got a little plant up in Little Chiba where they assemble cyberdecks. I guess shipping them into the CAS in pieces and then assembling them saves money.]<<<<<
—Io (18:17:47/2-21-52)

>>>>>[There're a couple places in those Chibatown areas where shadowtech is available if you've got the right connections. Not all of it is black-market, either.]<<<<<
—Icepick (19:33:25/2-27-52)

## NORCROSS (C)

Norcross and Marietta are sister districts. Like Marietta, Norcross experienced a huge influx of people at the turn of the century. The differences were that Norcross became overcrowded much sooner, and most of the Japanese bypassed the area. In general, housing in Norcross is much older and the standard of living is a little lower than in Marietta.

Global Business Computers is the only top-500 firm whose home base is in Norcross. The company's main production facilty and its home offices are located in the southern portion of the district. The site and nearby residential areas are all part of the GBC's corporate sector. Security is stringent.

GBC is known for its pioneering work in high-temperature semiconductors and its manufacture of custom supercomputers. The current GBC president, Elliot Wilson, has been instrumental in keeping the company moving forward and up the top 500. Despite the company's excellent performance under Wilson's management, his differences with the Board of Directors threaten to deprive him of his position.

The City of Atlanta's desire to annex a major portion of the North Georgia mountains into the Norcross district has become a serious point of contention between Mayor Anderson and Governor Prester. The foothills of these mountains are dotted with the homes of some of Georgia's wealthiest families and corporate elite who commute to work by air. Several of these residences might more aptly be called palaces, so elaborate are their accoutrements, grounds, and armies of security. The reason Atlanta wants to annex these regions is for the property taxes it could collect from these multimillion-nuyen residences. The residents oppose the annexation and resulting tax increase, while Governor Prester is against the city taking over the entire northeastern corner of the state. This could be the last straw in the conflict between city and state governments.

>>>>>[I've seen one of those mountain places. Even from a brief aerial view, I could see that the place was HUGE. The folks who live there must get lost going to the water closet.]<<<<<
—Krieg (04:56:20/2-15-52)

>>>>>[Norcross is wage-slave city, chummer. No reason to go there unless you've got biz with a corp.]<<<<<
—Kid (16:34:44/2-17-52)

>>>>>[Water closet, ain't we quaint?]<<<<<
—Loomer (22:51:39/2-19-52)

## SOUTHTOWN (E)

Crossing beneath I-20 is like passing between night and day. To the north of the interstate is Atlanta's prosperous Downtown district, and south of I-20 is Southtown, the blight of the Atlanta sprawl. Filled with the poor, homeless, and the violently criminal, it is a pit out of which rises Atlanta's dark tide of crime.

The only area of Southtown that the APF makes any real attempt to patrol is the zoo. The police maintain a tight cordon around the zoo, and they come down heavy on all types of misbehavior. Despite this protection, zoo attendance has dropped every year. The zoo authorities are hoping that their new paranormal collection, which opens in April 2052, will renew tourist interest.

The Atlanta Zoo already has a few paranormals, including a cockatrice, three harpies, and a naga. The zoo is a forerunner in developing handling techniques for these animals, and is also one of the leading facilities for observation and study of paranormals. The zoo also offers an excellent collection of mundane animals, particularly primates.

The most dangerous place in Southtown is the area around the Fulton County Stadium. After sports teams stopped using the large coliseum in 2024, Georgia Tech turned it into a research project. Researchers covered the coliseum with an experimental biotech membrane that was supposed to photosynthesize to produce food, turn solar radiation into usable energy, and purify the air it released into the domed interior of the coliseum. In effect, the coliseum was an experimental model for enclosed cities of the future.

Before the project could yield results, however, conflicting business interests and corporate sabotage resulted in a cut-off of funding, which eventually shut down the project. The dome was abandoned for almost ten years before the homeless began moving in and using the coliseum for shelter. Here, increasing numbers of homeless built their own microsociety based on primitive principles such as "might makes right." The City of Atlanta had no reason to interfere. All it meant to city officials was that a thousand "problem" homeless were no longer wandering the streets.

Ten years later, the people of the dome left in a mass exodus. On September 8, 2045, they poured out, taking refuge around the coliseum, building crude shelters in the old parking lots. Media teams who investigated the scene reported that the dome's membrane had gradually deteriorated to where it no longer allowed enough food to be produced for the masses living inside the dome.

The former leaders of this domed society had remained inside with their families, taking what food the dome membrane produced. The rest were reduced to scrounging for food wherever they could find it. This has gradually evolved to a kind of ritual of trial by combat whereby an outside "domer" can earn a position inside the dome. On seemingly random nights, the masses crowd back into the dome to view a kind of gladiatorial battle in which an outside domer tries to dethrone an insider. The domers refer to the special battlefield where these fights occur as the killground.

The rest of the time, the outside domers cluster about the coliseum, occasionally making forays out into the city for food. These outsiders still take orders from their leaders inside the dome, who have turned the outsiders' struggle to return to the dome into a kind of spiritual quest.

By day, the parking lots around the coliseum are quiet villages of sheet metal and plastic. At night, the residents either crowd into the dome or run mad through their streets of makeshift homes. The APF never goes near the domers, because beyond occasional theft, the domers rarely bother the outlying neighborhoods.

Some biotech and cyberimplant corps have taken advantage of the domer culture, using the domers as experimental subjects for new implants and cross-breed grafts. The domers clamor for these implant opportunities, hoping that the implant will give them the edge they need to win a spot inside the dome through combat. In reality, the majority of these crude surgeries end in useless metal appendages, savage disfigurements, and insanity. Most domers have at least one implant, with animal-part grafts particularly common. Unfortunately, these grafts also spawn the worst surgery catastrophes because the ex-perimental immuno-suppressants that make the grafts work often produce permanent hallucinogenic responses or physiological mutations in the patients.

Except for corp scientists, outsiders are not welcome in domer territory. Criminals and others fleeing their pasts may try to enter domer society, but the initiation required is said to be mysterious and potentially lethal. Only domers are allowed to witness the killground battles, which the domers will never speak of to any outsider. If rumors can be believed, the killground fights are exotic and deadly.

Besides the violence of areas such as domer territory, Southtown also offers all the known vices. Chiphouses have replaced the crack and ice houses of the 20th century. These dens are filled with BTL abusers who come to the houses to chip into their deadly fantasies. Some chip houses run by Seoulpa Rings also offer prostitution. The house "employees" are usually paid with a BTL hit, a destructive pleasure also available to any client so inclined.

On the streets, youths push BTLs for the Seoulpa Rings. Gangs often battle over the best street corners for pushing in order to earn more nuyen from their Seoulpa Ring bosses. The gangs also make rounds to collect extortion money from neighborhood businesses. At night, gangs roam the hardtops looking for mugging victims. Only a brave few individuals walk these streets after sunset.

Several warehouses in Southtown are centers of black market trade. Here is where the Yakuza store their contraband and where they handle any large-volume transactions. The security is actually rather light because the gangs and the Rings know which buildings are off-limits.

No matter how bleak the picture of Southtown, nearly a million people call the slums home. Some neighborhoods are simply places of poverty, where people are trying to survive as decently as possible. Many such Southtowners work either for local businesses or corporations in Douglasville, commuting by public transportation.

Local businesses range from the plethora of bars and disreputable night spots to discount food marts and Stuffer Shacks. Paying extortion to the local Ring has become a normal business expense that most owners simply accept without question. The APF extracts its own protection money, but business-owners know that unless the APF actually stops a crime in progress, they will never apprehend any criminal because follow-up police inves-tigations are rare in the district. On the other hand, the APF rarely questions shopkeepers who kill thieves in "self-defense."

>>>>>[I'd rather meet a whole gang on the street at night than one of those "brave few individuals." Southtown's got a lot of bad stuff, which includes some of the meanest samurai I've ever seen.]<<<<<
　　—Doog (02:31:21/2-14-52)

>>>>>[Yeah, I'm sure you've met a lot of them, Doog. They come looking for you, Mister Console Cow-boy?]<<<<<
　　—Io (12:03:53/2-14-52)

>>>>>[O.K., wise-off, I've met two dudes in Atlanta that I would call true samurai. And they were both bad to the bone. That specific enough for you?]<<<<<
　　—Doog (20:49:26/2-14-52)

>>>>>[Hey Doog, were they bad to the bone or bad to the chrome?]<<<<<
　　—Kid (17:12:24/2-15-52)

>>>>>[Southtown generates a lot of work for shadowrunners. The zoo's been known to hire runners to swipe paranormal specimens, and those biotech corps that butcher the domers are always looking for someone with the guts to snatch a look-see at the killground fights. The biotech boys want to know how well their latest Rottweiler jaw graft does in a real field test, and they hire dumb saps to go see. A friend of mine took one of those jobs. He never came back.]<<<<<
　　—Icepick (19:01:00/2-22-52)

>>>>>[Sorry about your friend, Icepick. I heard tell of a time when some domers broke into a Yak warehouse lookin' for food. Whatever they found and carted out was so valuable that the Yak want it back bad. They still haven't been able to find a team that can succeed at retrieving from the dome whatever the domers stole from the warehouse that night.]<<<<<
　　—Krieg (06:57:29/2-25-52)

# DALLAS/FORT WORTH

## HISTORY

By the late 1990s, Dallas residents could no longer scorn their Cowtown neighbors. With the crime rate soaring in Dallas, Fort Worth was attracting more of the international business traffic. Development around the Dallas/Fort Worth International Airport leaned heavily toward the smaller, safer city.

Large corporations with headquarters in Big D hired mercenaries to protect their property, leading to frequent clashes between the Dallas Police Department and heavily armed security teams over incidents of "excessive force." Undermanned and outgunned, the DPD could never hope to disarm the private armies within their city.

In 2009, United Oil Industries, whose headquarters were in Dallas, announced plans to build a multimillion-dollar convention complex at Eagle Mountain Lake, west of Fort Worth. Enraged unemployed and homeless workers stormed Uni Oil's headquarters and took control of the tower. While less righteous rioters looted the richly appointed offices, the leaders of the revolt demanded that fascist corporations be held accountable for the city's plight, that their assets be liquidated and used to revitalize the Dallas side of the metroplex.

Governor Hunter Carstairs called in Texas Ranger Assault Teams to quell the riot. After the smoke cleared, six mercenaries were dead, five Uni Oil employees were seriously injured, and 167 rioters were killed. Soon after, the state legislature passed laws giving corporate security forces carte blanche in dealing with armed intruders.

## STATE OF EMERGENCY

In 2011, thousands of refugees from the bloody dissolution of the Mexican government crossed the border into Texas, despite the efforts of the National Guard and Texas Rangers. Some fugitives headed for southern California, but most ended up in San Antonio, Austin, and Dallas/Fort Worth.

This influx of people overtaxed an already-crumbling welfare and housing system, leaving most of the new-comers on the street. Squalid shanty towns sprang up in vacant lots and under highway bridges. Incidents of racial violence increased as the crime rate soared. The police departments, severely outnumbered, voted to strike.

Declaring a state emergency, re-elected Governor Carstairs called in the National Guard. Meanwhile, Dallas

residents lived under siege, unsure which to fear more, the governor or the refugees. Before negotiators struck a bargain with the police department, 27 National Guardsmen were killed. Six shanty towns were razed in the struggle, but more sprang up to replace them, mere blocks away from the originals.

The corporations stepped in quickly, offering funds to shore up Dallas' failing welfare system following the "Year of Chaos." A battalion of lawyers drew up the terms of the assistance, requiring corporate approval of welfare dis-tribution. Governor "Headhunter" Carstairs had no choice but to agree to any terms they wished. The rules were drawn up to favor Fort Woth and Tarrant County. The poor-house system of relief was reinstated and work farms were established to contain the growing masses of homeless and to supply labor to the new construction projects in the area.

By 2014, a board of regents composed mostly of corporate executives and token government representa-tives was running the Dallas/Fort Worth municipal welfare-and-education system. Despite widespread dissatisfaction, the situation turned out well. Education programs were developed to teach the refugees English and a trade. Graduates from the program were guaranteed jobs with the corporations, as long as they kept their noses clean. The crime rate dropped significantly and economic stability began as the per-capita income rose.

## TREATY OF DENVER

In 2018, the Treaty of Denver precipitated another tide of refugees into the Dallas/Fort Worth metroplex. Over the next ten years, the population increased by 120,000 people. Most of these fugitives were better off both financially and in terms of education, however. Despite the increased crowding these newcomers added to the cities, they were welcomed for their new skills and business acumen.

## THE AWAKENING

The "goblinization" of 2021 drove out the traditional racial prejudices that formerly divided residents of Dallas/Fort Worth, unifying the two cities in a common fear. Governor Melissa Santiago-Ortega joined other governors throughout the United States and Canada in establishing metahuman detention centers. She strong-armed the Welfare Board into allocating the funds to provide adequate

shelter and sanitary facilities for the newly transformed population. Psychologists were brought in to find out if orks and trolls could be safely reintegrated into society. Specially trained units of the Texas Rangers ensured that the new metahumans did not fall victim to attacks like those their like suffered in other cities.

Though it was established that goblinization is not contagious in 2022, Governor Santiago-Ortega refused to release the metahumans without legal provisions for their safety. The Texas legislature was rocked when the Governor personally escorted ork and troll representatives into the senate hearings. In a moving speech, she stressed that the metahumans had been taxpayers before goblinization and, like victims of any disease, still deserved the protection and support of the government they had trusted.

It wasn't until 2023 that the Texas state legislature passed the Metahuman Bill of Rights, however, guaranteeing voting privileges and equality in housing, medical care, education, and employment. In 2024, re-elected Governor Santiago-Ortega presided at the opening of a multimillion-dollar Metahuman Resource Center in eastern Dallas.

### INDEPENDENCE

Angered over the newly formed United Canadian and American States' demand for revenue to help finance the nascent government, Texas exercised its constitutional right to secede in 2034. Together with nine other southern states, Texas became part of the Confederated American States. Though the UCAS was not happy about losing Texas' natural resources, the secession went smoothly and articles of cooperation between UCAS and CAS were drawn up.

Now that the armies of the United States no longer protected Texas' borders, Aztlan (newly seceded from NAN) moved into southern Texas. The Texas State Guard, originally part of the National Guard, joined Texas Ranger units in an attempt to stop the invaders. Despite the best efforts of these two, both San Antonio and Austin were lost before the forward push could be stopped. Dallas/Fort Worth became the new Texan capital.

When the other members of the CAS refused to send military aid to help drive out Aztlan in 2035, Texas resigned from the CAS. After support from the UCAS also fell through, the Texas state legislature realized its precarious position and applied for re-admittance to the Confederacy.

### UNEASY PEACE

A steady stream of refugees has been flowing to Dallas/Fort Worth from Aztlan since 2035, facilitated by an underground railroad run by the Aztlan Freedom League. The AFL is a nonprofit organization dedicated to sending medical supplies and food to the impoverished areas of Aztlan. Unofficially, it specializes in filtering people through the tight border and setting them up in a new life within the CAS. Many of these refugees end up in Dallas/Fort Worth, but their patrons take great pains to ensure that the government takes as little notice as possible. Most of the Freedom League's contributors are corporate executives and government officials.

Security along the Aztlan border remains high, but an uneasy peace reigns between the two nations. Trade resumed after the boundaries between the countries solidified, though Texas led the CAS in economic sanctions against Aztlan when it annexed the remainder of Mexico in 2044. When it soon became apparent that the territories were prospering under the Aztlan government, the strictures were lifted. In 2049, following the lead of NAN, Aztlan officially opened an embassy in Dallas/Fort Worth.

>>>>>[Not that we show them much hospitality around San Jacinto Day.]<<<<<
—Old Timer (12:22:44/03:27:51)

## BUSINESS

In direct contrast to the general domination of American business by Japanese firms, two D/FW firms made two major buy-outs of Japanese corps and changed the face of business in what was then still the United States of America.

In 2006, Texas Instruments executed a major coup by successfully suing Miroyama Electric for gross violation of patents. TI had to take the lawsuit through all levels of the Japanese legal system before finally forcing the appeal to its highest levels. In a surprise decision, it was ruled that Miroyama was guilty of the charges, and the management of the company was ordered to turn over its assets to TI. This they did, then committed seppuku.

>>>>>[Well, not quite. Mirayama was an embarrassment to many other Japanse *zaibatsu* because the company was actually partly owned by certain Hong Kong concerns. The TI situation was a perfect way for the *zaibatsu* to deal with them, believing that TI was on the verge of losing a major suit to Hitachi that would have handed the company over to them. TI didn't lose. Oops.]<<<<<
—Farmer Brown (13:41:15/12-10-51)

Two years later, Tandy Corporation surprised the world economic community by succeeding in a bid to purchase much of the assets of Nippon Electric (NEC). The funds to make the purchase came entirely from Texas millionaires.

>>>>>[And who in the area had recently come into a lot of cash? One guess...]<<<<<
—Farmer Brown (13:58:02/12-10-51)

This sparked economic warfare between Japanese and American firms. The resulting political and economic battles did much to destroy the independence of American business.

TI took the assets that it gained from Mirayama and has become the major supplier of semiconductor products at the wholesale level, competing with the Japanese cartels. There is little love lost between TI and Japan.

As a result of these two coups against Japan, the Dallas/Fort Worth business climate is tight and hot in international commerce. Japanese business intrusion has only recently begun to grow beyond a minor level.

Tandy Corporation has maintained its corporate headquarters in the downtown Fort Worth-area since the Tandy Tower complex was built in the late 1970s. The current management has just seen the end of a massive habitat project that extended the original Tandy complex over the Trinity River.

TI now covers the entire area around the intersection of Highway 75 (North Central Expressway) and IH 635. It towers over North Dallas as a symbol of Texas power and prestige. It contains manufacturing, research, residence, and entertainment facilities. TI has other buildings in Dallas/Fort Worth, but they are being slowly moved into the habitat. Only the government defense-research facility in Lewisville will remain.

In the mid-90s, General Dynamics Corporation purchased the major aircraft manufacturing assets of Lockheed Aerospace Corporation in order to control the lucrative advanced tactical fighter project. Lockheed had been the project leader on the contract bid, but the Fort Worth division of General Dynamics was the major manufacturing facility for the contract. The General Dynamics plant in Fort Worth was already huge, but now experienced an amazing increase in its capability, giving the economic recovery of the Dallas/Fort Worth area a major boost.

The good fortune of General Dynamics was late coming to the rest of the metroplex's aerospace industry. LTV and Bell Helicopter both had a hard time in the late 80s until the Osprey tilt-rotor heliplane and the C-17 heavylifter projects received full government backing. After several years, Bell and LTV began to cooperate to make better use of their combined expertise in composite materials, automated production, and CAE/CASE. When the UCAS/CAS split occurred, the two companies formally merged. Today the BeLTV company is the major producer of tilt-rotor aircraft, helicopters, and large aircraft components.

## FACTS AT YOUR FINGERTIPS

### WHEN TO GO

The average annual temperature in Dallas/Fort Worth is 19 degrees C. July and August are the hottest months, with a normal high of 30° C. January, the coldest month, has a normal low of 7° C. The humidity is high throughout the year, with an average of 82 percent in the morning and 55 percent in the afternoon. When combined with the high humidity, temperatures soar to levels that elves and dwarfs find constraining, especially in June, July, and August.

>>>>>[Oh great, five lines in and already we start getting the racist comments.]<<<<<
—Weaver (07:41:29/11-24-51)

>>>>>[Biology is not racist.]<<<<<
—Doc Dumain (10:13:03/12-02-51)

>>>>>[Unfortunately, there is no reason for the previous statement, other than bias.]<<<<<
—Medical Services Online (18:38:17/12-17-51)

The area has only 75.18 cm of rain annually, with May the wettest (10.92 cm) month and December and January the driest (4.32 cm). Pollutants hang over the city, trapped by the high humidity, until one of Texas' sudden storms cleans the air. This stagnant mist is pleasing to orks and trolls, who are often seen going about their business before the haze burns off in the afternoon heat.

>>>>>[Again!]<<<<<
—Weaver (07:48:06/11-24-51)

The best time to visit Dallas/Fort Worth is from late March through late May, when the temperatures are mild and the humidity low. June through September is also pleasant, but hotter and more overcast.

## GETTING THERE

### Plane

D/FW is a major hub for flights to and from the southwestern portion of the continent, as well as a stopping point for flights from around the globe. The DART line services both Dallas and Fort Worth, as well as the D/FW complex itself. These buses cost 9¥, one way. Cabs are also available. A cab ride to downtown Dallas or Fort Worth costs 25 to 30¥.

Love Field, a small air facility used by corporations, state officials, and Texas Ranger tactical units, is located in west central Dallas. Well-guarded, it is not open to the general public and does not offer interstate flights. Love Field is for intracity and intrastate travel by helicopter and other tilt-rotor craft.

### Automobile or Bus

Access to Dallas/Fort Worth from the UCAS is easy, with guards making only a cursory check of transit passes at the border. Entry from Aztlan or the Native American Nations requires more effort. Travel restrictions vary widely from nation to nation, and it can take several months to obtain the proper passes. Transit passes cost in excess of 40 nuyen. Dealing with a travel agent can significantly reduce the expense (they know who to bribe). Travelers should update the passport files on their credsticks before attempting to make any travel arrangements.

>>>>>[If ya know the right people, a shadow transit pass will run you between 200¥ and 500¥, depending on the quality. The checks that go down at the Aztlan border are much tougher than the NAN checks.]<<<<<
—Schemer (16:43:09/12-19-51)

For persons entering Dallas/Fort Worth through the Native American Nations, it is simpler to purchase a ticket on bus lines licensed to travel through tribal lands. Two lines offer regular trips to CAS: Jackdaw Ltd., a subsidiary of Spectrum Holoflix Entertainment Systems (SHES), and Falcon Express, partially owned by the Pueblo Council. Currently, there is no bus service from Aztlan. Most bus trips from the West Coast to the CAS cost about 175¥.

### Train

If traveling from Houston or Oklahoma City, visitors can take the NASA high-speed rail link to Dallas/Fort Worth. Built in 2009 by NASA and United Oil Industries, this above-ground train was constructed as a prototype for use in a proposed lunar colony. Propelled by a frictionless cushion of magnetic repulsion, it travels great distances at high speed.

Unlike the underground trains in cities like Seattle, the NASA Bullet Train is well-maintained and runs a continuous hourly schedule of departures. First-class tickets, which include a sumptuous buffet in the dining car, are 300¥. Second class is 200¥, while tourist class is 145¥.

>>>>>[We'll see how much longer it stays well-maintained. Currently supervised by a partnership formed by United Oil, who helped build the thing, and Ares Macrotechnology, who bought NASA, it's supposed to be handed over to the Texas government in 2055, per the provisions of the NASA buy-out.]<<<<<
—Hermes (21:19:13/01-08-52)

## WHAT IT COSTS

Prices are high in Dallas/Fort Worth, as in most CAS cities. Transit costs add 7 to 10 percent to the price of goods not manufactured in the CAS. Prices on citrus products, clothing, and locally produced electronic products are extremely low.

>>>>>[Not entirely true. Citrus products come in from the Rio Grande Valley and are subject to tariffs. There is also a great deal of truck farming done to the west and south of Fort Worth that keeps prices low and quantity high. Other fruits (watermelons, cherries, and especially peaches) are popular in season.]<<<<<
—Flute (11:09:34/02-15-51)

Hotel prices range from 30¥ on up. Barracks-style accommodations are available through the YMCA, YWCA, and Metahuman Salvation Army for as little as 2¥ a night. Breakfast is included with the deal, if you can take their brand of dogma before you eat.

Visitors new to Dallas/Fort Worth should take great care when dining out. The Tex-Mex food popular in the area produces volcanic results in the stomachs of the uninitiated. Though many restaurants offer a "temperature guide" on their menu, it is still best to inquire about the spices used in a dish before ordering.

>>>>>[If you look like an out-of-towner, odds are you'll get the "super spicy" sauce, whether you want it or not.]<<<<<
—Been There (23:58:41/12-16-51)

>>>>>[The best comparison is Mongolian or Szechwan Chinese…Look *OUT!*]<<<<<
—Been Burned (18:30:11/01-06-52)

## MAJOR BUSINESSES AND CHAINS

Following is a partial list of businesses with four or more stores in the Dallas/Fort Worth area.

### Department Stores
Luxury: Theimann-Markles, Ford & Stitcher
First Class: Filsons, Dali's
Family-Style: Wordsworth, Lears and Mervins, Penley's, Tintinnabulation
No Frills: TexMart, Winner's

### Groceries and Convenience Stores
Luxury: Solomon Ben David's
First Class: I.F.C. Groceries
Family-Style: Orchard Grocery, StopMart
No Frills: Pick 'N Go, You Bag MiniMarts

### Restaurants and Fast Food Places
Luxury: The Alamo, Mister H's, L'Escargot, The Haven, The Mansion
First Class: Mario's Gourmet Mexicano, Tokyo Royal, Old World
Family-Style: Pompanio Seafood, Mem'Sahib, Farfellow, Krunch's
No Frills: Burger Shack, Speedy Wok, Soy Salon, Hanna's Revenge

### Hotels
Luxury: The Busch Hotel, Loew's Resort, TripleTree Hotels
First Class: Hyatt Regency, The Pavilion
Family-Style: The Stratford, Red Carpet Inns, Sheraton Hotels
No Frills: Spenda Day Hotel, Cattleman's Rest, Comfort-Cubed

### Computers and Electronics
Luxury: Thin Ice, Maxwell's Electronic Emporium
First Class: The Wizard's Palace, Business Computers International
Family-Style: The Maze, Jack In, The Rescue Net
No Frills: Main Stream Computer Store, Bits O' Bytes

### Body Enhancement Centers
Luxury: Maverick Body Design
First Class: Lone Star Enhancements
Family-Style: BioTech
No Frills: The Clone Zone

## TRAVEL WITHIN D/FW

### Air

All Dallas/Fort Worth government buildings, as well as most corporate skyscrapers, major shopping malls, and hotels, have heliports for use by helicopters, tilt-rotors, and lighter-than-air vehicles. The heliports of the government and corporate structures are heavily guarded and a special permit is required to disembark on many of the towers. There are four intracity airlines: Lone Star Limousine Service, Armadillo Air Shuttle, Alamo Air, and Lockheed International Carriers. Loomis Armored Air Couriers provides transportation of sensitive materials or excellent armed escort for VIPs. Intracity air travel is an expensive service. A typical trip from Loew's Resort to

The Haven costs 145 nuyen, but many executives prefer the speed, efficiency, and security of air shuttles.

>>>>>[Hah! Once my shipment of Rapier III SAMs shows, there'll be hell to pay in this city!]<<<<<
— Texas Terrorist (18:41:45/11-29-51)

>>>>>[Oh, were those your SAMs? Well, sorry, but they came in handy.]<<<<<
— Avenging Angel (05:38:55/12-04-51)

>>>>>[Funny, I hear the air over the Aztlan-controlled section of Austin has been mighty quiet lately.]<<<<<
— Alliterative Anarchist (21:50:33/12-12-51)

**Car**
Dallas/Fort Worth has three local car-rental agencies, plus the larger CAS chains. All offer a variety of vehicles, with something for every taste and budget. A valid Confederated American States driver's license and insurance are required. Drivers from outside the CAS may obtain a provisional license for a 50-nuyen fee. Travelers from Aztlan are not covered by their insurance in Dallas/Fort Worth and must purchase short-term CAS insurance. Though such insurance is pro-rated according to the length of stay, it can be quite prohibitive. The typical cost of a week's insurance for an Aztlan driver is 400 nuyen. All drivers not native to the area are advised to check their insurance policies before attempting to drive in Dallas/Fort Worth.

>>>>>[I find all these mentions implying easy travel and access to Texas by Aztlan citizens troubling. The truth is that it is virtually impossible for a citizen of Aztlan to acquire a CAS entrance permit. Also, anti-Aztlan bias runs deep throughout Texas, making any kind of travel or business almost impossible for an Aztlan citizen.]<<<<<
— Aztlan Sentinel (09:30:12/10-29-51)

>>>>>[Listen, chummer. Take a good, hard look at a map of Texas someday and you'll notice large missing chunks. Then ask me why we hate you Az-ticks.]<<<<<
— Longhorn (13:45:18/11-02-51)

>>>>>[The land you refer to is now, and has ever been, historically ours. Learn to live with it, Longhorn. You'll never see it again.]<<<<<
— Aztlan Sentinel (21:48:49/11-17-51)

>>>>>[On the contrary, I see it all the time. In fact, I expect to be seeing you real soon now, too.]<<<<<
— Longhorn (10:41:12/11-22-51)

>>>>>[Remember Goliad! Remember Mexica! Remember San Jacinto! Remember El Paso!]<<<<<
— Darling Marie (11:41:12/11-22-51)

>>>>>[Three out of four ain't bad, chica, and remember what we did in Goliad.]<<<<<
— Mexican Streetfight (07:18:34/11-25-51)

Streets within the city are in good repair, though the city maintenance department seems to close lanes for repair in a haphazard fashion. A web of highways gridded for electric cars was added to the existing combustion-engine system, doubling the traffic load. However, the entrance and exit ramps were not upgraded and so present a constant hazard. Fuel-powered vehicles cutting into lanes designed for electric cars are also a danger, but the 500¥ fine is heavily enforced. Rush-hour traffic turns the city into a parking lot for hours on end. Traffic violence is not usually a problem except in poorer sections where go-gangs have been known to shoot up grid-locked cars just for sport. Highway travel after dark is not advisable, and the safety of residential areas depends on the section of the city.

**Bus**
DART offers free service within the downtown areas, with many routes and stops throughout the city. Bus schedules may be obtained at any restaurant or public office, as well as being permanently posted at the larger stops (when not painted over). Bus travel is no quicker than by car, but it leaves the worry to a combat-trained driver. Transit between Dallas and Fort Worth costs 2¥.

Violence on DART buses persuaded the company to include an armed guard (two after dark) on all routes. The addition of bullet-proof glass has also reduced the number of passenger casualties. Most larger bus stops are well-lit and include a manned security booth. Those stops without a manned booth have an emergency call box.

**Monorail**
The newest addition to the Dallas/Fort Worth metroplex is a monorail system, which travels around the downtown areas and between the cities. Stops at the major shopping facilities, hotels, and the Eight Flags Over Texas political park make this quick, air-conditioned mode of travel very popular. Progress is underway to add two additional monorail trains to the system: Cost is .5 nuyen.

## TOURIST INFORMATION

The Dallas/Fort Worth Convention and Visitor's Bureau is located just outside the Eight Flags Over Texas political park. The Bureau offers brochures, maps, and personal assistance. Tours of the cities, as well as excursions to Oklahoma City or Houston via the H-S rail link, may be arranged here.

Technicians in the Texas Ranger booth next to the Bureau will adjust a visitor's portable telecom to transmit a PANICBUTTON signal should he need help. The cost for this service is 2,000¥, and guarantees that Rangers will arrive within five minutes of receiving the signal. Heavy concrete, steel, or high-tension wires may affect the signal, so visitors are advised to avoid such areas if the possibility of trouble exists.

Visitor information may also be obtained in any Texas Ranger station or by dialing 2-FIND-IT. Operators will answer most questions about the city.

## LEGAL ASSISTANCE

The Confederated American Barrister's Association (CABA) has offices in Dallas/Fort Worth and can be reached at CABA-LAW. The CABA maintains a complete listing of lawyers able to meet most needs and budgets.

Metahumans will be referred to competent lawyers skilled in handling their special problems. Native Americans and Aztlan residents will be put in contact with their respective embassies.

## MEDICAL ASSISTANCE

Dallas/Fort Worth has numerous clinics and nine major hospitals capable of handling any medical emergency. Parkland Memorial Hospital provides excellent trauma care, specializing in wetware reconstruction. Baylor University Medical Center is a leader in cyberware development and installation, as well as organ-cloning and replacement. The Santiago-Ortega Metropolitan Hospital provides excellent care exclusively to metahumans. The D/FW paramedics are Texas Rangers with combat medical training. They maintain a large fleet of vans and helicopters to transport patients to hospitals. The DocWagon corporation recently signed a contract to operate inside CAS territory, adding their large, armored vans and helicopters to care for their customers.

>>>>>[The organization of the city's various "fast-response" medical assets has created an extremely volatile situation. The D/FWPD has its own paramedic/emergency service branch, which serves the city. The Rangers also respond to emergency calls within the city, as do dozens of private ambulance services. With DocWagon also on the scene now, the opportunity for conflict over a call has reached flash-over levels.]<<<<<
—Doc Dumain (09:32:16/12-16-51)

>>>>>[What Doc Dumain fails to realize, most likely because he is *not* a doctor, is that all the medical services he lists are professional. None would ever allow rivalry or unclear jurisdiction to place a client at risk.]<<<<<
—DocWagon Support (12:17:53/12-22-51)

>>>>>[What about that Hughes Stallion of yours that went down last week near Hurst? Any plans to deal with Blackthorne Medical over it?]<<<<<
—Programmer (14:12:51/12-23-51)

>>>>>[No comment.]<<<<<
—DocWagon Support (11:52:38/12-29-51)

Dallas/Fort Worth has the largest ratio of insurance companies per capita of any city in CAS. Visitors are encouraged to review their medical policies before visiting CAS. If their coverage is inadequate, they can purchase a short-term policy for as little as 175¥ per week. Visitors should carry an updated medical file on their credstick and keep a duplicate somewhere safe.

## CHIPS AND ALCOHOL

Located in the heart of the "Bible Belt," Dallas/Fort Worth maintains rigid control over the sale and distribution of legal drugs and alcohol. Beer and inexpensive wines are readily available in all grocery stores. Beer prices are extremely low, with a six pack costing as little as 3¥.

After a prominent senator's teenage daughter died from BTL-chip abuse three years ago, Dallas/Fort Worth cracked down on the trade in illegal simsense chips. Programs bolstered by private funds allow the city to run extensive education and rehabilitation programs. Sentences for possession of, and dealing in, these items are always the maximum, even for first-time offenders. Dallas/Fort Worth is building a maximum-security prison in the west Texas desert specifically for those convicted of dealing in illegal drugs and BTLs.

>>>>>[And public demand makes the dealers richer and richer. It's estimated that the smuggling of BTLs into D/FW is up 21 percent over last year. BTL-related crime is up 34 percent from this period last year. It is suspected that much of the BTL that reaches the streets is coming in from Aztlan.]<<<<<
—D/FW Observer (21:15:38/11-18-51)

## ENTERTAINMENT

Dallas/Fort Worth is the home of the Mesquite Rodeo, a southern phenomenon. This extravaganza of calf-ropin', bronc-bustin', and bull-ridin' takes place every weekend from April to September. Only non-chipped entrants are allowed.

The Dallas Cowboys home games are held in Texas Stadium. Visitors should plan to arrive several hours prior to game time. All spectators are scanned for weapons before entering the stadium.

For those who follow baseball, Dallas/Fort Worth has the Texas Lone Stars, a chipped team, whose games are played at Arlington Stadium. An unchipped team, the Texas Rangers, plays at the Southern Methodist University diamond.

For basketball fans, the Dallas Mavericks play in Reunion Arena, adjacent to the Hyatt Regency Hotel complex. The Dallas Diamonds play at Moody Coliseum on the SMU campus. These ladies are title champions and always a good draw.

For those who like their sport on ice, the Dallas Black Hawks play at Fair Park. A new combat bike team, the Texas Rattlers, opened a franchise here last year. They play their home games at Reunion Arena. Both Southern Methodist University and North Texas State University field fine Urban Brawl teams.

The Eight Flags Over Texas political park has a magnificent collection of Texas history and western art. The Reunion Arena hosts most megastars on tour, from the Maze to Nightmares to Classic Crystal.

For those who have the money, "members only" after-hours clubs offer entertainment from dusk until dawn. Take a full credstick, your best manners, and tell the cabbie you're a "member." He'll know where to go.


>>>>>[Yeah, the place that pads his pockets the most.]<<<<<
—Rattler (08:48:16/10-30-51)


## LAW AND ENFORCEMENT

Dallas/Fort Worth operates three levels of law enforcement (four, counting the private security forces of the corporations). Each has its own official jurisdiction, but overlap is inevitable.

### National Guard

Known for a time as the Texas State Guard following the short-lived secession, the National Guard is now an operational branch of the great CAS Army. It takes its orders from Atlanta. Should hostilities with Aztlan ever resume, the National Guard will operate as a true reserve, supplementing the front-line CAS Army units bearing the brunt of the fighting. Because of this, the Texas National Guard is well-trained and well-equipped.

### Texas Rangers

Technically the Texas State Police, the Rangers have evolved into more of a military organization since the year 2000. Comprised of many former and reservist members of the CAS military, the Rangers behave very much as the governor's private response force. Conflicts often develop with local law enforcement and corporate security over the involvement of the Rangers, whom the other two view as interlopers.

### Dallas/Fort Worth Police Department

The D/FWPD is still a municipal agency, though it is currently heavily subsidized by various corporate interests. Its juridiction extends only to the D/FW border; anything beyond is considered to be Ranger territory.

## DOWNTOWN

### DOWNTOWN AT A GLANCE

**Population**: 17,837,900
   Human: 48%
   Elf: 11%
   Dwarf: 3%
   Ork: 18%
   Troll: 19%
   Other: 1%
**Population Density**: 112.7 per square kilometer
**Per Capita Income**: 143,000 nuyen
**Below Poverty Level**: 37%
**On Fortune's Active Traders List**: 1%
**Corporate Affiliation**: 84%
**Education**:
   Drop-outs: 33%
   High School: 42%
   College Degree: 16%
   Graduate Degree: 9%
**Hospitals and Clinics**: 10
**Bishop's Crime Probability Level**: 7
**Felonious Crime Rate**: 24 per 1,000 per annum
**LTG Access Number**: 1214

### GEOGRAPHY AND DEMOGRAPHICS

Like most of Texas, the Dallas/Fort Worth area is broad flatlands, though it is covered with towers of glistening steel and glass. In the late 1990s, Dallas and Fort Worth were separate cities, with the bedroom community of Arlington serving the wealthy of both. By the early teens, floods of refugees from Mexico and the Native American Nations poured into the metroplexes, sending the crime rate soaring and the cities sprawling across the void between them. By the time Texas seceded from the remnants of the United States, the only division between Dallas and Fort Worth was one of public opinion.

The majority of the population lives in apartment skyscrapers around the downtown areas of Dallas and Fort Worth. Most low-level corporate executives live between the two in Arlington. The wealthiest corporate officials have walled villas along one of the many lakes around the metroplex. Garland is now almost exclusively an ork and troll neighborhood, with the wealthiest living near Lake Ray Hubbard. The elves have settled around Benbrook Lake on the southwestern edge of the metroplex, as far from Garland as possible.

>>>>>[Watch out for some of these villas, chummers. A friend of mine got geeked in her ultralight when she strayed too close to one on the northern edge of Joe Pool Lake. I'm not sure if it was a SAM or magic.]<<<<<
—Firebrand (08:51:62/12-12-51)

## POLITICS

There are two things that Texans are noted for, their passion for sports and for politics. The only major difference is that they like their sports clean but rough, and their politics dirty and rougher still. Mudslinging is not only favored, it is expected.

The upcoming gubernatorial race offers a good example. Incumbent Governor Angus Bilbruck maintains that the Texas Rangers stationed outside the embassies are for the purpose of protecting the occupants. City Manager Marla Abernathy, a troll and Bilbruck's popular opponent, insists that the governor posts guards on the embassies to satisfy his own xenophobia.

A political debate in Texas requires rigorous weapon-screening prior to the event, for both the audience and the politicians. Though this precaution has lessened the explosiveness of the debates, it has not totally prevented bloodshed. In 2023, Senator Franklin Moss became so incensed during a debate over metahuman rights that he challenged his opponent, Senator Victor Sanchez, to a duel. Moss' death the following morning was widely televised.

>>>>>[And has spurred a grassroots movement to settle all election run-offs in this manner. I can hardly wait.]<<<<<
—Wango (12:15:32/12-18-51)

>>>>>[Sounds wiz to me.]<<<<<
—Hugo (18:59:41/01-04-52)

## ECONOMY

The center of power in Dallas/Fort Worth is among the glass skyscrapers of both downtown areas, where many corporations maintain their world headquarters. However, the heart of the metroplex's economy is in the industrialized neighborhoods like Farmers Branch, Haltom City, Hurst, and Irving. The unique educational system in the Dallas/Fort Worth metroplex provides corporations with highly trained, motivated individuals with a strong loyalty to their patron.

>>>>>[Read: wage slaves.]<<<<<
—Expatriate (18:59:51/01-15-52)

Top fashion designers from around the globe come here to produce their creations. Exclusive boutiques in Grand Prairie cater to the rich and powerful, offering one-of-a-kind outfits at exorbitant prices. Among their clientele are super-sexy megastars and the wives of pretentious politicians. High-ticket shops in the local malls also carry the latest fashions.

As the gateway into the CAS from the west coast and Native American Nations, the Dallas/Fort Worth metroplex is the home of excellent trucking companies and courier services. No matter what the item to be shipped, someone in D/FW will be willing to transport it, for the right price.

>>>>>[Though the government and the corps themselves will deny it, the trucking and courier industries in the D/FW area are almost completely Mafia-controlled. Pay your consultation fees, and everything is wiz. If not...]<<<<<
—Buffalo Girl (07:47:51/12-19-51)

>>>>>[In the old days, the Mafia used to send messages by having a thug or two pay you a visit and break maybe a limb or two. Now, of course, there's Ritual Sorcery...]<<<<<
—Shane (13:50:51/01-12-52)

## NEIGHBORHOODS

### Addison (A)

Addison has become the core of the leading edge in electronics. Small chip manufacturers hover at the fringes of the two giants, Spectrum Holoflix Entertainment Systems (SHES) and Business Computers International (BCI). These two megacorps maintain a working relationship unique to the city. Operating under a system of cooperation, they offer an executive exchange program that allows low-level executives from both corporations to learn the workings of the other.

Both those companies, however, tread very carefully around Texas Instruments. It supplies them with the "Jellybean" components and wafers that they then modify manufacture of into final product. Since TI abandoned the retail market, dozens of smaller companies take the output of the giant to feed the demands of the consumer world. SHES and BCI are two of the most successful of those firms.

Breakthroughs by one are quickly utilized by the other, much faster than the rest of the industry. This cooperation has doubled the profits and security coverage. A high-tech entertainment complex is located between the two corporations and is only for use by corporate employees.

>>>>>(Spectrum and BCI make most of their yen by marketing simsense chips to the Middle East. The chips they export don't have to meet the rigid CAS standards for sensory-output limits. The result is that the chips that BCI designs and builds and Spectrum produces and records are very near, if not completely, what you and I would call a BTL.)<<<<<
—Southerland (08:48:27/12-16-51)

### Arlington (E)

The rotten core of the D/FW Metroplex is southern Arlington. After the University of Texas at Arlington moved to a new campus area in southeast Grand Prairie, the core of Arlington died. The areas adjacent to the Eight Flags park and Arlington stadium continued to prosper, but everything south of Highway 80 is dying.

The old General Motors assembly plant is the largest displaced-persons charity center on the North American continent. Thousands of refugees from the Aztlan invasion were processed through this building. It is now a residence for four thousand homeless people, and acts as a food center for several thousand more.

### D/FW Airport (A–B)

Dallas/Fort Worth International Airport merged with Grapevine to provide a single political and law-enforcement structure. In 2018, Las Colinas merged with Grapevine to form an international business center. Most of the international trading firms have their offices in Las Colinas and their warehouses in the Grapevine free trade zone.

### Dallas and Surrounding Areas (varies)

The northwest corner of Dallas county has become a warren of small-to-medium custom software and hardware manufacturers. There is a small Chinatown in Carrollton that has the finest Chinese restaurants in all of Dallas/Fort Worth. The I35E strip to Denton is populated with apartment complexes for most of the people who work in the north Dallas area. Lake Lewisville teems with people during the weekends.

Massive demands for economic "Equalization" from increasingly powerful minority pressure groups eventually split the city along the I30-I20 highway line. Northern Dallas continued to prosper because of the existing wealth and the new companies that sprouted to the north in the Sherman-Denison-Plano corridor. South Dallas continued to decline. After several nasty riots, the communities to the south of Dallas joined in a loose coalition to block any further growth or movement by the existing Dallas population.

Downtown Dallas hosts the Texas Senate in the Dallas County Convention Center. Many of the buildings vacated by businesses that failed in the general crash after the New York earthquake are now filled with government bureaucrats and agencies. The rest of the Downtown area is filled with insurance companies, banks, accounting firms, and such. To the north of downtown are many apartment complexes, condominiums, park residences, and grand mansions, a mixture of old and new money.

East Dallas is much as it was in the 90s. Small family homes, light business, and the like still make up most of the area.

Southeastern Dallas County started to flourish as the superconducting super collider was built. The entire area to the southeast of Dallas county blossomed into a strong set of small towns and cities. Many new and old firms established offices to supply the SSC research park.

### Farmers Branch (A)

This section of the D/FW sprawl is devoted almost entirely to industry. Motorola-Hiatsu and Texas Instruments, the two largest chip manufactures in CAS, are located here. They employ many orks and trolls from Garland, as well as many residents from downtown Dallas. The area's few shabby apartment complexes are usually rented out to go-gangers. The corporate landlords don't care what happens there as long as it doesn't involve their workers.

### Fort Worth and Surrounding Areas (varies)

The rot extends into Fort Worth from Arlington. The southeast side of Fort Worth is also depressed and almost ungovernable. A small corridor of safety exists between highway 80 and 130, but it cannot do much to redeem the east side.

West Fort Worth is the shining jewel of the entire Metroplex. Stretching toward Granbury to the south and Rhome in the north, from downtown Fort Worth in the east toward the Highway 80 - 130 split in the west, this area is still growing. The rich and powerful in Fort Worth have lived in western Fort Worth since the city was settled. Security is heavy, even oppressive, though the residents like it that way. Major features of this area include the Fort Worth Arts District, Carswell Air Base, General Dynamics, the Hulen Shopping Colossus, and the Ridglea Cultural Resort Villa.

To the north of downtown is the "North side." This area includes several residential districts and the world-reknowned Stockyards district. Much of the North side is dangerous, but the stockyards area is well-patrolled to protect the flood of tourists and visitors to Billy Bobs' Texas, the biggest night club and bar in the world.

Tandy Corp. and BeLTV are the leading industrial employers in the Fort Worth sector of Halton City. Many elves work for Tandy. BeLTV maintains small apartment complexes in the area, which they rent to their employees. Several good restaurants also cater to the workers.

Corporate mercenaries provide security for the neighborhood, often harassing non-employee visitors, unless they can provide a legitimate excuse for being there. Employees straying out of their corp's boundaries are subjected to similar treatment. Jurisdictional disputes between TanSec and BeLTV security forces are common and violent.

>>>>>(BeLTV uses Lone Star Security, based out of beleaguered Austin, for security. Lone Star has also been pushing hard for the D/FW police contract, but I don't think it's gonna happen.)<<<<<
—Wango (05:28:19/01-25-52)

Downtown Fort Worth is now filled with the offices of the Texas House of Representatives. The House meets in the old Tarrant County Convention Center. The two other big businesses are the Tandy Corp. in its own complex at the north of downtown, and the Bass Investment and Resource complex that fills the old Texas American Bank building. No major new buildings are in the Downtown area, but many of the older buildings have been completely rebuilt inside and excavated underneath to provide more floor space.

The area directly around Downtown Fort Worth has been completely reconstructed to fulfill the needs of the government and its employees. Security is high, but petty crime is a constant problem during the day.

The other areas of Fort Worth are a mix of safe to uncertain areas. The better-kept the houses, the safer you probably are.

Snaking through the D/FW complex is the Trinity River. After a series of devastating floods in the 1940s, the river was channeled into floodplains and overflow zones. During the 1970s and 80s, both cities adapted parts of the floodplains into recreation areas and public parks. A certain amount of residential construction was carried out in the flood areas, but a repeat of the 1940 floods in the late 80s forced both cities to restore the floodplains to open land.

The city of Fort Worth slowly extended and linked the parks and recreational areas to fill the floodplains with a complex of nature reserves and public parks. Dallas slowly followed suit and in the early 2000s, the entire river bed was made over into the same pattern of parks and unimproved zones.

A popular bike and walking trail winds its way from one end of the metroplex to the other. The metahuman community has virtually taken over this area and it is not at all unusual to find elves and trolls working together to keep the place in good repair. Also, this parkway is where most area shamans have their lodges. Do not disturb these marked areas unless you want trouble from all the police departments and the shamans.

Presently, Fort Worth is growing much faster than Dallas. In gross area, Fort Worth exceeded the acreage of Dallas several years ago, but much of the claimed land is unused and not really considered to be part of the city. The population of both is about equal, and will continue to grow in favor of Fort Worth.

During the state government's evacuation of Austin, the state legislature split between Dallas and Fort Worth. The Senate began to meet in Dallas, and the House of Representatives settled into Fort Worth. This split in the seat of legislative power continues to this day. The governor's mansion is in Dallas, but the governor normally has a private house in Fort Worth for political balance.

### Garland (C)

This once peaceful, suburban neighborhood is now the stronghold of the ork and troll population. The stores and apartment complexes cater almost exclusively to the larger metahumans. Most of this area is in poor repair, though not necessarily because of the occupants. It was a troll consortium, for example, that owned a group of

condominiums primarily housing orks that was recently condemned by the DFW Welfare Board.

Wealthier orks and trolls have private, walled residences along Lake Ray Hubbard. These estates do not have many security systems, but are heavily fortified and patrolled. Disputes over land boundaries are explosive and bloody, despite the residents' veneer of culture.

Travel in this part of the city should be undertaken with the greatest caution at all times, as the Texas Rangers are notoriously slow in responding to alarms in this area.

Jack In, Bit O' Bytes and The Clone Zone all have large branch stores in the malls near the juncture of Highways 30 and 635.

>>>>>[It's a sad commentary that orks, trolls, and other metahumans feel they have to separate themselves from the rest of society in order to live like human beings.]<<<<<
—Cobra (05:16:31/11-16-51)

>>>>>[Give me a fraggin' break, Cobra. You of all people wimpering about "metahuman rights." Gawd. Well, at least I can die now knowing I've seen it all.]<<<<<
—Rand (22:19:24/12-01-51)

### Grand Prairie (A)

Grand Prairie is the biggest manufacturing center for fashions on the North American continent. The destruction of New York gave hundreds of small shops in Dallas/ Fort Worth an opportunity that they grabbed with a passion. The shops and designers slowly filtered into Grand Prairie to take advantage of the plentiful office and light industrial parks. The central location allows the businesses to draw on the huge manpower pools of Arlington, Irving, and southern Dallas. The Dallas Apparel Mart is still the grand showcase for the designers, but Grand Prairie is the backroom for those designers. There are dozens of small retail stores that sell the latest in mens' and womens' fashions. If you want the best in tailoring, Grand Prairie is your destination.

Many art galleries and antique stores are also located here. Gold's displays exquisitely carved dwarf sculpture, ranging in size from massive to minuscule. If you don't see what you desire on display, a dwarf craftsman will be more than willing to create a custom piece for you. This is also the place to come in search of finely wrought jewelry done in southwestern, elven, or orkish style. Artisans are available at most shops to custom-design a piece to fit your personality and pocketbook.

>>>>>[Can somebody please tell me what in god's name is "elven" or "orkish" style? I guess carrying the racism forward, "elven" is delicate with natural themes and materials, while "orkish" is rough hewn and crude, but compelling. Right?]<<<<<
—Eve M. (14:51:31/12-24:51)

>>>>>[I think it means that if the work is done by an elf, then it is in the elven style. If it is by an ork, it is in the orkish style, and so on. Seems fairly reasonable to me.]<<<<<
—Sunday (09:24:48/12-28-51)

>>>>>[Oh it does, does it? Shows how much you know. In the art world, "styles" don't work that way. A style refers to the manner of presentation and content, such as classic modern, post-industrialist, or neo-impressionistic. Style has nothing to do with the genetics of the piece's creator.]<<<<<
—Artiste (23:58:37/01-14-52)

>>>>>[Hey, I've got a whole shipment of velvet elven paintings that I'm trying to unload. Contact me on the DFW "CityLink" network at LTG# 2214 (62-7156).]<<<<<
—Shiner (02:39:49/01-19-52)

### Irving (C–D)

Irving hasn't fully recovered from the Great Crash of 2018. This is the common name of the largest loss of civilian life during the Aztlan conflict. A Boeing 787 heavylifter delivering military supplies to D/FW airport crashed with its full load of ammunition and bombs on the downtown Irving area. The shockwave from the blast shattered thousands of panes of glass throughout the metroplex, adding to the casualties. The accident has never been successfully explained, but many theories exist.

The remnants of Irving are devoted almost exclusively to transportation services and the packaging of preprocessed foods. Rows of warehouses line the streets, some more well-guarded than others.

Dr. Pepper, Inc. has an elaborate complex here. Complete with its own medical center, grocery store, trivideo theater, and restaurant, it is a city unto itself. Pepper's security teams are well-trained and polite, a pleasant change from other corporate forces. Lone Star Security Van Lines is the leading armored transport system in the city. With a fleet of delivery vehicles, ranging in size from a minivan to an 18-wheeler, they can accommodate a wide variety of cargoes. Safe delivery is guaranteed or your money back. Black Cat Cargo Lines is a truck rental agency. Though they are expensive, their equipment is clean and reliable.

An additional note is the presence of the large Universal Brotherhood chapterhouse on O'Conner. Since the location was set up four years ago, the homeless and squatter population of the area has fallen off dramatically; the Brotherhood takes them in and rehabilitates them into viable members of society.

### Mesquite (B)

Mesquite is now the major petrochemical center for Northern Texas. For security reasons, the refineries are not the flashy cities of lights of old, but are uninspiringly bland building complexes. The fire department stations in this area are triple the size of stations in other parts of the metroplex.

### Richardson/Plano (A)

The Richardson/Plano area has become one of the most technically advanced parts of the metroplex. Many of the major Japanese and Korean electronics and high technology firms have their major southern presence in this zone. Aztechnology does not have an office here. Their offices are all in Fort Worth. Renraku has started a corporate facility that will, when finished, rival its arcology in Seattle. It is not scheduled for completion for at least 50 years, however. Texas Instruments has just completed its own habitat that forms a bridge structure over SH75. It forms the southern marker of the Richardson/Plano/Sherman/Denison commercial zone.

### The Mid-Cities (AA–AAA)

The mid-cities area of Hurst, Bedford, Euless, Colleyville, and North Richland Hills united to form a single governmental body, but the area kept the old town names to attract new citizens. The Mid-Cities Management District eventually filled the northeast corner of Tarrant county, excepting D/FW airport and Grapevine.

The Mid-Cities Combined Police Force (MCCPF) goes out of its way to enforce the law within the city limits, and will escort undesirables out with a friendly warning to find an alternate route on the return trip. Heavily financed by private donations, the MCCPF is armed with all the latest equipment available to security forces. They are not shy about showing excessive force to maintain a safe and quiet neighborhood.

>>>>>[The MCCPF still maintains its autonomy from the DFWPD, though there is much pressure on the MCCPF to allow assimilation. There are even rumors of members of the DFWPD working after-hours to make life hell in The Mid Cities.]<<<<<
—Jeeper (14:52:41/12-05-51)

The Wizard's Palace, an up-beat simsense and software store, caters to the most obscure tastes. Two small lore stores, Leviathan Lore Store and Dust Devil Lore, operate under the protection of the MCCPF. It is common knowledge that Lieutenant Governor Carlos Villaneuva owns a controlling interest in the Dust Devil establishment.

>>>>>[The situation in D/FW and in most of the so-called Bible Belt, for that matter, is interesting. Historically and socially a religious, conservative region, D/FW has on a few occasions been rattled by theological and philosophical conflicts over the nature of magic. Fortunately, logic seems to be prevailing: there hasn't been any serious anti-mage violence reported in the region in over a decade. Bias-related, at any rate.

There does, however, seem to be a great deal of fear, undoubtedly stemming from ignorance, lurking just beneath the surface. I can see this easily exploding to the surface if the number of "magic-related incidents" continues to grow.]<<<<<
—Preacher (11:27:21/01-17-52)

### University Park (AA)

University Park is a fine example of the mixture of old money and new riches. This attractive residential sector has homes dating from the late 1800s, showpieces of elegant affluence. A monorail stop connects this wealthy neighborhood with the corporate centers throughout the metroplex. This is one of the few areas in the city where it is safe to stroll after dark. Well-manicured lawns and small parks make this a popular weekend family attraction. Security systems vary among the homes. Many powerful mages live here.

## PLACES OF INTEREST

### HOTELS

#### Busch Hotel

Luxury Hotel Archetype (24 floors)/1321 Commerce Street/Nikki Wallace, Manager/No Racial Bias/LTG# 2214 (22-4700)

Decor throughout the hotel is elegant, with just a touch of antiquity. The rooms have four-poster beds with fluffy down comforters, a separate seating area, and a dining table. Suites are soundproofed and come with all the amenities. A doctor and dentist are on call 24 hours a day, and a barber and hairdresser are on the premises. For a fee, the concierge can arrange for services not normally available.

A fine restaurant is in the hotel. The French Room, resplendent with muraled, high ceilings serves exquisite Nouvelle Cuisine until midnight.

#### Cattleman's Rest

No Frills Hotel Archetype (16 floors)/8051 LBJ Freeway (at Coit Road)/Rolf Ploutz, Manager/No Racial Bias/LTG# 9214 (34-2431)

This hotel, which offers only the barest of amenities, is mentioned only because it is clean and secure. The management recognizes its limitations and keeps the rates proportionally low.

#### Comfort-Cubed

No Frills Hotel Archetype (8 floors)/3800 West Northwest Highway/Diablo Burke, Manager/No Racial Bias/LTG# 8214 (91-9561)

Run by a huge troll and staffed by dwarfs and orks, this establishment has amazingly good security. Rooms have only a bed, and allow enough space for the door to open. The communal bathrooms, down the hall, are clean and well-lit, with several stalls and a separate shower area.

#### Hyatt Regency

First Class Hotel Archetype (24 floors)/815 Main Street/Rebecca Lynn Burwell-Stevens, Manager/No Racial Bias/LTG# 1214 (67-1234)

Formerly the old Hotel Texas, the Hyatt Regency is located across from the convention center. A typical room has a king-sized bed and a comfortable couch. The bathrooms are large, with luxurious bath towels.

#### Loew's Resort

Luxury Hotel Archetype (20 floors)/2201 Stemmons Freeway/Martin Alexander, Manager/Subtle Bias Against orks and trolls/LTG# 8214 (65-1200)

Loew's is a landmark in Dallas/Fort Worth. The red brick building is topped by three glass pyramids, which house tree-filled atria. The lobby is spacious, with an octagonal stained-glass dome overhead. Hallways overlook the atria. Each suite has a bedroom, parlor, and bath. An indoor swimming pool, health spa, and sauna are available free of charge to hotel guests. The barber and a beauty shop are located in the atrium, along with a florist, western-wear shop, and an art gallery.

#### The Pavilion

First Class Hotel Archetype (16 floors)/2821 Turtle Creek Boulevard/Raven Fireborn, Manager/Bias Against orks and trolls/LTG# 7214 (22-2100)

This restored mansion, complete with circular drive and fountain, is sumptuous but not pretentious. The lobby is a huge rotunda that resembles a fine art gallery rather than a hotel lobby. Standard rooms have a private terrace and separate seating area. The bathrooms are done in marble with brass fixtures. For an extra fee, a suite with a complete kitchen and dining area may be rented. The dining room serves a variety of dishes, all of them excellent.

#### Red Carpet Inns

Family Style Hotel Archetype (14 floors)/1011 South Akard Street/Neil Robertson, Proprietor/Subtle Bias Against Humans, Orks and Trolls/LTG# 6214 (36-1083)

This small, elegant hotel is decorated in rich earth tones, with wood paneling and thick carpeting. It is an elven delight. Lush plants decorate not only the lobby and halls, but the rooms themselves. Humans will not be turned away, but it is clear that they are unwelcome.

**Sheraton Hotels**

Family Style Hotel Archetype (20 floors)/601 Avenue H East, Arlington/Barry Oldham, Manager/No Racial Bias/ LTG# 5214 (25-1666)

Located across from Eight Flags Over Texas, the Sheraton is under new management and is staffed by employees anxious to please. Each room has a king-sized bed and sturdy wicker furnishings. The food here, though not spectacular, is plentiful and reasonably priced.

**Spenda Day Hotel**

No Frills Hotel Archetype (6 floors)/1015 Elm Street/ Kay Carstairs-Milliken, Manager/No Racial Bias/LTG# 2214 (98-9951)

The only thing of note about this hotel is its location near the city's financial and insurance sector. The rooms are small and sparsely furnished. The beds are of adequate size, though they tend to be lumpy. The manager is the great-niece of the infamous Governor "Headhunter" Carstairs.

**The Stratford**

Family Style Hotel Archetype (18 floors)/302 South at Houston Street (at Jackson)/William Keller, Manager/ No Racial Bias/LTG# 7214 (12-9090)

Newly remodeled, the hotel offers excellent security and reasonable comfort. The bathrooms are adequate, though the towels are small.

**TripleTree Hotels**

Luxury Hotel Archetype (26 floors)/8250 North Central Expressway (at Caruth Haven)/Dustin Blackwolf, Manager/No Racial Bias/LTG# 5214 (72-8700)

Located in one of three gold-toned towers a short distance from Greenville Avenue's restaurants and nightclub strip, this oval-shaped hotel offers a magnificent view of the city. The decor is modern, favoring bold, geometric prints. Each room has a floor-to-ceiling window, a minibar and refrigerator.

## RESTAURANTS AND BARS

### The Alamo

Mid-Sized Restaurant and Bar Archetype/2533 White Settlement Road/Papa James, Proprietor/No Racial Bias/ LTG# 4214 (94-0357)

Upon entering, customers are greeted by a huge stuffed bear. The decor is sparse, but the atmosphere is thick. The barbecue is the best in the city. There are no waiters. Everyone, from wealthy politicians to ork sanitation officers, waits in line. The spices are hot and the prices are reasonable. This is the place to find many of the city's freelance "security personnel."

### Farfellow

Mid-Sized Restaurant and Bar Archetype/12900 Preston Road (at LBJ)/Willow, Manager/Bias Against Non-elves/LTG# 1214 (62-0369)

Farfellow is Dallas/Fort Worth's only all-elven restaurant. Its decor is light and airy and the service quick and courteous. The menu is all vegetarian, though so well-prepared that even a meat-eater would not mind. The manager is a known member of the radical Elven Ascendancy League, which lobbies for more elven influence within the government. Elves new in town can usually find a room for the night upstairs.

### The Haven

Large Restaurant and Bar Archetype/8325 Walnut Hill Lane/Gregory Baca, Manager/Subtle Bias Against humans/LTG# 3214 (62-7487)

Decorated to resemble a sunny grotto, complete with a splashing waterfall, the dining areas are very private and secluded. The menu leans heavily toward vegetarian dishes, though the meat dishes are quite good, if a trifle overdone. Private rooms in back may be rented for larger, business meetings. Reservations are expected, but not necessary.

### Krunch's

Mid-Sized Restaurant and Bar Archetype/2755 Bachman Drive/Garl Steelmonger, Manager/Bias Against Non-orks and trolls/LTG# 3214 (87-4592)

This is the only dining establishment that caters exclusively to orks and trolls. The decor is early junkyard, with bumpers and hub caps from vintage cars adorning the walls. The food is rather greasy but plentiful. Drinks are served in Texas-sized cups suitable for the thirst of a large metahuman. The patrons are always loud and raucous. The waitresses are fast and heavy-handed. Humans willing to shake hands with Garl are welcome, if, that is, they aren't on their way to have their hand put in a cast.

### L'Escargo

Large Restaurant and Bar Archetype/2201 Stemmons Freeway (Loew's Resort)/Diana Johnson, Manager/Subtle Bias Against orks and trolls/LTG# 2214 (71-1200)

The food here is good, though not great. What draws most customers is the showmanship of the skilled chefs that prepare your meal at your table. This is the place to bring important business contacts you want to impress.

### The Mansion

Large Restaurant and Bar Archetype/200 Main Street/ Priscilla Matlioni, Manager/No Racial Bias/LTG# 2214 (24-1000)

Delightfully decorated in a rich, art nouveau style, the Mansion is a culinary treat for even the most jaded palates. As the name implies, this is a dining experience with a high, though well-justified, price. Visiting VIPs rarely miss the chance to come be pampered. Valet parking is provided by an impressive team of well-dressed trolls.

### Mario's Gourmet Mexicano

Mid-Sized Restaurant and Bar Archetype/4912 Cole Street/Mario Cervantes, Proprietor/No Racial Bias/LTG# 4214 (31-4211)

Authentic Mexican dishes and a lively atmosphere make Mario's a popular spot. Imported beer and iced tea flow freely to quench the fire of the spicy food. Knowledgeable and friendly waiters will explain exactly what

goes into each dish, a definite aid to travelers unfamiliar with the cuisine. This is also an excellent place to contact some of the city's most talented deckers.

### Mem'Sahib

Small Restaurant and Bar Archetype/Caruth Plaza (Park Lane at North Central)/Shakir Tahiri, Manager/Subtle Bias Against orks and trolls/LTG# 5214 (61-2301)

This charming restaurant offers a sumptuous Indian menu that is very light on the curry. Their bread is baked fresh on the premises. The food is spectacular—so is the bill.

### Mister H's

Mid-Sized Restaurant and Bar Archetype/Motorola-Haiatsu-East Tower (D/FW Airport)/Leonard Petorski, Manager/No Racial Bias/LTG# 6214 (66-8400)

The decor of this intimate restaurant is reminiscent of a 90s suburban home. Though the dining room is small and often noisy, the service is excellent. The menu features a delightful blend of continental cuisine and seafood. The desserts are sinful. Reservations are a must.

### Old World

Mid-Sized Restaurant and Bar Archetype/2610 Maple Avenue/Anna Cardonne, Manager/No Racial Bias/LTG# 3214 (21-0032)

Noted for its menu of European and Native American dishes, this is the hot night spot for the socially elite. The decor is plain and functional, but it's unlikely you'll notice once the meal has been served. The waiters are quiet and efficient, offering friendly suggestions if you don't know what to order. Be sure to ask to see the dessert menu. It's one of the best in town.

### Pompanio Seafood

Mid-Sized Restaurant and Bar Archetype/6950 Greenville Avenue/Alex Pompanio, Proprietor/No Racial Bias/LTG# 3214 (34-6728)

Owned by a retired fisherman, Pompanio's is like a visit to a very clean wharf. Filled with nautical mementos, it is almost a museum to a time when fishing was still done by small boats and not harvested wholesale. The seafood served here is only a few hours old, flown in directly from the coast daily. Alex likes to greet visitors himself, often remembering the names of repeat customers. He is a genial host but will not stand for any mischief. His waiters brag about the time he personally threw one of the local go-gang leaders out, without opening the door first.

### Tanstaafl

Restaurant and Night club Archetype/157 at Collins Avenue/Ayn Anson, Manager/Bias Against Politico Types/LTG# 6214 (88-0319)

A very political place, the restaurant gets its name from a slogan from the turn of the century. Anything you want set up can be set up here. The D/FWPD and the CAS civilian intelligence services try to keep the place under surveillance, but the watchers and the snoopers always seem to get broken, quickly. Nobody uses his real name.

### Tokyo Royal

Large Restaurant and Bar Archetype/7525 Greenville Avenue/Timothy Kwang, Manager/Bias Against orks and trolls/LTG# 6214 (98-3304)

The architecture is authentic Japanese, both inside and out. The elaborately prepared oriental dishes are served by slender Japanese women dressed in stunning traditional kimonos. A fine sushi menu is also available upon request. This restaurant is quite popular with the city's dwarfs. The maitre'd will turn away all orks and trolls, politely but firmly.

## NIGHT CLUBS

### The Almost New West

Night Club and Bar Archetype/3105 Winthrop/BillyJoe Summers, Manager/No Racial Bias/LTG# 7214 (88-0872)

Primarily a country and western club, the Almost New West has been known to give local high-tech bands their start during the monthly amateur night. There is a 5-nuyen cover charge only on the weekends.

### Belle Star

Night Club Archetype/7724 North Central/Starr Patterson, Manager/No Racial Bias/LTG# 7214 (45-4787)

This is the hot spot where the VIPs go to "get back to their country roots." Starr books big-name bands at least twice a month. The waiters and waitresses are professional dancers more than willing to teach the inexperienced how to two-step. They do not charge for this service, but a generous tip is appreciated. There is a nightly 10-nuyen cover charge.

### Billy Bob's Texas

Large Night Club and Bar Archetype/2520 Commerce/Jake Pierce, Manager/Subtle Bias Against orks and trolls/LTG# 6214 (90-6491)

Billy Bob's is the largest night club in the country. Where else but in Texas could you find a night club with its own rodeo and 40 bars as well? C & W megastars vie for club dates here. Jake employs a full staff of impressive bouncers to ensure that everyone has fun, but not at someone else's expense. Because some of the more memorable fights have been started by orks and trolls, they are closely watched while inside. There is a 20-nuyen cover charge.

### The Chicken Ranch

Night Club and Cheap Hotel Archetype/4111 Lomo Alto/Marilyn Powell, Proprietor/Bias Against orks and trolls/LTG# 5214 (03-8101)

The parlor and entry hall of this establishment are decorated in the style of the most elite men's club. Elegant oriental rugs cover shining hardwood floors. Overstuffed leather couches and chairs are clustered in well-lit conversation areas. A well-stocked bar is located in one corner of the parlor, tended by Django, the bouncer. The entertainment rooms are lush and richly appointed. All patrons are expected to behave in a gentlemanly fashion and formal attire is preferred. The ladies are gracious and witty, fitting dinner companions and highly trained professionals. Membership prices are steep, but well worth it.

### Daddio's

Night Club Archetype/111 East 4th Street/Quentin Sasser, Manager/No Racial Bias/LTG# 2214 (87-0752)

This is the place to hear the best jazz in Dallas/Fort Worth. Most of the music is done by local bands, but occasional out-of-town bands are featured. Daddio's is best known as the background for rising megarocker Sean Porter's latest trivideo. There is no cover charge, but the drink prices are high. This is a favorite meeting place for the city's mages.

### The Milky Way

Night Club and Cheap Hotel Archetype/4099 Valley View Lane/Margarite Bouchet, Proprietor/No Racial Bias/LTG# 5214 (26-9000)

A high-tech wonderland filled with neon lights and flashing strobe lights, this club appeals to younger clientele. The music is loud, the liquor hard, and the dress bizarre. Membership is co-ed. Drugs other than simchips are not allowed on the premises. Anyone found in possession of BTLs will have their legs broken before being thrown out. The rooms are clean and functional, though not well soundproofed. Membership fees are reasonable.

### The Satin Doll

Night Club and Cheap Hotel Archetype/2621 McKinney Avenue/Cynthia Kim, Proprietor/Subtle Bias Against orks and trolls/LTG# 6214 (22-1660)

Done in an opulent oriental decor, the Satin Doll is for members who wish to be pampered. The co-ed membership includes many corporate executives and government officials. Discretion is the word here. Many exotic pleasures are available, if you have enough money. A word to the wise: the bouncer may not look threatening, but should be treated with extreme care. One abusive patron recently "slipped on the sidewalk outside and broke his neck."

### Tumbleweed Sally's

Night Club and Cheap Hotel Archetype/300 Main Street/Salina Franklin, Proprietor/No Racial Bias/LTG# 4214 (256-8900)

This members-only club is a re-creation of a western dance hall. All employees are professional dancers, and many also sing quite well. The dress is casual and the atmosphere lively. The piano player doubles as the bouncer. Beer is served in large, frosted mugs, and gentlemen are politely reminded that spurs are not allowed in the back rooms. Membership fees are reasonable.

### The White Elephant Saloon

Night Club and Bar Archetype/106 East Exchange/Anthony Leland, Manager/No Racial Bias/LTG# 8214 (26-1887)

A replica of a stockyard saloon, the White Elephant offers a down-home atmosphere. Customers come here to dance and drink—and occasionally to get in fights. Hammer, the bouncer, is more than capable of handling the rowdy crowd.

### Wired Willy's

Night Club Archetype/6808 Camp Bowie/John Galt, Proprietor/Bias Against the Un-Wired/LTG# Find It If You Can

A hole in a wall that leads to a cellar hides the most popular wired club in the city. Nasty boys play here. Friday night is the traditional No Bozo Night where you can only get in if you can defeat the maglock on the front door.

## OTHER PLACES OF INTEREST

### Botanic Gardens
University, off I-30/Dixie Littlefield, Director/No Racial Bias/LTG# 9214 (42-7686)

Visitors may stroll through floral panoramas ranging from an English rose garden to a Texas Xeriscape to an intricate Japanese garden. Hours vary seasonally. Admission is free.

### Dallas/Fort Worth Art Museum
1309 Montgomery/Dr. Natalya McClain, Director/No Racial Bias/LTG# 3214 (29-2151)

This magnificent gallery houses a wide range of exhibits. It is recognized as having the finest collection of Southwestern art in the world, as well as an outstanding display of modern metahuman works. Admission is free.

### Eight Flags Over Texas
2201 Road to Eight Flags near Arlington Stadium/No Racial Bias/LTG# 5214 (58-8900)

The eight flags flying over the entrance commemorate when Texas was part of Spain, France, and Mexico, as well as when it was a Republic, part of the Confederacy, and the United States of America. The two most recent flags date from the secession from the US and CAS: when Texas became a Republic again, and now as a part of the Confederated American States.

Visitors to EFOT travel from Texas' lawless frontier days to its current place as a member of CAS. Rides and pavilions extend off the park's focal point, the relocated Alamo. With gates flanked by the goddesses of Liberty that once graced the dome of Austin's capitol building, the Alamo stands as a shrine for those Texans who died fighting for freedom. It was moved block by block, including a large portion of the land on which it rested, from San Antonio while the Texas Rangers struggled to hold back the advancing Aztlan forces in 2034. Though San Antonio fell to the invaders, the Alamo still belongs to Texas.

### Fair Park
Parry and First/Edward Fitzhugh, Co-ordinator/No Racial Bias/LTG# 1214 (12-9931)

Located on the eastern edge of D/FW, this huge park is the site of the annual Texas State Fair in October. Several museums are located within the park: the World Weapons Expo, the Texas Hall of State, and the Paranatural History Museum. Admission to the park is free, though the museums have a small entrance charge. All the buildings on the grounds were recently refurbished and the security increased. The park closes at dark, except during the State Fair.

### JFK Memorial
Commerce, Main & Record

In the center of this 50-square foot space stands a plain black marble marker engraved with the name John F. Kennedy. Nearly 90 years ago, a short distance from this spot, the young President of the United States of America was assassinated.

### The Galleria
Shopping Mall Archetype (8 floors)/Dallas Parkway North/Nicholai Corelli, Mall Association President/LTG# 6214 (25-2133)

This is the major shopping mall in the metroplex. The stores feature merchandise aimed at the middle and upper class shoppers. There are numerous restaurants and fast food joints located throughout the complex. An independent lore store, Desert Winds, offers a wide variety of talismans and lore books, as well as plenty of friendly advice. Business Computers International has a large store here, as well as the Maze and the Rescue Net. For cyberware, there is Maverick Body Design, two BioTech stores and three Clone Zone stores. Maverick is high-priced, but well run. The Clone Zones are inexpensive, but remember that you get what you pay for.

### Northpark Center
Shopping Mall Archetype (10 floors)/North Central between Park & Northwest Highway/Mercedes Donnovan, Mall Association President/LTG# 8214 (87-7441)

This is the only mall in the metroplex with an attached hotel, Comfort-Cubed. Though it is one of the lower-class hotels in the area, you won't spend much there anyway. The manager has a locker facility for your shopping purchases. Theimann-Markles, Ford & Stitcher, and many other quality stores rub elbows here with the lesser-priced shops. There are several lore and electronic stores here, along with BioTech and Clone Zone stores.

### The Quadrangle
Shopping Mall Archetype (3 floors)/2800 Routh/George Sands, Mall Association President/LTG# 8214 (22-8679)

This trendy mall is filled with specialty stores. This is the place to look for one-of-a-kind items. Thin Ice has a store here dedicated to custom cyberware. Lone Star Enhancements has a branch here, run by Dr. Richard Edelman. It is well-staffed by concerned professionals. The rules can be bent slightly, for the right fee.

### Water Gardens
I-20 at Main/James Oliver, Director/No Racial Bias/LTG# 5214 (90-5534)

Built not far from the old Chisholm Trail, the park offers visitors the chance to experience water in various states. At the Active Water Pool, 4,000 liters of water a minute plunges 15 meters below ground level. The Quiet Water Pool sends sheets of water cascading silently down 6-meter walls. Admission is free. The park is open 24 hours a day, though the fountains are activated only from 9:00 A.M. to 4:00 P.M. It is not wise to be here after dark, as this is a favorite dueling spot for gangs from around the metroplex.

### Zoo
2727 Zoological Park Drive (Forest Park)/Dr. Gerald Purga, Director/No Racial Bias/LTG# 3214 (29-7050)

Though the zoo is known mostly for having the largest reptile display in the world, it also houses over 850 species in elaborate settings depicting their natural habitats. It also features a large aquarium with seals and sea lions. The Forest Park Train, running from the park's entrance to the zoo, is the longest miniature train ride in the world. Admission is 5¥ for adults, 2.50¥ for children.

# REPUBLIC OF QUÉBEC

The Republic of Québec. A peaceful nation-state endowed by nature with a spectacular range of beautiful terrain: from serene lakes and rolling woodlands to rugged mountains. A prosperous land where friendly people strive to make you welcome, and where new opportunities for a rewarding and fruitful life are around every corner…. *Drek!*

Forget it, chummer. But if you're looking for a tight-assed, contradictory, schizoid, and pretty-damn-close-to-loony-tunes country, this is the place. If any country ever needed its lid blown off, it's the good old "Belle République." (Time out: Before you get the wrong idea, I didn't write the schlock at the beginning, even as a joke. I copped it, bit for bit, from the Republic's "Voix de Québec" BBS, and I took no liberties with the translation. Check it out if you want a good laugh.)

## HISTORY

I'm not the best resource for ancient history before about 2030, but this is the way I read what went down. In the weird old days, way back in the 1700s, Québec was the center of a sprawling colonial empire called New France, which spread from what's now the Atlantic coast of the Republic down to Louisiana.

During the 18th century, Québec was also a military power worthy of respect. In 1704, Québecois scragged the town of Deersfield, Massachusetts, and 50 years later, gave a lesson in skirmish tactics to an American unit led by a young hack called George Washington. Come 1759, though, the tide turned and the British army defeated Québec's French forces on the Plains of Abraham just west of Québec City. Like it or not, Québec got dragged into the newly forming country of Canada.

And they didn't like it. Throughout the next two and a half centuries, the people of Québec clung to their French roots, even though they were part of a predominately English-speaking ("Anglophone") country. They had political clout, and they used it. Canada maintained French as its second official language, and the government "expressed grave disappointment" over any community that brought out English-only laws. In Québec, however, the provincial government could and did promulgate laws that made it illegal to use English in a number of areas.

Throughout the 1960s and 1970s, the Québecois kept jerking the leash on the rest of the country by threatening separatism. (Time out: That's probably too drekking cynical. There was this group of hotheads who really wanted to separate, but the majority wouldn't vote them into office. Not yet, anyway.) Things got interesting in the late 1980s, when the government of Canada was trying to bring in some kind of constitutional accord. Québec was holding out for constitutional recognition as a "distinct society," and when they finally got it, the backlash started. The earlier argy-bargy about the few communities declaring themselves English-only was just a warning.

When the "distinct society" provision came in, a couple of whole fragging provinces declared themselves English-only, just to spite Québec.

Now, the population of Québec saw this as French-bashing, which it was, so in 1998, they finally went and elected the separatist hotheads who'd been waiting 40 years for their chance. On January 1, 2000, Québec declared itself independent from the rest of Canada.

If the truth be told, it didn't make much difference…except to the few Anglophones stupid enough to stay in Québec at this point. Québec had always been a distinct society, with its own legal system based on the French "Napoleonic Code," and laws against the use of English in business. Now those laws got even stricter, and Québec tried to close its borders.

Try is about as far as it got because Québec just wasn't self-sufficient enough to survive as an independent sovereign state. The separatist government had expected some help from France, which had enough troubles of its own and so left Québec to sink or swim. Though the ties with the rest of Canada remained, the government tried to keep these as unobtrusive as possible, which tended only to complicate matters further. The economy of Québec began to falter, as the food crunch set in in earnest.

Things became progressively worse, but not catastrophic, until 2011, the "Year of Chaos." During the past century or so, Canada had become a bipolar country. Most of the country's wealth was concentrated in central Canada, (mainly Ontario) though Québec had its fair share before separation. The two coasts, the western provinces and the Maritimes, perceived themselves as the "poor relations."

RICK HARRIS '91

As things went from bad to worse, the Maritimes suffered even more than the west (which had always kept close ties with the Pacific coast of the U.S.). In 2011, the Maritime provinces formed themselves into a "loose confederation."

Though they remained nominally part of Canada, they began to build up their own internal infrastructure for eventual separation. They also extended "most favored nation" status to the Republic of Québec. The signs were there, for anyone with the sense to see them, that eventually the Maritimes would secede.

The Great Ghost Dance of August 17, 2017 was the trigger. Celinne DeGaulle (no relation), then President of the Republic, recognized that the Treaty of Denver or something very much like it was now inevitable, and acted before anyone else could usurp her initiative.

On December 11, 2017, the Québec government invited the Maritime provinces to join the Republic. To their surprise, all but Labrador, the mainland portion of Newfoundland, refused with a resounding no. Either way, most of Canada's Atlantic coast was now in the hands of the Republic. When the Treaty of Denver was signed in April 2018, Québec abstained, confident that its historically close ties with the Native Americans of the region and its recent rapprochement with others who felt disaffected would protect it from reprisals.

In this, President Celinne DeGaulle was totally correct.

The remaining Maritime provinces, Nova Scotia, New Brunswick, Prince Edward Island, and the island of Newfoundland, were not in an enviable position. Nominally still part of Canada, they were cut off from the rest of the nation. They still shared their loose confederation, however, which would let them act with some kind of coordination. In 2019, the Premier of Newfoundland, acting as spokeswoman, approached the state of Maine and asked to be annexed. Maine had seen this coming for some time, and agreed.

After goblinization began on April 30, 2021, Québec showed the kind of schizoid reaction that's become so typical of the government. While other countries were reacting to goblinization with repression, Québec immediately extended full rights to all UGEs—as long as they were French-speaking ("Francophones"). Anglophone, pure-strain humans had been considered second-class citizens, or worse, for years. God help anyone who was now an English-speaking ork or troll. (Time out: I know, I know. Drek, you say. But I cordially invite you to visit me in Québec City and check it out for yourself, chummer.) Québec is still trying to build the level of prosperity it had before separation. President Joel Jénache, a real hard-ass borderline psycho if ever there was one, is trying to woo corporate investment, but most of the multinationals aren't that keen. (After all, the two languages of international trade and finance are English and Japanese. French doesn't even come in third.) Some more moderate elements of Jénache's government have been trying to get him to back off on the more outré language restrictions, but Joel won't budge.

One recent innovation that makes things more attractive to outside investors are "Enterprise Zones." (I'll give you the scoop on those later.) The key thing here is that they seem to be working.

Québec's building up some interesting secondary industry, but so far nothing much in the software area. (Jénache's response to this? Slap gross tariffs on imported software and firmware, to try to "protect" the non-existent "domestic" industry. Makes you fragging despair over politicians, doesn't it?) The standard of living is climbing faster than in some parts of the UCAS, but not fast enough for many people. There's an election coming next year. Oh, yes, Québec is still a democracy. Everyone has a vote, that is, as long as they can identify themselves and explain their career and background—in impeccable French. This one may turn out to be a real horse race. Facing off are Jénache and the Parti Québecois, another real psycho called Jean-Paul Turbot (pronounced Tur-bo) leading the hard-right Alliance Francophone, and Thérése Monpitard of the more moderate Démocrates Mondains. Place your bets, chummers.

## ECONOMY

The currency of the Republic of Québec is the New Franc ($f$), which is divided into 100 centimes. Currently, the exchange rate is bouncing around two francs to one nuyen ($2f = 1¥$). By law, the rate is considerably lower when you go to a government-sanctioned bank to exchange your nuyen, which is required as soon as you enter the Republic. One nuyen converts to as little as $1.95f$ (1 franc, 95 centimes).

When buying nuyen, 1¥ will cost about $2.05f$. The government pockets the difference. The shadows offer less official venues for exchange. The rates are sometimes better than in the banks, especially if the exchange is part of some other kind of deal.

Québec is not a particularly prosperous country. It has some secondary industry, and is quite successful in the manufacture of toys like body armor, certain weapons, and some kinds of groundcars. Almost nothing in the way of tertiary industry (information-based industry, like software) exists. Taking Seattle as the baseline, which everybody seems to want to do, Québec's standard of living is lower. The costs for such staple goods as food and clothing are less than in Seattle, but salaries, bonuses, and so on are lower still.

The following list compares the average costs for certain types of goods in Québec with what you'd pay in Seattle. I'll discuss the discrepancies later.

| QUEBEC COST OF LIVING | |
|---|---|
| **ITEM** | **COST MULTIPLE** |
| **Weaponry** | |
| Ammunition | 130% |
| Explosives | 200% |
| Firearm Accessories | 140% |
| Firearms | 120% |
| Melee Weapons | 95% |
| Projectile Weapons | 100% |
| Throwing Weapons | 100% |
| **Armor and Clothing** | |
| Armor | 120% |
| **Security and Surveillance** | |
| Communications | 130% |
| Security Devices | 200% |
| Surveillance Counter-Measures | 250% |
| Surveillance Measures | 250% |
| Survival Gear | 90% |
| Vision Enhancers | 350% |
| **Lifestyle** | |
| Lifestyle | 80% |
| **Electronics** | |
| Electronics | 180%+ |
| **Cybertech** | |
| Biotech | 380% |
| Bodyware | 300% |
| Cyberdecks | 500% |
| Headware | 300% |
| Internals | 300% |
| Programs | 500%+ |
| **Magical Equipment** | |
| Hermetic Library | 100% |
| Magical Supplies | 95% |
| Magical Weapons | 200% |
| Power Foci | 90% |
| Ritual Sorcery Materials | 100% |
| Spell Foci | 90% |
| **Vehicles** | |
| Aircraft | 150% |
| Boats | 120% |
| Ground Vehicles | 120% |
| Military Vehicles | Hah! |

What does this mean? It means that a Radio Shack CD-100 cyberdeck that costs 6,200¥ in Seattle is going to run something like 62,000$f$! A 1,000¥ katana will set you back about 1,900$f$.

Now check out some of the discrepancies. It all comes down to software and firmware (which is basically just software blown into an optical chip, right?). The government slaps a nasty tariff onto any software or other item with a significant software component that enters the country, supposedly to stimulate the (non-existent) domestic software industry.

Doesn't seem to be working. Of course, the black market is doing a jim-dandy business in anything connected with software.

## GOVERNMENT

The Republic of Québec is governed by a so-called National Assembly and led by a President. Nominally a democracy (as long as you speak French), Québec is divided into 65 "ridings."

Depending on population and historical factors, individual ridings have one, two, or even three seats in the Assembly. (Riding boundaries, and the number of seats each commands, can be changed at the whim of the government in power. For a good laugh, watch the boundary lines shift around just before an election.) Individuals vote for representatives running for election in their riding. The president is the leader of the party that gets the most seats or, in the case of a coalition, the one who is the best horse-trader and favor-broker.

Québec is basically a tri-partite system. The major parties are the Parti Québecois (moderate/right; currently in power); the Alliance Francophone (hard right; psycho and potentially genocidal); and the Démocrates Mondains (moderate/left; the best of a bad lot). The many lunatic-fringe groups include the Greens, the Alliance Metahumaine, and the Force Populaire (a real radical outfit that makes Alamos 20,000 look like bleeding-heart liberals), but they're lucky to get one seat in the assembly among them. Despite apparent differences between the three major parties, their policies are similar, except with regard to issues they believe are "hot buttons" for the electors. If the Parti Québecois gets beat in the next election, things will get a little better or worse for anglophones and metahumans, depending on who wins. Otherwise, nothing much else will change.

## LAWS

This is really what you want to learn, isn't it, chummer?

As I said earlier, Québec's legal system is based on the Napoleonic Code, which means that judges aren't the (supposedly) objective, uninvolved arbiters of other legal systems. In the Napoleonic system, the judge is an active participant in the trial, the person responsible for bringing out all relevant facts. The relationship between the prosecuting attorney and council for the defense is not adversarial. Instead, everyone's supposed to cooperate in bringing the truth to light.

So what does all that mean? First, chummer, take my advice. If you're going to court, hire yourself a Québecois attorney. No matter how good your out-of-country lawyer is, you'll end up losing big-time unless you've got someone who plays by the rules. (Remember, too, that French is the official language, and your trial will be totally in French. No official translators, no exceptions. Another reason to get some good local talent in your corner.)

Second, a judge is a much more valuable purchase in Québec than anywhere else. Because he takes a more active role in a trial, a bribed judge can help you one frag of a lot. (They're harder and more expensive to suborn, but it's well worth the expense—and the trouble.)

As for laws in general, Québec has one of the more schizoid systems in the world. I'll just hit the high points.

### LANGUAGE LAWS

French is the official language. Though English is not yet forbidden in casual conversation, using it will not make you popular. It is illegal to conduct business dealings in a language other than French, and any deal so transacted is null and void. All contracts must be in French. Dealings with the government, the civil service, and the police forces must be in French. All printed material sold in Québec, and all signage, must be in French. Addressing a Québecois in English is considered a high insult; if he or she is operating in an official capacity, it's a misdemeanor. (Sound pretty draconian? You got it, chummer.)

### WEAPONS

Explosive, armor-piercing, and belt-fed ammo is illegal. Possession is a felony, and you'll end up doing hard time. Auto-fire weapons are outlawed. (A word to the wise: You can possess a gun that could normally auto-fire as long as it's been government-modified to prevent it being switched to auto-fire. Got that? Now, it so happens that the government-authorized modification can be reversed, but said reversal requires high-tech, intricate tools such as a small screwdriver or a nail file.)

Smartguns are legal as long as they're not auto-fire-capable, but smartgun adapters or smart goggles are hideously illegal. (Didn't I tell you the laws were schizoid?)

There are conflicting laws concerning the carrying of weapons.

Packing concealed heat is a no-no (felony), but carrying a weapon in the open is considered "flagrant disregard for public safety" (another felony). Fragged if you do, fragged if you don't.

Got all that? Well try this: it's fine to pack heat as long as it's for the express purpose of hunting and you're on your way from your residence to a hunting area. ("Certainement, officer, I always go hunting with my Colt Manhunter and katana.") Exceptions for people engaged in legal bounty-hunting also exist, but they're too fragging convoluted to go into here. If you plan to play rough in Québec, hire yourself some local talent or see one of the many "personal security consultants" just dying to take your money for legal advice on this kind of thing.

## ENTRY RESTRICTIONS

The population of Québec is low, considering its size. In fact, the government offers a "child bonus" for each young'un a Québec family manages to pop. You'd think a place like that would have easy immigration laws, right?

Wrongo, chummer. If you ain't already living here, the odds are real good you never will be. Anyone applying for permanent residence better be prepared to show that some close relative was a bona fide Québecois or member of a local Indian nation. Otherwise, things don't look good. To work here requires a temporary permit renewable every six months, but only if a non-Québecois will be filling a job for which there are no qualified Québecois applicants (this usually limits you to software/firmware or other information-technology areas). And you'd better be damn sure you can speak good French.

Other visitors must post bonds when they enter the country. Visitors who aren't particularly desirable—anglophones and convicted felons, for example—often must pay a large deposit that works something like bail. If you don't leave when you said you would, your money is forfeit.

For others, it's more like parole, where a visitor must check in with a supervisor every week or so. The government waives many of these restrictions for employees of any large multinational with a presence in one of Québec's Enterprise Zones.

From a more practical standpoint, the border is long and not that well-patrolled, though the Québecois Defense Force has recently caught onto the idea of motion detectors and remotely piloted vehicles to patrol their turf. It's still fairly simple to get across if you use your head.

## BOUNTIES

For a country that classifies anglophone humans as just one step above animals, and anglophone metahumans even lower, it's no surprise that Québec does not recognize the sentience of any paranormal creatures. (Yes, chummers, that includes the sasquatch.) As a rule of thumb, if another, more enlightened country is even considering a species sentient, Québec has a bounty on it. (I guess their rationale is that sasquatches and others will never learn French.) The local Shadowland BBS reported that a bunch of trolls with a dzoo-noo-qua kind of mutation and an attitude problem geeked an entire fishing village a couple of weeks ago. The bounty on dzoo-noo-qua is up to 1,200ƒ a pelt, and the Alliance Francophone is pushing to have that bounty extended to all trolls. If I were a troll in Québec, I'd be watching the news real close.

## WEAPON FINES AND PUNISHMENT TABLE

| Weapon Type | Offense and Fine | | | | |
|---|---|---|---|---|---|
| | 1 | 2 | 3 | 4 | 5 |
| Type | Possession | Transport | Threat | Use | Intent |
| (A) Sm. Bladed Weapon | 50ƒ | 50ƒ | 500ƒ | 1,000ƒ | 1,500ƒ/3 mo |
| (B) Lg. Bladed Weapon | 250ƒ | 250ƒ | 1,000ƒ | 1,500ƒ | 2,000ƒ/3 mo |
| (C) Blunt Weapon | 75ƒ | 250ƒ | 500ƒ | 1,000ƒ | 1,000ƒ/2 mo |
| (D) Projectile Weapon | 50ƒ | 200ƒ | 500ƒ | 1,000ƒ | 1,500ƒ/3 mo |
| (E) Pistol | 300ƒ | 1,000ƒ | 5,000ƒ | 8,000ƒ/ 6 mo | 20,000ƒ/ 1 yr |
| (F) Rifle | 600ƒ | 2,000ƒ | 8,000ƒ | 10,000ƒ /1 yr | 3 yrs |
| (G) Automatic Weapon | 1 yr | 2 yrs | 3 yrs | 5 yrs | 10+ yrs or death |
| (H) Heavy Weapon | 1 yr | 3 yrs | 5 yrs | 10 yrs | 20+ yrs or death |
| (I) Explosives | 20,000ƒ | 50,000ƒ | 1 yr | 4 yrs | 10 yrs or death |
| (J) Military Weapon | 1 yr | 3 yr | 5 yrs | 8 yrs | 20+ yrs or death |
| (K) Military Armor | 2,000ƒ | — | — | — | — |
| (L) Ammunition | 10,000ƒ /1 yr | — | — | — | — |
| (M) Controlled Substances | 10,000ƒ | 1 yr | — | — | — |
| (CA) Class A Cyberware | 1 yr | — | — | — | — |
| (CB) Class B Cyberware | 10,000ƒ | — | — | — | — |
| (CC) Class C Cyberware | 10 yrs | — | — | — | — |
| (CD) Unlicensed Cyberdecks and Matrix Software | 50,000ƒ | 100,000ƒ | | | |

## PUNISHMENTS

Québec is a big proponent of criminals doing hard time. Where another country might just slap someone with a nasty fine, Québec's more likely to toss offenders into the can. And don't forget the death penalty for murder, kidnapping, insurrection, and various other crimes. Nor does it pay to agitate openly against the government because the "defense of state" law defines civil insurrection as a capital crime as well. The death penalty is implemented using the guillotine. (No fragging drek. For major crimes like the kidnapping of a member of the Assembly a couple of years ago, they put the whole show on the national trideo channel. The government tells us that the increased number of executions broadcast during ratings sweep week is just a coincidence, and sure I believe them.)

## INJURY/DEATH OFFENSES

Watch this stuff, chummers. Madame Guillotine is always waiting, and Québec has no parole.

### Reckless Endangerment

Fines range from 500ƒ to 30,000ƒ, depending on the severity of the endangerment.

### Assault

Fines range from 5,000ƒ to two years in jail.

### Attempted Murder

Punishment ranges from two years in jail to a death sentence, depending on how hard you attempted.

### Manslaughter

Punishment is five years in jail per person geeked. Special cases like "vehicular manslaughter," driving while brain-fried, can draw worse.

### Murder

The offense can be punished by as little as ten years in the can, but the death penalty is quite common.

### Premeditated Murder

This is the big one, folks. If premeditation can be proven, the punishment is death.

### Accessory to a Crime

Punishment ranges from 25 percent to 50 percent of the penalty for the actual crime. There is, of course, no accessory for either murder charge.

## RELATIONS WITH OTHER STATES

Though Québec sends diplomatic missions to just about every country on earth, the government is not on the best of terms with anybody except the Algonkian-Manitoo Council. The UCAS keeps up diplomatic relations with Québec, but just. (The UCAS, particularly the northeastern section, has never forgotten the 2017 invitation to join Québec, which they view as an attempted power grab.) The relationship with France is little better. That somewhat more enlightened country finds Québec a bit of an embarrassment.

# QUÉBEC CITY

**Population:** 1,200,000 (Greater Québec)
  Human: 81%
  Elf: 11%
  Dwarf: 4%
  Ork: 3%
  Troll: 1%
  Other: 0%
**Density in Populated Districts:** 400 per square mile
**Per Capita Income:** 40,000$f$ (about 20,000¥)
**Below Poverty Level:** 29%
**On Fortune's Active Traders List:** 0.2%
**Corporate Affiliation:** 38%
**Means of Commuting to Work:**
  Internal Combustion Vehicle: 7%
  Grid-Guide Electric Vehicle, Individual: 10%
  Grid-Guide Electric Vehicle, Group: 71%
  On-site Workers: 7%
  Other: 5%
**Felonious Crime Rate:** 8 per 1,000 per annum
**Education:**
  High School Equivalency: 65%
  College Equivalency: 30%
  Advanced Studies Certificates: 5%
**Hospitals:** 31
**LTG Access Number:** 1418

## FACTS AT YOUR FINGERTIPS

### WHEN TO GO

The weather in Québec City is similar to that of New England. In January and February, temperatures are well below freezing, often dropping below −18° C, with plenty of snow and sleet. The short, muddy spring occurs in May. June and July are the most comfortable months, for August temperatures climb as high as 32° C, and humidity can be unpleasantly high. Autumn is the preferred tourist season, with warm days and cool nights. It is also the time when prevailing winds tend to blow off-shore, carrying the reek of chemical effluvium in the St. Lawrence River away from town.

### GETTING THERE

#### Plane

Most international carriers, with the notable exception of Air France, land at Québec City's major airport. Costs are typical, depending on city of origin, time of day/

year, and so on, plus a 75$f$ airport tax on each arrival or departure. The shuttle bus into the city (15$f$ one way, 28$f$ round trip), leaves on the hour. Alternatively, a taxi ride into town costs about 50$f$.

Local carriers handle limited runs. Québecair connects to Montreal, Toronto, and New York (fast copter service, five or more flights a day for most routes), while Québec Aviation has one daily fixed-wing flight to Boston. Costs for these routes are about 400$f$, and no airport tax is levied on domestic carriers.

(Security checks at the airport are real strict, boys and girls: chem-sniffers, metal detectors, even government wage mages. If it's not kosher, leave it at home. You can always pick up another in the shadows anyhow.)

#### Automobile or Bus

Québec City isn't as far off the beaten track as it looks, only about 800 klicks from New York and less than 650 klicks from Boston. From New York and points south, pick up I-91 at New Haven and follow it to the Québec border; from Boston, take I-93 until it links up with I-91. Three bus lines service Québec City: Voyageur Lines, Autobus Fortin Poulin, and Whippet Bus Company (the latter two from late June to early September only). Tickets on the first two are about average cost; Whippet fares carry a 5 percent surcharge.

Québec border guards are suspicious, trigger-happy, and completely lacking any sense of humor. Expect at least an hour's delay getting through the border. (A word to the wise. The border guards have the right to totally disassemble a vehicle if they have "reasonable cause" to suspect someone is packing contraband. They are under no obligation to help the owner reassemble it afterward.)

#### Train

No rail service runs across the border. Within Québec, however, an efficient maglev links Québec City and Montreal, run by VIA Rail. In Québec City, Gare du Palais train station has been restored beautifully in the Lower Town.

### WHAT IT COSTS

Hotel prices run the gamut. It costs about 60$f$ a night for a single room (without bathroom) in an old building, and from there to 300$f$ a night and higher for the best. At the upper end of the scale, you're rubbing shoulders with politicos, local trideo stars, and other glitterati; at the lower end, you're butting heads with rats and roaches.

Parking is a fragging nightmare. The only public parking is at hotels, and that's only for guests or people willing to pay through the snout. Your best bet is to leave your wheels at home and bus it in to town.

If that's not an option, join the "parking club," Société Parc Auto (no, I'm not fragging kidding). Ten francs buys a parking pass good at any of the club's lots, allowing up to 24 hours' parking and two entries and exits from the lot within that period. It's worth it.

The city's towing company is an arm of Busters, and everybody knows how zealous they are. Standard impound rate is 100ƒ, plus a further 250ƒ surcharge (plus expenses for ammunition expended, medical fees, and so on) if Busters tow drivers have to scrap it out with anyone else interested in taking off with a vehicle.

Other costs are in line with the rest of Québec (see p. 66). Locally caught seafood is ridiculously cheap, considering that fisherman could probably make more selling their catches to industry for the fishes' mercury content alone.

(As for some of the pleasurable biological functions, Québec is straight-laced. Customers can find services for any orientation or combination thereof, but prices reflect their illegal nature. Suffice to say that there are less expensive places to answer Mother Nature's siren call.)

### GETTING AROUND

Within Québec City, public transport is good (considering the parking nightmare, it had bloody well better be). The city's admirable grid-guide bus system has a large fleet of mini-buses, each seating twelve. It's galling to admit, but the city's claims that bus service is 95 percent on-time is, if anything, conservative. The system works.

Québec City is not as bad as some other places, but has its share of nighttime street violence. After nightfall, the buses double their speed, making them tougher targets for gunfire but also giving passengers a rougher ride. The buses are armor-plated, and their autopilots have an emergency "bug-out" routine that returns the vehicle to the central station at ultra-high speed and by the shortest possible route if hit by any single round larger than 9mm or with a velocity of over 960 KPS. The "bug-out" routine can also be triggered by an internal PANICBUTTON. Improper use of this device is considered a felony, and you'll be up for manslaughter if the bus runs someone down on its way back to the central station.

Most of the larger buildings, including all major hotels, have heliports and landing flats. A number of intracity "short-hop" services will gladly ferry you around. A flight from the Hilton International Québec to the city of Levis across the St. Lawrence River costs about 150ƒ. At night, air traffic is limited to narrow corridors, and kept under the watchful eye of missile-armed Gendarmerie rotorcraft.

A high-speed ferry takes passengers and vehicles across the river to Levis. The ferry docks in Lower Town at the foot of Saint-Pierre. The fare is 8ƒ for a foot passenger, 40ƒ and up for a vehicle.

## TOURIST INFORMATION

The Québec City Region Tourism and Convention Bureau operates two well-staffed tourism information centers, one at 399 rue St. Joseph Est, the other on Boulevard Laurier, near the Québec and Pierre Laporte bridges on the way into the city. The Québec Government's Tourism Department operates an information office on the Place d'Armes, down the hill from the Château Frontenac, at 12 rue Ste-Anne. All public telecomm booths have an auto-access key for a tourist information hotline.

For internal (i.e., cyberware) telecomm, access local 101. All communication is in French. Don't count on finding an operator who will switch to English; it's against the regulations and the individual would risk losing his job.

### LEGAL ASSISTANCE

The North American Civil Liberties Union (NACLU) operates a single and highly unofficial office in Québec City (LTG# 1418 (87-0010), and these guys do speak English. If you're in trouble, they can refer you to a good local lawyer. Québec offers no services tailored to metahuman rights problems. The NACLU will do their best to help, but their unofficial status in Québec ties their hands somewhat.

### MEDICAL ASSISTANCE

Québec City has a central medical emergency hotline called Info-Santé at LTG# 1418 (90-9000). They give real-time advice for health problems and will dispatch paramedics if necessary. If someone had the correct hook-up hardware, he could dump medical telemetry right to them, and they could run it through their diagnostic computer. Again, don't count on finding someone who speaks anything but French. DocWagon™ does not operate in Québec, nor is there a local equivalent.

In an emergency, just about any hospital will perform life-saving surgery, no matter what the balance on the victim's credstick, provided the victim is delivered to the hospital or a paramedic pick-up can be arranged. Once the victim is stabilized, however, the hospital will not release him until satisfied that they will get their money.

### CHIPS, DRUGS, AND ALCOHOL

Québec in general and Québec City in particular are quite rational in their attitudes toward most mind-altering substances. You can buy beer, wine, and equivalent substances in corner stores, but hard liquor, mild hallucinogens, and simsense chips are only available from government-sanctioned Société des Alcools stores. Prices are twice as high as you'd pay in Seattle because of the added heavy taxes. The legal age for the consumption of alcohol is 18 and for hallucinogens is 21. Only the mildest simsense chips are available, and the legal age for them is also 21.

Choice mind-benders like full-on BTL chips and ataractics like mindfragger, electric lady, and cram are not available through legal channels. Simple possession of anything that interesting is usually considered a felony, and possession with intent to traffick might even get you an audience with Madame Guillotine.

### ENTERTAINMENT

If you only hear what they tell you at the tourist information bureaus, Québec City will be a dull time. Even "traditional" entertainment like theater, serious music, and pro sports is rare, not to mention the dearth of legal night spots.

But entertainment is where you find it, right, chummer? Québec City is home to a whole drek-load of shadowclubs. These are like the old after-hours spots of 50-some years ago: no advertising, no signs, no official protection, and no patience with troublemakers. The atmosphere ranges from the same techno-pop disco you'd find anywhere in the world to some really, um, unique establishments that cater to rather select tastes. Be sure you know what you're getting into before stepping through the door, because after that it might be too late. (Time out: How come the Gendarmerie doesn't find out about these places and close them down? you ask. They know, all right, chummer. It's just not worth their while to admit it.)

## CITY AT A GLANCE

Though the sprawl of Greater Québec is like that of just about any post-industrial city, the center of Québec City is unique.

Québecois are big on history, particularly that dating back to when Québec was the center of New France. The motto on the country's coat of arms is "Je me souviens" ("I remember"), so it's no surprise they've maintained buildings that any other city would have torn down for low-cost housing. Among these are La Citadelle, a huge,

bastioned fort rising 85 meters above the bank of the St. Lawrence River (now the headquarters of Québec's Defense Force) and the walls that still surround parts of so-called Upper Town. There's also Château Frontenac, a castle-like creation built originally as a hotel, but now used as the official residence of the President and his advisors. (Time out: A whole hotel for the President and cronies? You got it, chummer. The Québec government doesn't do things by halves.)

As you can see from the felony figures in the opening table, crime isn't as serious in Q.C. as in other sprawls. That's thanks to the Gendarmerie, the city's answer to a police force. Like most places, Q.C. swung away from civic-supported police forces when they started demanding too much in the way of hazard pay, and so on. Around 2020, the Mayor phased out the normal police department and replaced it with a private outfit. (There's some connection between that corporation and Lone Star, which means that Lone Star, whether directly or indirectly, handles security for an uncomfortably large percentage of North American cities. I haven't yet been able to establish exactly what the connection is. Stay tuned, chummers.) The name "Gendarmerie" was apparently chosen to give the illusion that these aren't, in fact, hired guns.

The Gendarmerie is an efficient paramilitary organization. Many of their officers have done Desert War tours, and some of the higher-ups have oh-so-shady connections with various Special Forces units. They're good, they know it, and you don't want to slot around with them. They're usually equipped with non-lethal toys like narcoject rifles, net guns, stun batons, and tasers, but when the going gets nasty, they pack enough real heat to guarantee a one-shot takedown on just about anything. Their cars are armored, and their patrol Yellowjackets pack enough ECM to throw off anything fired their way. They keep a tight grip on the city. Again, if you value life and liberty, don't slot with these guys.

In general, the people of Q.C. are open and friendly—if you speak French. It's a liberal place when it comes to purchasing alcohol and other mind-altering substances as long as you buy them from government-sanctioned sources. (Their rationale is that if you want to fry your brain, it's your choice.) What they do come down on are people who do damage while jazzed out of their brains. (A real healthy way of handling things, I have to admit.)

Québec City has more hospitals per capita than in Seattle, and they're a little less tight-assed about ability to pay. If your credstick comes up somewhat short, they'll put you back together, then go see a judge about garnisheeing your wages. (From what I hear about Seattle, they'll let you bleed to death in the lobby if you're one nuyen short. And then turn around and charge your estate for cleaning expenses.)

## GEOGRAPHY AND DEMOGRAPHICS

Québec City is divided into two major regions for historical reasons. The Lower Town, down on the river, was initially home to traders, shipwrights, and fishermen. After a few run-ins with various enemies back in the 18th century, the locals got tired of rebuilding their town every time it got the drek shot out of it by cannon. So they built Upper Town on this fragging great cape looking down on Lower Town, which became an area of wharves and warehouses only. Of course, this didn't work out quite as planned because better cannon could sure as drek lob ordnance into Upper Town, but the division was made and still remains.

Two hundred years ago, Lower Town was a rough neighborhood, home to thieves, alleybashers, and ne'er-do-wells. About 100 years ago, things took a turn for the better, and people started putting up good stores and restaurants. But with all the upheavals since the dawn of the new century, Lower Town began another downward slide. Today it's not quite a slum, but it's seen better days. There are some areas in Lower Town where the Gendarmerie travel in squads, and even then, they're looking over their shoulders.

Upper Town was the richer area, and it's managed to hang on a little better than Lower Town. Some roads and a couple of staircases will take you from one to the other, but for just centimes, lazy people can travel the 65 or so meters in a funicular, a little slotting railway car thing.

Lower Town is where the less desirable elements of society live. In good old Q.C., that's English-speakers. Unlike most other cities, neighborhood divisions are not based on race. In Upper Town, for example, francophone orks rub shoulders with francophone humans. (Of course, not many metahumans live in Québec City anyway. Slot me if I know why, but the city is more predominately human than just about any other on the map.) The one racial division exists in Lower Town, where trolls and orks tend to be concentrated on the waterfront docks.

Québec City has some anachronistic features, but its economy is fairly modern and successful. There is a thriving manufacturing industry mainly to the west, out of the city center, and considerable use of the St. Lawrence river for trade (some of it even legal).

## POLITICS

A mayor and seven aldermen run Québec City's municipal government. Term of office for mayor and alderman is three years, with no limit on the number of consecutive terms.

For the past nine years, the mayor has been Jocelynne Geuvrement (pronounced "Gay-ver-mon"), a drek-hot hermetic magician as well as a politician. Each election, the aldermen play musical chairs, in for a term, out for a term, but Geuvrement has just been sitting pretty. Her gruff manner may not be especially lovable, but she is exceptionally gifted at building and maintaining a consensus among aldermen, despite the fact that each has his own private agenda.

She's a master at favor-trading, influence-peddling, and all the other skills involved in back-room diplomacy. Much as I despise her personally, I have to admire her abilities. When Geuvrement's too old to play the politics game (she's in her 60s now), Q.C. will be the loser.

The rest of the aldermen are typical, undifferentiated political hacks. In contrast to the federal government, the municipal arena has no organized political parties, but a few unofficial groupings exist.

One faction is in favor of free-enterprise and against any restrictions on big business. Another is about as left-wing as possible in a basically right-wing society. On general principles alone, they're against anything that will benefit big business. Then there's the middle faction, which includes Geuvrement, trying to balance off the two extremes.

Elections are conducted electronically, and the voting is open, not based on wards or other political divisions. Each citizen can cast his vote for mayor, and vote for up to three aldermen. The seven aldermanic candidates with the most votes win, pure and simple. Of all candidates for the position of alderman, 20 percent must be Amerind in extraction.

One member of the city council about whom nobody says much is the Chief of the city Gendarmerie. Theoretically, he's an observing member, able to vote only on issues that directly affect the security of the city. But when you get down to it, what doesn't affect the security of the city?

Whether he votes or not, the Chief's voice carries great weight with most aldermen. If the Chief has a strong opinion on something, the aldermen will usually vote his way. The current Chief of the Gendarmerie is Sebastien Hull. He is about 45 years old, a multi-season Desert Wars veteran, almost more cyberware than human, and not a man to cross. Though some of my colleagues think Hull may be planning a coup, I believe he is satisfied with being a very real "power behind the throne." We'll see, though.

Q.C. is also home to the Republic's federal government. As mentioned, the President, his family, his staff and hangers-on all live in luxury in good old Château Frontenac, whose lower floors have been set up as meeting rooms, status rooms, and so on. The National Assembly itself meets in the Hôtel du Gouvernement, near where Grande-Allée meets Avenue Dufferin. The old Hôtel du Gouvernement got scragged back in 2015 in a riot that convinced the government to make civil insurrection a capital offense. Though they rebuilt the edifice, the final result is an eyesore. The current Hôtel du Gouvernement looks as though someone threw all the worst features of classical-style architecture into a bag, shook them up, and then poured them out in a heap. The one good feature, from the government's point of view, is that it's defensible. The crenelated walls will stop a small rocket, the gargoyles all have surveillance cameras in their mouths, and the faux turrets have machine-gun emplacements concealed in their tops.

The members of the National Assembly stay in Q.C. only when the Assembly is in session. The rest of the time, they're back in their home ridings, stumping for votes, or off on "official" junkets and fact-finding missions, usually to the Caribbean or Hawaii. When in Q.C., they live in a huge luxury compound built on Cap Diamant, surrounded by enough high-tech security drek to protect them from a small army.

In general, citizens of Québec City are complacent about the government. As their standard of living slowly inches upward, they don't seem to notice or care what trade-offs might be making that possible. President Jénache and Mayor Geuvrement have collaborated on setting up

Enterprise Zones, which give the big multinationals a free hand to do whatever the drek they want. Québec needs investment, and that means wooing the big corps. The corps know that Québec needs them more than they need Québec, and that puts them in the driver's seat in any negotiations.

Their requirements for setting up shop in Québec are becoming more and more demanding, including beneficial tax status and extended boundaries of the Zones. Once the corps are in, all they have to do is mention the possibility of winding up their affairs in Québec, and both levels of government get whiplash showing how fast they can kiss butt to make the corps stay. The government is slowly giving away its power to the corps, but all the people seem able to see is how great it is that the government is bringing in investments, jobs, and generally jazzing up the economy. Any elected official who even whispers about restrictions on corporate investment would be committing political suicide, and the corps know it.

## POWER DYNAMICS

In most cities, the power flows among a triad of factions: government, the corps, and the Yakuza. In Q.C., one of the legs of that triad, the Yakuza, is missing. This is probably because the Yakuza were slow to recognize the potential of Québec. If they'd made their move right after separation, when the country was unstable and scrabbling to stay alive, they might easily have taken over. As it was, they played a waiting game, watching to see if the Republic would survive or crash and burn. When Québec stabilized, relatively speaking, the Yaks made their move, but it was too late.

The Yaks played things the way they always do when scoping out a territory: they put out feelers and sent in negotiating teams to set up "strategic alliances" that they could eventually take over. The negotiators came back in lots of very small bags. In reprisal, the Yaks sent hit squads to take out a certain percentage of the gangs who'd scragged their negotiators, intending to teach the others a lesson, Yakuza-style. Usually this works just fine; the gangs not hit directly usually hang back, and the Yaks can move in. Not this time. The way it looked, the entire fragging Québec underworld—hundreds of small outfits—had temporarily put aside their differences to hunt down each and every one of the Yakuza hitters. Not a single Yak soldier made it out of Québec alive.

The Yakuza never tried to move into Québec again, but they're probably behind much of the anti-Québec demonstrations in northeastern UCAS. As soon as the Yak threat was gone, the Québec gangs happily turned back to scragging each other.

The other two legs of the triad are stable, but the balance is shifting toward the corps. Unless the government takes some action, pulling their support of the Enterprise Zones, for example, it will lose real power and become a mere puppet government.

The wild card in Q.C. is the Gendarmerie. Sebastien Hull, the Gendarmerie Chief sitting on the Council, behaves as though he's dead-set against any initiative obviously promulgated by the corps. On the surface, he seems to be a counterbalance to the heavy corporate influence, but why do I keep hearing reports that Hull has had a number of oh-so-confidential meets with the heads of MCT and Aztechnology, hmm?

## ECONOMY

Upper Town has fewer corporate skyscrapers than one might expect for a city of this size, but that is because Q.C. has only recently become an attractive place for corporate investment. As in other cities, most corp buildings offer tours, priced anywhere from 5ƒ to 15ƒ. They usually have PR offices as well, staffed with flacks who are very slick at feeding drek to the gullible.

The light and medium industry, situated to the west of the city center, has been responsible for most of the cash-flow into Q.C. Until recently, that is. Now the major money-makers are the Enterprise Zones. These, too, are generally to the west of the city center, but closer than the real manufacturing areas.

## ENTERPRISE ZONES

There are currently five Enterprise Zones in greater Q.C., and three more are scheduled to open in early 2054. As you cruise east along Georges VI or Grande-Allée, these zones look like old-style industrial parks, whose layout and manicured grounds look attractive, unobtrusive, and non-threatening. (These zones wiped out whole drek-loads of residential neighborhoods, however, displacing thousands whose homes were razed to make space for the Zones.)

Zones are usually surrounded by multiple layers of fencing. Depending on whose Enterprise Zone it is, the fences may be alarmed or electrified. The open ground between the layers of fence may be patrolled by dogs, mined, or criss-crossed by X-ray lasers. (At least, so I've heard.)

The five Zones belong to some of the largest of the big corps: MCT, Aztechnology, Fuchi, Yokogawa-Honeywell, and Yamaha. The details of their security arrangements vary according to the "personality" of the company involved. Aztechnology, for example, has more magical protection, while MCT uses characteristically brutal overkill. Whatever the type of security, the Zones are almost impossible to penetrate. Most use biologicals to patrol certain areas. (These biologicals are probably just trained guard dogs, though I keep hearing rumors that the Y-H security has more arcane critters.) Both MCT's and Y-H's Zones are considered null-zones: nothing unauthorized can get in, and even if it did, it wouldn't live long.

What's with all the security, you ask? And how can the corps get away with such lethal force? That's the beauty of Enterprise Zones, chummer. By law, an Enterprise Zone is extraterritorial, beyond the laws of Québec. As long as the corps keep their affairs quiet, the Québec authorities don't want to know about it. (I'm not sure I blame them after some of the stories I've heard about the heavy drek going down in the Zones.)

## NEIGHBORHOODS

### OLD TOWN

The areas within the walls of Old Québec show a wide range of architectural styles. A few buildings date back to the origins of the city, with the most aggressively avant-garde architecture of newer shops and offices standing right alongside. The eyesores are the "bastardized" buildings: new edifices whose construction mimics styles of the past.

Q.C. has tried to limit the height of buildings in the walled area of the Upper Town to 30 floors or less. The area includes some pleasant shopping areas and many cafés and restaurants.

This neighborhood is classed as AAA. Law enforcement is severe on all levels of offenses.

### LATIN QUARTER

Though the Latin Quarter is also within the old walls, and might be considered part of Upper Town, it has a totally different personality. It's an area of narrow, winding streets, generally bounded by Côte du Palais, Côte de la Fabrique, Sainte-Famille, and Université. The Latin Quarter used to be an area of cheap accommodations, where students and artists lived in garrets and congregated in coffee houses and wine bars. Unfortunately, a fire wiped out the area in 2010. The city tried to rebuild the area in the old style, and frag it if they didn't succeed. It really looks like it's more than a hundred years old.

Not many artists or students live here anymore; the old buildings now house offices. The cafés and wine bars are still there, but they're targeted more at tourists than at residents. During the day and until the bars shut down at 1:00 A.M., the area is safe. It is classed as AAA, with heavy enforcement on all levels of offenses. Between about 2:00 A.M. and dawn, however, the Quarter would be lucky to get a single-A classification. Enforcement on transport and possession of knives and pistols is light, but heavy on all others.

### OUTSIDE THE WALLS

This area is still strictly Upper Town, because it's on top of the cape, not at its foot. But its personality is different from that of the Old Town. Here are located the main corporate headquarters. Apart from a few incongruities such as Château Frontenac, the architecture is generally modern. This is the business hub of the city, where the corporate money is—and it shows.

All corporate buildings have their own landing flats and underground parking facilities. Employees and authorized visitors enter the buildings by these two means; only tourists and other pseudo-desirables enter off the streets. This is why law enforcement is not as strict as in Old Town. The real heavy-hitters are never on the streets, except in well-armored personal cars or in the mini-buses. The corporate area is perhaps security rating AA during daylight hours on possession and transport of knives and pistols, heavy on everything else, but drops as far as security rating B light enforcement on possession and transport of bladed, blunt, and projectile weapons and pistols, and possession of rifles, but is heavy on everything else late at night after the restaurants and clubs are closed. (This is not the place for roaming the streets at night.)

### THE CITADEL

Not really a neighborhood, this is the headquarters of the Québec Defense Force, and they take their own security pretty seriously, thank you very much. The walls, formerly those of the old fort, are reinforced, and the ground at their foot is laced with sensor grids. The auto-cannons atop the bastions are quite capable of engaging anything up to a full-armored panzer on the ground or high-speed fighter-bombers in the air. (Time out: These guys are full-on military, remember that. You might be tough on your own turf and against other shadowrunners or sec-guards, chummer. But military is something else again. Do not slot with these guys.) If I had to give this place an enforcement class, it would be quadruple-A in big quivering letters, with lightning bolts and celestial fanfares. If you're not authorized, breathing is treated as a capital crime.

### LOWER TOWN

Now we come to the interesting place. Lower Town is downright slimy, grimy, boisterous, dangerous, and a frag of a lot of fun if you've got an edge. This is where the Anglophones live and work, and anyone who likes the shadows will love this area.

The main business in Lower Town is transport. Transport of what, you say? Well, the traders of Lower Town will transport anything, buy or sell anything: information, people, ordnance, drugs, chips…even legal drek like food, clothing, or trideo sets. Information and disinformation are also big sellers.

Down in Lower Town are the flop houses, rough bars, warehouses, businessmen going down for the last time, and hot-shots on their way up. I'd tell you the names and locations of my favorite night spots down there, but by the time you scan this, they'll have changed. That's the way it is in Lower Town.

It's no surprise that law enforcement is not a big issue on anyone's list. During the day (on a good day), enforcement might be classed as security rating D (light for possession and transport of, and threatening with, bladed, blunt, and projectile weapons and pistols; light for possession of automatic weapons, ammunition, or Class A cyberware; heavy for all others). At night, the bottom drops out to security rating E (light for possession and transport of, and threatening with, bladed, blunt, and projectile weapons and pistols; light for possession and transport of automatic weapons; light for possession of ammunition and Class A and B cyberware; heavy for all others) but that can vary…usually downward. The closer you get to the docks, the rougher it gets. The docks themselves probably merit the mythical Z class: light to no enforcement, no matter what you're up to. As the locals say, "If you're on the docks at night, you're too dumb to live…or too tough to die."

## PLACES OF INTEREST

### HOTELS

**Hotel Auberge des Gouverneurs**

Luxury Hotel Archetype (18 floors)/St-Cyrille Est and Avenue Dufferin/Jean Flauvier, Manager/No Racial Bias/ LTG# 2418 (65-0956)

The original Auberge des Gouverneurs got torched in 2015 (the same riot that scragged the old Hôtel du Gouvernement). The outer facade of the new building tries to emulate the style of the original, but doesn't quite get it.

The interior is frighteningly modern. The building is connected to Q.C.'s well-appointed Convention Center. Expect to pay through the nose.

**Hilton International Québec**

Luxury Hotel Archetype (25 floors)/Conroy and Avenue Dufferin/Gérard Laplace, Manager/No Racial Bias/ LTG# 2418 (18-0418)

Looks like a Hilton, smells like a Hilton, costs like a Hilton. From inside, you could just as easily be in Cleveland, Cairo, or Copenhagen.

**Manoir Ste-Geneviève**

Family Style Hotel Archetype (15 floors)/Avenue Ste-Geneviève and D'Aiguillon/Karin Balsamme, Manager/No Racial Bias/LTG# 2418 (65-5820)

Another god-awful attempt at period architecture. The rooms are spacious and the service exceptional, considering the moderate prices. Cornucopia, the restaurant atop the building, is worth a visit, and the wine cellar is un-fragging-believable.

**La Maison de la Fleuve**

Cheap Hotel Archetype (2 floors)/Saint-Paul and Côte Dinan/Gary Botwell, Manager/No Racial Bias/LTG# 3418 (56-1476)

This is one of the few hotels where you can check in speaking English and not get a broom closet. It's down in Lower Town, and has 15 rooms (with, I think, a grand total of three bathrooms). Gary is a Troll who puts up with no drek on his premises. If you want to save some money and don't care about multilegged bed-mates, check out "the riverhouse."

### RESTAURANTS AND BARS

**Table Haute**

Mid-Size Restaurant and Bar Archetype/Saint-Patrice and Ste-Geneviève/Serge Bruyère, Manager/No Racial Bias/LTG# 2418 (51-2973)

If you can afford it, this place is a must: the best and unarguably the most expensive restaurant in the whole fragging city. Don't ask for a menu, just go with the "menu découverte": it's whatever the chef thinks is freshest and best on that particular day. Dress up, and make sure you've got a good balance on your credstick. Dinner for two, without wine, runs 200ƒ and up-up-up, but it's well worth it. (Time out: If you're interested in such things, there are persistent rumors that Serge the manager was

into something hot and heavy with our beloved Mayor Geuvrement a couple of years back.)

**La Ripaille**

Mid-Size Restaurant and Bar Archetype/Buade and Fort/Claude Wallace, Manager/No Racial Bias/LTG# 1418 (21-4754)

Nowhere near as expensive as the Table Haute, La Ripaille is still a four-star eatery. The decor is a little overdone, with computer-generated "photographs" of how ancient Québec must have looked, and the atmosphere is much more stuffy than the Table Haute, but the food is still worth the aggravation.

**Le Marie Clarisse**

Small Restaurant and Bar Archetype/Foot of Côte de la Montaigne/François Pinard, Manager/No Racial Bias/ LTG# 3418 (65-4819)

An interesting place for those who want to pretend they're slumming but don't want to take any risks. Located in Lower Town, this seafood restaurant has got

almost enough security to rival one of the Enterprise Zones. Patrons are ferried back and forth to Upper Town on a special mini-bus. The "doormen" pack heat, and are quite ready to use it. This novelty aside, the prices are high and the food totally uninspired. It's popular with tourists anyway.

**Le Bistro**

Large Restaurant and Bar Archetype/St-Jean and St-Augustin/Gilles Connolley, Manager/No Racial Bias/LTG# 2418 (02-5849)

A typical high-tech disco, Le Bistro features lots of light and sound, which is sometimes painful without aural dampening. It's a lot safer than equivalent places in other cities, because the real street life prefers the shadowclubs. The patrons are mostly tourists, many middle-aged and trying to pretend they're younger, and some operators waiting to hit on same.

**Eden**

Large Restaurant and Bar Archetype/Near Lockwell and Avenue Turnbull/No Known Manager/No Racial Bias/ LTG# 2418 (32-4060)

This is one of the most stable of the shadowclubs (it's been in the same place for almost nine months now). No guarantees it'll still be there when you scan this. Hot place, good music, and an electric current of danger running through everything. Here's the kind of place where the people with an edge spend their nights.

## OTHER PLACES OF INTEREST

**Universal Brotherhood Chapterhouse**

Richelieu, between Ste-Geneviève and St-Augustin/ LTG# 2418 (32-0100)

This place opened its doors about two years back, and it's been picking up members ever since. I don't really know what the Brotherhood's about, but I hear it's one of these "inner truth" scams. In any case, the building includes a soup kitchen for the destitute, a counselling service, and a small but well-equipped (and free if you happen to be broke) clinic.

**Hôtel de Ville (City Hall)**

Cook and Chauveau/LTG# 1418 (70-2200)

Hôtel de Ville is the seat of the municipal government. A detachment of Gendarmerie is on 24-hour guard duty outside the building. As a pleasant change of pace from the pseudo-antique architecture of some other public buildings, this is a good 2040s-style office block with a central atrium garden. Visitors are tolerated, if not welcome.

**UCAS Consulate**

St-Louis and Terrasse Dufferin/LTG# 1418 (06-5000)

Looks like a fortress, defensible like a fortress. If you're a UCAS citizen, this is a good place to go for help in time of need. The staff speaks English, and they're well-versed in Québec's weird legal system. There is an official extradition treaty between UCAS and Québec, so don't depend on the Consulate's extraterritoriality to protect you for too long. The place is guarded by a detachment of well-trained marines.

# UNITED CANADIAN AND AMERICAN STATES

UCAS is the top dog in the political shark-tank of North America these days. The United Canadian and American States (no, it doesn't stand for United Capitalists and Sheep) was built on the corpse of the old United States of America, and carries on the proud tradition of that country all too well. The UCAS has a total population of 173,201,800 SINners, and Washington, FDC (the DeeCee sprawl) serves as the capital. Estimates on the SINless population are all over the place, but the median figures are about 3 to 4 million.

So how did the dear old UCAS come to be? Follow me, children, and we shall see.

## FALL OF THE UNITED STATES

We cannot fully understand where we are until we know how we got here. So to understand the UCAS, we have to examine the toppled giant from which it sprang.

### U. S. PRESIDENTS FROM 2001–2032

| | |
|---|---|
| Martin Hunt | 2001–2004 |
| Philip Bester | 2005–2008 |
| Jesse Garrety* | 2009–2016 |
| William Jarman | 2016–2028 |
| Andrew MacAlister** | 2029–2030 |

*Assassinated December 12, 2016. Succeeded by Vice President William Jarman.
**United States is dissolved on October 15, 2030. MacAlister is chosen as the provisional president of UCAS, and later first president of UCAS.

### FALSE DAWN

The last decade of the 20th century was a kind of false dawn, for it seemed to be the beginning of an era of global peace. Though it definitely produced such major changes as the superpowers reducing their strategic nuclear arsenals by 90 percent, it was only the calm before the storm.

The candidates in the presidential campaign of 1992 played on the American people's desire for peace, security, and prosperity. The winner, Jeffrey Lynch, was swept into office on a huge majority, which he referred to in his inaugural address "as a mandate to cure the ills of the nation and bring a new vitality to America." Seeing how easily the voters bought this line, Congress quickly fell into step behind President Lynch's programs.

By the end of Lynch's second term in 2000, the U. S. power structure had undergone some fundamental changes. A wave of deregulation had begun in 1996, touted by the slogan "Invest in America, Inc." The U.S. Postal Service was the first to go, broken up and sold to private messenger companies. Following in quick succession were the U. S. Weather Service, Forest Service, Amtrak, and a half-dozen other public services. This altered relationship between the U. S. and big business ended the necessity for the various regulatory agencies. The high (or low) point of this trend came when President Philip Bester approved the dissolution of NASA and the sale of its facilities to private interests. Except for a pair of shuttles retained for intelligence and military missions, the U.S. had abandoned space exploration.

By 1998, the defense establishment had been cut by almost 40 percent, with even bigger cuts in procurement and R&D for new weapon systems. Many companies saw their defense contracts dry up, while predicted increases in peacetime markets failed to materialize. Congress was concentrating on reducing a huge deficit, which also meant trimming or eliminating many social service programs as well.

As international tensions decreased, domestic unrest increased dramatically. The unemployment rate climbed to 50 percent in some regions as overloaded welfare services began to break down all over the country. The last years of the century brought widespread strikes, culminating in 1998 and 1999 in the teamster strikes that led to food riots in many cities.

### THE ORDELL COURT

Three of the Supreme Court justices appointed during the Burger court died or retired between 1993 and 1998. Justices who supported the policies of the current administration were appointed to replace them, neatly stacking the deck.

Chief Justice Burger retired for health reasons in 1994 and was succeeded by Terence Ordell, an outspoken conservative law professor from the East Coast. Ordell's court handed down decisions based on a narrow interpretation of the Constitution and his abrasive opinion on laws that "…gave criminals a 'Get-Out-Of-Jail-Free' card."

In the next decade, many of the Ordell Court's decisions overturned or significantly eroded earlier rulings on the laws of evidence and probable cause. The Court also reduced government controls of corporate practices. Other Ordell court dicisions increased the executive branch's decision-making power, relative to that of the legislative and judicial branches. All that now stood between the whims of the government and the rights of the citizens was the government's promise of good faith. The citizens didn't have a chance.

With the Supreme Court's landmark Seretech vs. The United States (1999) and Shiawase Corporation vs. the Nuclear Regulatory Commission (2001) decisions, multinational corporations gained virtual autonomy on American soil. The age of the megacorp had arrived.

## MILITARY WITHDRAWAL

The first decade of the 21st century saw the decline of the U. S. military presence worldwide. Troop strength in Europe was drastically reduced. The burgeoning military strength of Japan, which was growing to match the country's economic power, led to a phase-out of U. S. bases in both Japan and Okinawa. By 2010, no significant American military presence existed west of the Philippines.

## ROAD TO DENVER

Martin Hunt served as U. S. President from 2001–2004, and was the last president who could have averted the collapse of his nation. Blocked by a stubborn Congress and a hostile Supreme Court, Hunt failed in his attempts to wrest economic and political control of America from the megacorporations. After only one term in office, Hunt was succeeded by Philip Bester in 2004, following a bitterly fought campaign. Bester, the former governor of Colorado, was for all practical purposes a puppet of the corporations.

Hunt had managed to block the megacorps' politically motivated efforts to open federally protected lands to exploitation during his administration. Once Bester was in the White House, however, the government almost tripped over its own feet giving industry access to federal resource reserves.

Bester's successor, Jesse Garrety, who served from 2008–2016, followed by William Jarman, elected in 2016, treated opposition to exploitation of government resources as virtual sedition.

Garrety's "cowboy" attitude was not, however, the worst part of his administration. What made him infamous was the so-called Re-Education And Relocation Act of 2009, which herded the Native American population and their supporters into camps. This act also made possible pits of brutality like the maximum-security enclosure in Abilene. William Jarman, who had supported Garrety's policies for four years as vice president, won the 2016 presidential election by campaigning stridently against his predecessor's "inhumane" actions in dealing with the Sovereign American Indian Movement.

This about-face did not last long, however. Once in office, Jarman began to exterminate members of NAN. The Ghost Dance and its bloody results, which led to the shattering of North America, can be blamed directly on these two men.

It says something about the desperate mentality of the country that Jarman was returned to office in 2020, despite a disastrous first term. Then came the 29th Amendment to the Constitution, which allowed a president to serve an unlimited number of terms in office. This radical development could have come about through the powerful control that the corporations exerted over government and the people's confusion in the midst of chaos. Jarman won the election in 2024, becoming the first three-term president since Franklin D. Roosevelt.

Jarman's administration would have had its hands full even if the only challenge it had faced was restructuring the country. The year 2021, as everyone knows, was the year of Goblinization. Perhaps the experience with Howling Coyote and his Ghost Dancers made Jarman loathe to try his usual solution to whatever he perceived as a threat— annihilation. In any event, his administration did not start rounding up the Awakened and slapping them into concentration camps. Indeed, government research teams from the Center for Disease Control and elsewhere were instrumental in proving to a terrified public that the change was not a contagious condition, and that there was no medical justification for isolating the victims of goblinization. This response was one of the U.S. government's few enlightened actions in these years.

### THE FINAL BLOW

From 2001 to 2029, the U. S. lost almost a third of its population to VITAS and more than a third of its territory to NAN. Meanwhile, the national debt continued to skyrocket, resulting in even more drastic cuts in social programs.

The Computer Crash of '29 shattered what remained of the economy, along with telecommunications and transport systems. On April 9, 2029, for example, the virus infected the national air traffic-control network. As a result of inaccurate signals and scrambled communications, 27 major air accidents occurred within two hours, with a death toll in the thousands. Non-essential air traffic remained grounded for almost a week following the disaster, until a new control network could be cobbled together.

North America's cities were cut off from one another and from outlying regions. Riots erupted everywhere. For food. For fear. For the hell of it. Everyone lived in a terrorized bunker mentality. Straying onto the wrong street could get you shot, or at least detained by private security forces or the neighborhood militia. Government and corporate centers became fortresses.

For a time, it looked like the final collapse of state-based culture in North America, setting the stage for the emergence of neo-anarchy. But the big boys had a rabbit in their hat, and chose this moment to produce it.

## BIRTH OF THE UCAS

### THE ACT OF UNION

While up to their necks in disaster, the leaders of the U.S. and Canadian governments were also deep in secret negotiations to salvage both nations. The result of those negotiations was the Act of Union, which was signed into law simultaneously by U. S. President Andrew MacAlister and Canadian Prime Minister Harold Frazier on Oct. 15th, 2030. Known as Union Day, October 15 is now a national holiday in the United Canadian and American States (UCAS), and a day of mourning for all Neo-Anarchists. Against all odds, those two troubled countries managed to come together in a working union.

By Spring 2031, a constitution was submitted to the Provisional Congress. Within six months, two-thirds of the new country's states had ratified the UCAS Constitution.

Canada got to put its name first and the new flag had some maple leaves, but in the ways that mattered, it was a U. S. show from the word go. The Canadians were in terrible shape and needed the union desperately. They didn't have the leverage to force MacAlister's government into any major concessions, which meant that the U.S. simply absorbed them.

MacAlister became Provisional President of the UCAS after the Constitution passed, and served out the remainder of his elected term as president of the UCAS. His vice president "stepped down," to be replaced by Harold Frazier—the former prime minister of a defunct government.

In 2032, the voters also seemed to believe in kindness to ex-heads of state, allowing the MacAlister/Frazier ticket to win re-election handily.

### SECESSION FEVER

The southern UCAS became increasingly dissatisfied with the policies being made in the Federal District of Columbia, the new capital of the UCAS. The situation came to a head in 2034 when the governors and legislatures of ten southern states seceded from the UCAS, protesting that MacAlister seemed to behave as though everything outside the northeastern megasprawl could go hang.

Despite saber-rattling on both sides, neither the UCAS nor the new Confederated American States (CAS) could afford civil war. In 2035, the Treaty of Richmond was ratified, peacefully settling boundaries between the two nations.

When California withdrew from the UCAS in 2037, Japan backed it up with diplomatic recognition and hefty military aid. The leaders of the California Free State lived to rue that day, for the Japanese have established so much influence in that region that California is nearly an Imperial client-state at this writing.

Hawaii bailed out of the UCAS in 2038, and set up shop as a constitutional monarchy. Japan backed this new nation as well, but Malama, Hawaii's queen, has done a better job of walking the tightrope between accepting Japanese aid and losing independence.

In the midst of these events, the voters turned down Andrew MacAlister's bid for re-election in 2036. The newly organized Technocratic Party, pushing a platform of technology as the salvation of the UCAS (new party, same old drek), successfully beat him with their candidate, Martin Vincenzo, a charismatic businessman from Massachusetts. He introduced a new level of coalition politics into UCAS elections by naming Republican Vernon Washington as his running mate. In fact, most presidential slates since 2036 have featured a coalition ticket. (Ever feel as if the politicos are ganging up on you?)

## EUROPEAN MILITARY WITHDRAWAL

When the Euro-War broke out in 2031, the fledgling UCAS ordered its troops to withdraw from the conflict areas on the grounds that the Provisional Government did not have the constitutional authority to commit them to battle. This policy did not change, however, even after ratification of the UCAS Constitution. The former allies of the old U.S. were on their own and out in the cold.

Speaker of the House Kenneth Steiner summed up the prevailing attitude in the UCAS when he argued against sending American troops into a "border skirmish." By the end of 2032, more than half the UCAS ground and air forces stationed in Europe were withdrawn by the increasingly isolationist government.

When the CAS seceded, some North American units still stationed in Europe got into a few "border skirmishes" of their own. The European nations retaliated to being dumped by interning those units, then repatriating them to North America. By 2035, the UCAS had no military presence anywhere outside North America.

## TERROR IN THE CITIES

Then came 2039 and the Night of Rage. Anti-metahuman groups were blamed for the fires that killed hundreds of metahumans trapped on the Seattle docks on the night of February 7, 2039, and later for the deaths of thousands more as the violence spread across the continent and throughout the world. Since then, fanatics of every stripe have crawled out of the woodwork to write a message of blood and destruction in the streets. Meanwhile, every ten-yen street gang in the country is buying and carrying military weapons, too. In this climate of fear, police tactics have become much more military and much less likely to respect due process and citizens' rights.

Urban terrorism is a fact of life in the UCAS today. In addition to racist terrorist groups like Alamos 20K and militant metahuman groups like the Sons of Sauron, there are still some hard-line Amerindian terrorist groups who have vowed not to rest until the whole continent is restored to native rule. Then there are the the ideological terrorist groups who go after whatever offends their beliefs. The Hammer of God, for instance, attacks sex shops, brothels, simsense theatres, birth control clinics, and media that support "permissiveness." Criminal gangs also use massive force to control their territories. The perpetrators usually wield power in the lower and middle levels of the underworld. The big boys have other means to achieve their ends. Last, but not least, are unethical shadowrunners who use urban terrorism to cover their activities.

According to conservative estimates, an act of terrorism occurs somewhere in the UCAS every twelve hours, ranging from drive-by assassinations to heavy bombings to ritual magical attacks.

## CIVILIAN RESPONSE

In 2008, Texas passed a law creating urban militia units, which allowed residents of an area to sign up for limited combat training and obtain military weaponry with minor restrictions. New laws also defined the right of residents to contract private security firms to provide armed protection for their communities and homes. This paved the way for many cities to contract with private firms to provide police and other public safety services. These days, the typical urban militia unit operates in middle- and upper-class and higher neighborhoods. In areas populated heavily by salaried workers, the local corporations usually help bankroll the militia.

It's not all fun-and-wargames being in the Urban Militia. Members spend one weekend a month training. If a unit's specified level of readiness falls too low, their charter can be revoked. No one wants to give up the pretty hardware that militia members get to carry, so units work hard to stay up to snuff.

Militia members may be called up to reinforce the National or Metroplex Guard in controlling civil disorders, but it's only in their assigned neighborhood that they have real power.

## UCAS STATES AND TERRITORIES

The UCAS consists of 30 states and two special administrative districts (the Seattle Metroplex and the Federal District of Columbia). Some metroplex areas are virtually independent jurisdictions, but remain nominally part of their state, electing members to Congress and voting in Presidential elections on that basis. The UCAS has held no territory outside the North American continent since the secession of Hawaii.

Each state and Seattle has an elected governor, two Senators, and a varying number of representatives to the Congress of the UCAS. The Federal District of Columbia is administered by a government-appointed Commissioner and has no representatives in either House.

## UCAS FLAG

Modelled on the United States flag, the UCAS flag retains the field of 13 red and white stripes, with a blue canton in the upper left-hand corner. Set against the canton are five maple leaves (representing the states that were originally Canadian) and 27 stars (representing the states and territories originally part of the U.S. ) reflecting the 32 states and territories of the UCAS.

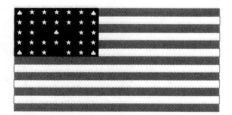

## UCAS GOVERNMENT

### PRESIDENTS OF THE UCAS

| President | Term |
| --- | --- |
| Andrew MacAlister* | 2030–2036 |
| Martin Vincenzo | 2037–2040 |
| Carl Preston | 2041–2048 |
| Alan Adams | 2049– |

\* U.S. President from 2028 to 2030 and Provisional President of UCAS until the Constitution was ratified in 2030.

### THE CONSTITUTION

*We, the people of the United States of America and the Dominion of Canada, in order to form a more perfect union, establish justice, restore domestic tranquillity, provide for the common defense, promote the general welfare, and procure the blessings of liberty and security for ourselves and our posterity, in spite of all enemies foreign and domestic, and the travails of our two nations, do ordain and establish this Constitution for the United Canadian and American States.*

So goes the preamble of the UCAS Constitution. Though similar to the old U.S. Constitution, its differences are telling enough to reveal the terrifying social disorders that gave birth to the Act of Union and the establishment of the UCAS.

Many amendments to the U. S. Constitution were incorporated into the body of the UCAS document. Deadwood was eliminated, including the 18th and 21st Amendments (Prohibition and its repeal).

The president and vice president are elected to four-year terms, but by a simple majority of the popular ballot. The UCAS has no electoral college. There is also no limit on the number of terms a president may serve.

The UCAS legislative branch is constituted much as it was under the U. S. Constitution, with a Senate and House of Representatives. Each state, and Seattle, elects two senators to six-year terms. Representatives are elected by districts of approximately 50,000 full citizens, with districts reapportioned based on a census held every ten years. Neither probationary citizens nor out-and-out SINless inhabitants count toward congressional districts, and they cannot vote.

The federal judiciary is structured exactly as it was in the U.S., and U.S. Supreme Court decisions are considered binding precedents in UCAS law.

The UCAS can suspend habeas corpus and various other civil rights in time of war, insurrection, or declared national emergency. Over the past two decades, various regions of the country have been declared in a state of emergency for periods of up to two years.

The first ten amendments of the U. S. Constitution exist unchanged in the UCAS Constitution, and are still referred to as the Bill of Rights. Much of their effectiveness has been weakened by recent Supreme Court decisions, however.

Other amendments to the UCAS Constitution include:

• **11th Amendment**—The rights of UCAS citizenship, by birth or naturalization, are not to be denied to any individual due to race or creed.

• **12th and 15th Amendments**—Expanded powers to state and local (i.e., Metroplex) governments. The central power of the UCAS government is greatly reduced.

• **13th Amendment**—UCAS recognizes contracts between corporations and their employees as binding. Upon due process of law in a Contract Court, corporations may extradite persons found guilty of unlawfully breaking their employment contract.

• **14th Amendment**—The so-called "SIN Amendment," ratified in 2036, established the System Identification Number, requiring the registration of every UCAS citizen. Individuals residing in the UCAS without SINs are defined as "probationary citizens," with sharply limited civil rights. Probationary citizens are not permitted to vote in federal elections. Species other than *Homo sapiens* are eligible for probationary citizenship in UCAS, but full citizenship may be granted to a non-human/non-metahuman only by act of Congress.

## GOVERNMENT OFFICIALS OF THE UCAS
**(In order of their succession to the presidency)**

**President:** Alan Adams (Dem.)
**Vice President:** Thomas Steele (Tech.)

**Speaker of the House (10th Congress):** William Sorenson (D-Ind.)
**President Pro-tem of the Senate:** Marianne Plaut (T-Md.)

**Department of State:** Gerald Humphrey, Secretary
**Department of the Treasury:** Quentin MacDonald, Secretary
**Department of Defense:** Malcom Dowling, Secretary
**Department of Justice:** Douglass Freeman, Attorney General
**Department of Agriculture:** Sheila Erdeky, Secretary
**Department of Business:** Harcourt Pierce, Secretary
**Department of Resources:** Jay Stein, Secretary
**Department of Human Services:** Alexander Dominello, Secretary
**Department of Health:** Dr. Charles Hands-That-See, Surgeon General
**Department of Information:** Randall Gartner, Secretary

## POLITICAL PARTIES

The following table is based on voter registration in the 2048 elections and indicates the relative influence the major political parties wield with the electorate.

### INFLUENCE OF POLITICAL PARTIES

| Party | Percent of Voters |
|---|---|
| Republican | 23% |
| Democrat | 22% |
| Technocrat | 22% |
| Archconservative | 14% |
| Libertarian | 10% |

The remaining 9 percent of voters are registered as independents or else adhere to one of the numerous policlubs or other splinter parties in the UCAS. None of these groups has more than a small fraction of the registered vote.

## LAW AND LAW ENFORCEMENT

Federal jurisdiction in the UCAS covers:
- Crimes committed in federally controlled areas
- Crimes involving interstate conspiracy or flight across state lines
- Kidnapping
- Terrorism
- Computer crime
- Crimes involving foreign nationals
- Violation of laws passed by Congress

Federal law enforcement agencies include the Federal Bureau of Investigation, the Secret Service, the U. S. Marshal's office, and various local police forces in federal areas like the District of Columbia. All these are under the control of the Department of Justice.

Civil or criminal proceedings against extra-territorial corporations, their subsidiaries, and employees are heard in Contract Court. Should the Contract Court find that a case is more properly a matter for a UCAS or local court system, it may order a change of venue.

Decisions of the Contract Court have been enforced in the past by corporate security forces, economic sanctions against recalcitrant corporations or governments, federal law-enforcement agencies, and in extreme cases, by overt military action, depending on the nature of the decision and the response of the party that lost the case.

## CONTROLLED EQUIPMENT AND MATERIALS

Controlled equipment and materials, including guns, are the concern of local jurisdiction. Transport and sale of controlled weapons and materials is, however, subject to federal jurisdiction. Military weaponry and equipment, and cyberware are all subject to federal statutes, and illegal possession or use of such equipment carries harsh punishment.

Any drug defined as physically addictive (with the exception of alcohol and nicotine, thanks to almost a century of high-powered lobbying) is a federally controlled substance, and may only be dispensed legally by a state-licensed biotechnician. Similarly, any biotechnical device that induces permanent neurological change is controlled in the UCAS. BTL chips, for example, are outlawed, as are most head-jobs that affect the pleasure centers of the brain.

Various non-addictive substances and most forms of the lesser simsense psycho-addictives are not controlled by UCAS law, though local statutes may impose controls, as in the case of Seattle's liquor monopoly.

## ENFORCEMENT

The following material augments or replaces the Sprawl Law Weapon Fines and Punishment Table on pp. 122-23 of **Sprawl Sites**.

Note two new classes of controlled items:
- **Class M:** controlled substances or biotechnical devices.
- **Class CD:** Unregistered cyberdecks and Matrix program software.

## WEAPON FINES AND PUNISHMENT TABLE

| Weapon Type | Offense and Fine | | | | |
|---|---|---|---|---|---|
| | 1<br>Possession | 2<br>Transport | 3<br>Threat | 4<br>Use | 5<br>Intent |
| (A) Small Bladed Weapon | — | — | 2,500¥/3 mo | 5,000¥/6 mo | 10,000¥/1 yr |
| (B) Large Bladed Weapon | — | — | 2,500¥/3 mo | 5,000¥/6 mo | 10,000¥/1 yr |
| (C) Blunt Weapon | — | — | 2,500¥/3 mo | 5,000¥/6 mo | 10,000¥/1 yr |
| (D) Projectile Weapon | — | — | 2,500¥/3 mo | 5,000¥/6 mo | 10,000¥/1 yr |
| (E) Pistol | — | — | 5,000¥/1 yr | 10,000¥/2 yrs | 25,000¥/3 yrs |
| (F) Rifle | — | — | 5,000¥/1 yr | 10,000¥/2 yrs | 25,000¥/3 yrs |
| (G) Automatic Weapon | 5,000¥ | 10,000¥/3 mo | 25,000¥/2 yrs | 25,000¥/5 yrs | 50,000¥/5 yrs |
| (H) Heavy Weapon | 10,000¥/2 yrs | 20,000¥/2 yrs | 5 yrs | 7 yrs | 10 yrs |
| (I) Explosives | 500¥ | 2,500¥/3 mo | 3 yrs | 10 yrs | 15 yrs |
| (J) Military Weapon | 10,000¥/2 yrs | 20,000¥/2 yrs | 5 yrs | 7 yrs | 10 yrs |
| (K) Military Armor | 5,000¥ | — | — | — | — |
| (L) Ammunition | 1,000¥ | — | — | — | — |
| (M) Controlled Substances | 500¥ | 1,000¥ | — | — | — |
| (CA) Class A Cyberware | 5,000¥ | — | — | — | — |
| (CB) Class B Cyberware | — | — | — | — | — |
| (CC) Class C Cyberware | 15,000¥ | — | — | — | — |
| (CD) Unlicensed Cyberdecks and Matrix Software | 2,500¥ | 10,000¥/6 mo | — | — | — |

The possession or transport of weapons in Classes A-F is not prosecuted under UCAS law, but may be prosecuted under state and local ordinances. Offenses involving weapons in Classes A-F other than possession or transport would be prosecuted in a federal court only if they occurred in connection with a crime under federal jurisdiction. For example, threatening or even shooting one's neighbor is of no interest to a federal court, but pulling the same gun on a guard in a government building would constitute a federal case of Threat, or even Intent.

Similarly, Class B cyberware is not illegal under federal law, though many areas control or even outlaw it.

### MAJOR FELONIES AND CAPITAL CRIMES

Classifications of major felonies involving injury or death are on the books in the UCAS, as described in **Sprawl Sites**, p. 124-25. Unauthorized Access to Computer Resources is also a major felony, punishable by 25,000¥ and five years in prison if data is stolen, damaged, or altered. These penalties double if the invaded system belongs to the government.

Capital crimes, that is, crimes for which the death penalty may be invoked, are:
- Premeditated murder
- Felony murder (any homicide committed in the course of a felony)
- Murder of police or military officer in pursuit of his duty
- Treason against the UCAS
- Rape or kidnapping involving death of or grievous bodily harm to victim.

Periodic attempts by corps to get credit fraud added to the list of capital crimes have, so far, been unsuccessful.

## ECONOMY OF THE UCAS

The UCAS is one of the most technologically advanced countries on Earth, but it is poor in natural resources. While advances in recycling have helped the UCAS avoid severe shortages, the economy is increasingly dependent on the import of raw materials.

Income taxes are high, partly because corporations have managed to create numerous tax shelters for themselves.

The UCAS unit of currency is the dollar. The official exchange rate makes one (1) nuyen worth approximately five (5) UCAS dollars. In reality, the dollar fluctuates plus or minus 20 percent against the nuyen on a day-to-day basis.

Almost all financial transactions are handled electronically and are subject to government tracking. A thriving shadow economy based in cash and corporate scrip also exists, despite official attempts to quash it.

For gaming purposes, whenever a transaction is conducted in UCAS dollars, roll 2D6 and consult the Dollar/Nuyen Exchange table.

### DOLLAR/NUYEN EXCHANGE

| Die Roll | Result (One nuyen equals) |
|---|---|
| 2 | UCAS $6.25 |
| 3–4 | UCAS $5.75 |
| 5–6 | UCAS $5.25 |
| 7 | UCAS $5.00 |
| 8–9 | UCAS $4.75 |
| 10–11 | UCAS $4.50 |
| 12 | UCAS $4.00 |

## COST OF LIVING

Industrial capability, the cost of resources, legal controls, and taxes all contribute to the cost of living in the UCAS. The following table gives the differences between standard and UCAS prices, in nuyen, of various items and services. When shadowrunners are going shopping in the UCAS, apply the modifiers to the prices given in **Shadowrun**, **Street Samurai Catalog**, and other FASA products. Items not shown on this list sell at standard cost. If the runners are paying with UCAS dollars ($), adjust prices accordingly.

| UCAS COST OF LIVING | |
|---|---|
| **ITEM** | **COST** |
| **Weaponry** | |
| Ammunition | 120% |
| Explosives | 150% |
| Firearm Accessories | 120% |
| Firearms | 120% |
| **Armor** | |
| Armor | 110% |
| **Surveillance and Security** | |
| Communications | 110% |
| Security Devices | 150% |
| Surveillance Countermeasures | 80% |
| Surveillance Measures | 120% |
| Vision Enhancers | 120% |
| **Lifestyle** | |
| Lifestyle | 125% |
| Medical Care | 120% |
| **Electronics** | |
| Electronics | 120% |
| **Cybertech** | |
| Bodyware | 115% |
| Cyberdecks | 150% |
| Headware | 110% |
| Internals | 105% |
| Programs | 200% |
| **Magical Equipment** | |
| Foci | 150% |
| Hermetic Libraries | 120% |
| Magical Supplies and Materials | 200% |
| **Vehicles** | |
| Aircraft | 110% |
| Boats | 125% |
| Ground Vehicles | 120% |
| Military Vehicles | 250% |

## BLACK MARKET

Stringent federal controls on the equipment needed by deckers and magic-users has created a successful and lucrative black market for these items. Because federal laws against data-crimes are particularly severe, cyberdecks, software, and other tools of the decker's craft are regulated out of the reach of shadowrunners on the legitimate market.

The pure and natural raw materials needed for magical work are hard to find in the heavily built-up and often highly polluted areas that make up most of the UCAS. Imports of magical materials are subject to high duties, and even locally produced magical equipment and materials carry a high sales tax.

The black market is sometimes the only source in the UCAS for the shadowrunner looking to practice his craft for a living.

# FEDERAL DISTRICT OF COLUMBIA

**by Prof**

*DeeCee is a cancer in the guts of North America, brothers and sisters. Home of the gummint, the spooks, and the sojers. DeeCee is where the buttons live that can blow us all the frag off Momma Earth. But they don't admit it, oh no—it's all 'national security' and 'deep cover.' Drek!*

*They all hunger for the power! They keep on gettin' more control! Control! That's what the fat cats of DeeCee grind out year after bloody-fraggin' year. And that's what they'll keep grindin' out until we amputate this disease with the knife of revolution.*

*—Excerpt from speech by the late Harvey Moon, founder of the Youth Organization for Undermining National Governments*

Brother Moon's position is stated with more vigor than logic, but it captures the feelings of all true neo-anarchists when contemplating the capital of the UCAS. Not all of us see things in the simple black and white terms of Y.O.U.N.G., however. Dramatic confrontation with authority, however satisfying to the spirit, can often cut short a productive revolutionary's career. Brother Moon discovered this when a police raid interrupted the address I have quoted above.

The Federal District of Columbia, the DeeCee sprawl, is indeed a major site of infection in the disease of government, and a sizable fraction of its three million inhabitants are part of the machinery of that government.

While the power is much less centralized in the UCAS than it was in the late and unlamented United States, this is still one of the pivotal marketplaces for power in North America. Power is the true currency of those who aid and abet the regime, from the most minor lobbyist up to the President and Congress.

Here are some useful tidbits of information for those who might have cause to pursue their shadowy vocation under the bright lights of the capital of the UCAS.

## A LITTLE HISTORY

Since the District of Columbia was created in 1791, assorted attempts have been made to break it up and turn its territory back over to the neighboring states of Maryland and Virginia. Congress took over city government in

1871; home rule was returned to residents in 1974. The city government was ousted by Congress again in 2003, amid charges of widespread corruption and incompetence. The decision was challenged in court by city officials and public-interest groups, but the challenges were defeated. In 2007, the Supreme Court declined to review the decision.

By 2024, the economy of the Delmarva area—the intersection of Delaware, Maryland, and Virginia—was completely dominated by the "business" of government and its attendant private industry. Local governments had a hard time keeping up with the demand for services. In an attempt to impose some order on the crazy quilt of competing local authorities, the federal government negotiated an agreement with the state governments of Maryland and Virginia that resulted in the Federal Capital District Act of 2024. This extended the boundaries of the District of Columbia to include Montgomery, Prince Georges, and Howard counties in Maryland, and Arlington, Alexandria, and Fairfax counties in Virginia. Tax revenue lost by the two states was to be made up by increased allocation of federal tax monies to their budgets.

The new jurisdiction was chartered as the Federal District of Columbia, colloquially known as DeeCee. When the United States of America was restructured into the United Canadian and American States, DeeCee continued as the capital of the new nation.

One of the more delicate compromises in the Treaty of Richmond, negotiated in 2033, involved the northern part of Virginia. While a second Civil War seemed unlikely, the president and Congress did not want the safety of DeeCee dependent on the good will of Atlanta.

Accordingly, part of Virginia remained UCAS territory, and was admitted to the UCAS as the state of North Virginia. This buffer zone is the portion of the state north of the Rappahannock River. Fredericksburg, straddling the Rappahannock on I-95, became the capital of Northern Virginia. Legitimate and black market goods moving between the CAS and UCAS change hands round the clock in this bustling border city.

**FEDERAL DISTRICT OF COLUMBIA**
**Area**: See map
**Population**: 3,436,000 SINners

# REGIONAL GOVERNMENTS WITHIN FDC

**ARLINGTON (Population: 240,000)**          Security Rating
**Alexandria**                                          A
  Upper Middle Class residential
**Arlington**                                          AA
  Upper Class residential and office neighborhoods
**National Airport**                                   AAA
  Reserved for specially cleared flights
**Old Towne**                                          AA
  Upper Class residences, with a historic district, high priced
    shops, restaurants, and clubs
**Pentagon-Crystal City**                              AAA
  Upper Middle Class residential and business, major govern-
    ment offices, and the Pentagon
**Rosslyn**                                            AA
  Major office blocks and business area

**FAIRFAX (Population: 776,000)**          Security Rating
**Fairfax**                                            A
  Middle Class residential and business areas
**Falls Church**                                       B
  Middle and Lower Class residential and business areas
**Lorton**                                          Special
  DeeCee prison complex—extremely high security
**Reston**                                             AA
  Upper Middle and Middle Class residential areas
**I-66 Corridor**                                      B
  Major business and Middle Class residential areas
**I-95 Corridor**                                      A
  Major business and Upper Middle Class residential areas
**Tysons Corner**                                      B
  Major business district
**Vienna**                                             A
  Upper and Upper Middle Class residential district
**Dulles International Airport**                       AAA
  FedPol provides security for this major airport

**HOWARD (Population: 853,000)**          Security Rating
**Baltimore-Washington International Airport**         AAA
  Security provided by Knight-Errant
**Columbia**                                           A
  Middle Class residences, medium office district
**Ellicott City**                                      B
  Mostly undeveloped with a large shaman population. Lore
    stores in the historic district. Several Upper Class devel-
    opments
**Fort Meade**                                         AA
  Major military reservation

**MONTGOMERY (Population: 853,000)**          Security Rating
**Bethesda-Chevy Chase**                               A
  Upper Class and Upper Middle Class residences, major office
    blocks
**Rockville**                                          D
  Run-down business district
**Wheaton**                                            C
  Lower Class residential and business districts

**Gaithersburg**                                       A
  Middle Class bedroom community
**Germantown**                                         A
  Middle Class residential and medium business area
**Silver Spring**                                      B
  Lower Class residential and business area
**Takoma Park**                                        B
  Middle Class residential, artists' district, lore stores

**PRINCE GEORGES (Population: 695,000)**          Security Rating
**Capitol Heights-Marlboro**                           D
  Severely depressed business area, Lower Class residential
    district
**College Park**                                       B
  Run-down residential areas surrounding the huge University
    of FDC campus
**Greenbelt**                                          AA
  High-security corp facilities and their employee residences
**Hyattsville**                                        B
  Middle and Lower Class residences and light industry
**Laurel**                                             A
  Middle Class residential and commercial areas
**Mount Rainier**                                      D
  Severely depressed residential, warehouse, and light indus-
    trial district
**National Technical Center**                          AAA
  A major concentration of R&D facilities, operated jointly by
    government and corporations

**WASHINGTON (Population: 657,000)**          Security Rating
**Adams Morgan**                                       A
  Middle and Upper Middle Class urban residential area
**Anacostia Barrens**                                  Z
  Urban combat zone
**Foggy Bottom**                                       AAA
  High-priced residences for government and corp bigwigs,
    George Washington University
**Georgetown**                                         AA
  Extremely high-priced urban homes, historic area, shops,
    clubs, and other high-priced consumer businesses galore,
    Georgetown University
**Government Zone**                                    AAA
  Site of main UCAS government buildings, monuments, and
    museums. Extremely high security at all times
**LeDroit**                                            B
  Middle and Lower Class residential area, Howard University
**Northeast**                                          D
  Lower Class business and residential areas
**Shaw**                                               B
  Middle and Lower Class residential area with diverse ethnic
    population and numerous small restaurants offering a va-
    riety of cuisines
**Upper Northwest**                                    AA
  Upper, Upper Middle and some Middle Class neighborhoods,
    American University
**Waterfront**                                         A
  Upper Middle Class condos, houseboats, marinas
**West End**                                           AA
  Major downtown business area

## WHO'S IN CHARGE?

The FDC has an interlocking system of federally appointed rulers and locally elected officials. Each is ultimately accountable to the president and Congress, but the entire farrago is obscured by a set of bureaucracies of legendary complexity and questionable efficiency.

The Federal District Chief Commissioner is appointed by the president, subject to confirmation by the House District Committee. The Commissioner chairs the Federal District Commission, composed of elected Regional Commissioners from the six divisions of the District and an at-large member. The Chief Commissioner serves as the tie-breaker. Congress must approve most decisions made by the Commission.

Each Regional Commissioner heads his or her regional government, which provides and coordinates for residents the services that city and county governments supply in other jurisdictions.

The Chief Commissioner heads the DeeCee executive branch. Departmental directors are, with one exception, accountable to him. In a burst of paranoid folly peculiar for even this kind of administrative structure, the Federal Capital Chief of Police is appointed by the attorney general, so is not accountable to the Chief Commissioner. DeeCee police follow a different chain of command than other government services. This is supposedly required because of the importance of security in the capital city. My own suspicion is that some brilliantly subtle neo-anarchist slipped this provision into the Act of 2024 to illustrate the absurdity of what had been created.

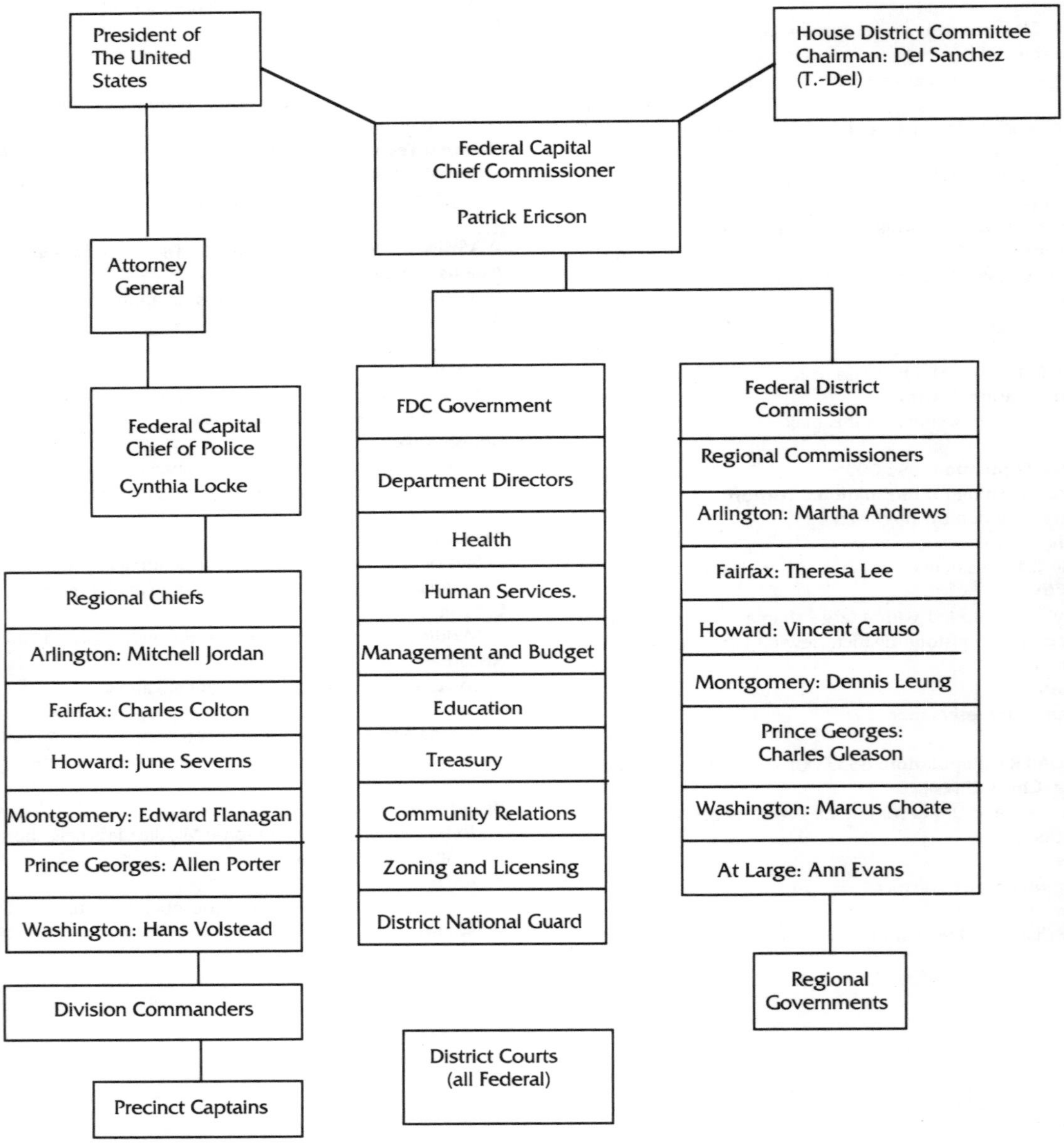

```
President of                                    House District Committee
The United                                      Chairman: Del Sanchez
States                                          (T.-Del)

                     Federal Capital
                     Chief Commissioner

                     Patrick Ericson

Attorney
General

Federal Capital          FDC Government              Federal District
Chief of Police                                      Commission
                         Department Directors
Cynthia Locke                                        Regional Commissioners
                         Health
                                                     Arlington: Martha Andrews
Regional Chiefs          Human Services.
                                                     Fairfax: Theresa Lee
Arlington: Mitchell Jordan   Management and Budget
                                                     Howard: Vincent Caruso
Fairfax: Charles Colton      Education
                                                     Montgomery: Dennis Leung
Howard: June Severns         Treasury
                                                     Prince Georges:
Montgomery: Edward Flanagan  Community Relations      Charles Gleason

Prince Georges: Allen Porter Zoning and Licensing    Washington: Marcus Choate

Washington: Hans Volstead    District National Guard At Large: Ann Evans

Division Commanders                                  Regional
                                                     Governments
                         District Courts
Precinct Captains        (all Federal)
```

## MAJOR GOVERNMENT FIGURES

### PATRICK ERICSON

The 57-year-old Ericson is Federal Capital Chief Commissioner. A flamboyant party hack from Detroit, he was appointed by Adams to pay off political debts in that region. Long on talk, short on action, Ericson is prone to spend enormous resources studying the irrelevant details of minor problems instead of tackling the issues. He is largely regarded as a rubber stamp for the House District Committee.

### MARTHA ANDREWS

The Regional Commissioner of Arlington, the 48-year-old former schoolteacher is a Technocrat. Andrews is known for an acid wit and impatience with bureaucratic drek.

### VINCENT CARUSO

Vincent Caruso, the Regional Commissioner of Howard, is a Democrat. The 51-year-old developer is active in support of metahuman rights.

### MARCUS CHOATE

The Regional Commissioner of Washington, Choate is a Democrat. He is 51 years old and a staunch civil libertarian who supports home rule for FDC.

### ANN EVANS

The At-Large Commissioner, Evans is a Technocrat. The charismatic former newsnet investigative reporter is 45 years old and acts as the gadfly on the Commission, as far as the Chief Commissioner is concerned. Evans is a strong supporter of returning home rule to FDC.

### CHARLES GLEASON

As Regional Commissioner of Prince Georges, Gleason has maintained a tough platform on civil disorder and improved services for residents. Several contracts issued under the 48-year-old Democrat's administration have been questioned, but so far no misfeasance has been proved.

### THERESA LEE

The Regional Commissioner of Fairfax is Republican, age 52, and very conservative. Lee is also known to support anti-magical programs and is suspected of connections to Alamos 20,000.

### DENNIS LEUNG

The Regional Commissioner of Montgomery, Leung is a Technocrat. He is 42 years old, a microtronics engineer by profession, and supported by numerous megacorp PACs.

### CYNTHIA LOCKE

The 41-year-old Locke is Federal Capital Chief of Police. She is the Former Assistant Chief of Police in Boston. Locke is ambitious, tough, and a bad person to make an enemy. She believes in using an iron fist in an iron glove when security in government areas or upper-echelon residential zones is threatened.

## EVERYBODY WHO IS ANYBODY

### by Mimosa Boy

Well, children, Prof has bored you to tears with what the DeeCee dictators *say* the rules are. Now M-boy is going to take you by the grubby hand and lead you through the maze behind the scenes.

What we have here in our mondo decadentissimo old town is a thriving little caste system. Either you are *SOMEBODY*, or maybe just a little somebody, or you're nobody at all. Just *guess* where grimy-nasty shadowfolks mostly fit, hmmm?

At the top of this little heap are the biggies in the federal government—Prexy Adams, of course, and the dear leaders of the House and Senate, and the Supremes. No, silly, not those old rockergirls. I mean the Supreme Court. Cabinet people and White House staff come next. Last in the tippy-top of the social register are plain, ordinary congress-things, high-level aides to the fatter cats I've already told you about, and ambassadors from countries we like.

If these folks want something, they get it. Parking spots in the G-zone, flight clearances into National, reservations at Trianon—all sorts of goodies come their way. If they *don't* like someone, that someone gets it, too—right in his little neck.

These people are only on each others' A-lists. Their A-lists are the ones everybody wants to be on.

---

### MAJOR FDC UNIVERSITIES

Campuses marked UFDC are part of the University of the Federal District of Columbia.

**Fairfax**
George Mason University (UFDC) (Falls Church)
**Montgomery**
Montgomery College (UFDC) (Rockville)
**Prince Georges**
UFDC at College Park (UFDC) (College Park)
**Washington**
American University (Upper Northwest)
Catholic University (Northeast)
Georgetown University (Georgetown)
George Washington University (Foggy Bottom)
Howard University (LeDroit)
Van Ness (UFDC) (Upper Northwest)

Next come the DeeCee biggies—the Commish and his merry band, *dear* Cynthia and her stout regional *commandants*, heads of District departments, and so on. They get almost the same perks as the top drawer, but sometimes not right away. If they have to ask a favor from some rival organization, the bargaining can just go on for days.

The plain old celebs and debs, big-time corporators, ambassadors we *don't* like, and all that crowd with fame and/or fortune rate the next slot on the old social ladder. When you're hot, you're on the in-list with this crowd, but slip just a teensy bit in the ratings or on the market, and gee, suddenly everyone has a previous engagement when you come to call. It is *so* rough at the top, you just can't think, children! Influence they have, but just because they know somebody who knows somebody who is very *much* a somebody. And one slip or scandal can wipe it all out. Makes one wonder what a few nicely placed skeletons in the right closets might do to get their attention, no?

It is a long way down to the next batch of flash and trash. Most of them work for the people on the top. Middle execs, government staffers, the less popular lobbyists, local top-cops, and the like, if you like. I for one usually don't, but maybe that's just me. They don't get to go to the parties, so the only way they'll be seen in the glitter palaces here in the sprawl is if they come to lick their bosses' boots. But if you want something done and can*not* cope with all the forms and questions and nasty trivia that those dreary dearies at the office of this-that-and-the-other always want filled out, well, if you can get to the right little cog in the wheel, it's just amazing how smoothly the process will go. The gears will turn if you have the right oil. M-boy has found something in four figures always seems just the right weight. Of course, if one is simply an honest citizen, or worse, some gutter scum who has washed his SINs away like *some* I could mention, then it is just a tad dangerous getting on the wrong side of these lower-level somebodies. Ration cards are so easy to lose, aren't they? But don't worry, we'll have you eating again in a few weeks, or months, at the outside. Oh, and *do* remember the stiff penalties for black-market consumption, darlings, that is, *if* you have anything the market could possibly want.

And way, way down at the bottom of the heap—why, we find you, and me, and Aunt Sally, and practically everyone you might know. All of us having to bow and scrape to the people up on top if we want to just go along minding our own little business—when our business is in the light. When we dance in the shadows, well, who can tell a knight from a knave, hmmm?

# INTO, OUT, AND AROUND

### by Rotormotor

There's a lot of biz to be had in DeeCee, but a runner's got to know his way around the turf before he can play in the shadows. I've been rigging round and about DeeCee for eight years now, and I'm here to pass on a couple things you chummers ought to know before you try a run in this sprawl.

## MAJOR AIRPORTS

Security is nasty at the big airports, so don't frag with them unless you've got solid, I mean *solid,* protections or connections. The smaller fields scattered around give you better odds on success. There're spots where you can bring in a multi-engine jet with zero perspiration, and others where you get maybe a beacon and just enough field to touch down a small chopper.

The Big Three are Ike, BWI, and Tommy.

Most of the major passenger and freight haulers have flights into one or more of the Big Three. The major airlines supply their own security, fleshing out the local heat. All three have good weapon-detection systems and explosive sniffers scanning luggage and passengers, and traffic control is hard to evade.

Natch, there are freeway connections at each of the Big Three. Ike has a private connector to the inner Beltway (I-495), while BWI and Tommy hook up to I-95. The FDC Metro subway serves Ike, and light rail connections will bring you in from BWI and Tommy to Union Station, smack in the center of DeeCee.

National is the fourth airport with major facilities in DeeCee, located in Arlington, just across the Potomac River from downtown DeeCee. A word to the wise, chummers: Don't even think about it. National's been restricted to flights with special federal clearance since 2012, which means government flights and planes carrying VIPS. When the feds play kissy-face with some top-ranked suit, they clear his plane for National. There's a Metro station there, left over from when it was a public 'port. Have heavy ID if you expect to get out of the station, or get some government clown to cut you an access pass. The place swarms with FedPols. On the upside, nobody at National sticks his nose too deep into the affairs of the bigwigs who use the 'port—and if you are cleared to land there, you must be a bigwig. Q-E-fragging-D. If you can wangle landing rights, you (and whatever you need to transport) are in like Flynn.

### BWI

Known as Baltimore-Washington International to the suits, BWI is located at the northern end of DeeCee, in Howard. Knight-Errant handles security at BWI. You know their name, you know their fame. Don't get cute with these boys or they'll blow your butt away.

### Ike

Eisenhower International, formerly Dulles International, is in the western end of Fairfax. The FedPols—the well-loved Federal Police, DeeCee's government heat—are the security outfit here. FedPols can be slow on the uptake, 'cause they love that red-tape drek, but they carry heavy heat. If they get on your case, you better finish your biz and buzz, 'cause DeeCee will be too hot to call home.

### Tommy

Opened in 2040, Thomas Jefferson International is just south of the District boundaries in North Virginia, off I-95. Security is provided by low-bid, local talent, UCASPro (UCAS Protective Services). They're real eager beavers, out to prove to Tommy's management that they can do the job. If you want to try anything fancy at one of the Big Three, Tommy's the place, since UCASPro still looks pretty lightweight.

## LOCAL AIR TRAFFIC

There's a mess of airbus, private charter, and other local air transport here in DeeCee. You can get a chopper or private plane heading into almost any part of the sprawl or nearby suit communities. Average cost of a scheduled commuter hop is $50. Air taxi service runs about $200 an hour. All nice and legal, with the flight plans going straight into the FedPol computers.

Any fixer worth his cut can set you up with a friendly neighborhood rigger for those little flights of fancy you'd prefer to keep out of the Fed database. Just keep in mind that the air space around DeeCee receives tighter surveillance than you'd ever want to see. Riggers don't come cheap, chummers. Low bid makes for low life expectancy around here. Most riggers learn fast that the best craft for a quiet hop over DeeCee is a low-signature ultralight with silenced turbines and as much stealth tech as you can cram on board. And that costs.

The Government Zone has incredible traffic control. A string of chopper raids by Policlub Blut und Ehre in 2047 convinced FedPol aircraft and surface defenses to develop major enforcement over the G-zone. Four "regrettable incidents" last year reminded us that these guys have orders to shoot first and radio for ID later.

Aerial runs anywhere in DeeCee need to go up fast, keep low, and land quick. Any other m.o. guarantees you'll attract attention within 10 minutes, 30 minutes tops. You've got 60 seconds or less if you go into combat up there.

## TRAINS

Union Station is in the Government Zone a couple of blocks from Capitol Hill. Both long-haul and commuter rail trains run from this combination terminal/mega-mall. The station has FedPol security rivaling the airports since the bombings of 2035, but the station is great for runners moving legally because it connects to Metro. Chopper

service is available from a rooftop pad, but it's covered by the G-zone air security blanket. Unscheduled departures make few arrivals, if you know what I mean.

Other areas of DeeCee are served by light rail—fast, clean, and electric. They can turn into a nasty little mousetrap if you're on the run, though, carrying your sad self straight into the arms of the waiting law. Don't frag yourself taking the train when you should be in the fast lane.

### GROUND TRAFFIC

You can use Interstates 95, 70, and 66, plus a lot of smaller highways, to drive into DeeCee. You can roll in on a superhighway or take back roads that are barely more than plowed ground. If you're running up from the CAS and want to give DeeCee a miss, the I-795 east and west bypasses are available. I-795E skips past the fringes of the District, along the route of old US 301. I-795W runs past the western side of DeeCee, before picking up I-95 near Baltimore.

The most vulnerable spots for running through DeeCee are the six bridges across the Potomac River. The FedPols can set up checkpoints on any or all of these with zero perspiration. Typical checkpoints have a squad car with two cops standing by for pursuit, and another two or three cops scoping the cars as they come through, checking ID and all that drek.

Daytime travel means heavy traffic on most major roads. Traffic speed averages around 60 to 70 KPH on the freeways, and maybe 20 to 30 KPH off them during rush hour. That's assuming nothing's messing up the flow. You can move 25 to 50 percent faster outside rush. Speed limits around DeeCee are 100 KPH highway, 70 KPH on side streets.

In most places, when the lights go off, the gangers come out to play. DeeCee is no exception. Also like most towns, some zones are rougher than others.

Major FedPol presence on the streets in the G-zone, and almost as much in the surrounding downtown areas, ensures your safety any time of day or night. Elsewhere, you find the usual go-gangs ruling the night streets if they can dodge or scare the local law.

### WATERWAYS

DeeCee is not a big water town the way Seattle is. But you do have Chesapeake Bay only 30 klicks east of town. After increased pollution wiped out the bay's fishing and oyster industries, a lot of local fishing families turned to smuggling. Today's watermen run low-signature muscle boats carrying contraband from the CAS and offshore pickups. They also carry shadowrunners who find it a bit too warm to travel on-shore.

The Potomac River runs through high-rent and government-controlled areas where the odds of observation and challenge are high, so it's not much use to runners as transportation.

### PUBLIC TRANSPORTATION

The DeeCee Metro subway system has grown over the last century to cover the entire sprawl. Trains run round the clock, departing every 5 minutes during rush hour, when tickets are $10. Off-rush tickets are $5, and trains run 10 minutes apart except from midnight to 0400, when they crank back to 20 minutes.

Stations are patrolled at the same enforcement levels as the neighborhoods in which they are located. You can feel real secure in a Government Zone station with certified credstiks hanging out of every pocket, but in some of the stations in Prince Georges and Anacostia, safety is what you carry in your holster.

Bus service feeds each Metro station. On major routes, buses run every 10 minutes during rush hour, and every 30 minutes during off-rush. Double this for minor routes. Not all lines run at night.

Taxi service in DeeCee is plentiful and cheap at $1 per klick, since the Feds like to keep fares affordable. Most cabbies will tell you where to stick the fare if you want an address in a low-enforcement zone after dark, and no driver in his right mind will enter an urban combat zone at any time of day or night.

# MEDIA

### by Prof

DeeCee is a saturated media arena. A dozen broadcast channels and an enormous trid network of cable and satellite signals, both licensed (useless) and not, compete fiercely, 24 hours a day, for viewers. The unlicensed channels run the gamut from stomach-turning splattervid to news broadcasts committing the ultimate crime in UCAS: revealing truth to the people.

The technology of communications has leaped ahead in the last few decades, and we've seen the evolution of three general classes of media programming.

## MAJORS

The major nets, continuing the programming trends of the late 20th century, degenerated into mindless pablum, tranq for the eye. The major networks extol the values of the government-industrial complex to viewers over "free" airways, and the basic service trid in every major urban area. All the majors offer premium-priced simsense as part of their service. Of course, "free" really means "paid for by taxes and ads," with costs passed right back to consumers.

Rick Harris '91

## INDEPENDENTS

Independent licensed media often are scaled-down versions of the major networks. Others walk a tightrope between keeping their license and broadcasting something other than bread-and-circuses.

There are also special-interest independents. These include the Battle Channels, providing coverage of corp wars all over the world, and Chessnet, offering coverage of major chess meetings and chess-related programming, and the sex channels, which provide material for every taste and orientation.

Many of the more praiseworthy independents are financed by grants from non-UCAS organizations and non-UCAS governments, though such arrangements are monitored closely by the Feds. Even the enlightened capital has been known to back an independent. Other independents are nothing more than house organs for less altruistic megacorps. Some independents offer simsense hookups. This is invariably a sign that the net is a puppet for a major corp, because the basic equipment for this kind of transmission is incredibly expensive.

## PIRATES

Finally, we have the media expression of the neo-anarchist ideal: the pirate stations. These range from half a dozen techies feeding signals into unassigned trid channels to megayen operations transmitting via satellite from outside UCAS jurisdiction.

Media piracy does not automatically mean enlightened programming. Vicious "killgames" are the stock in trade of many pirates. Deathstar-9, for example, is notorious for the Aztlan-based show *You, The Jury*. Viewers may register votes in capital cases, not only for the guilt or innocence of the accused, but for the method of execution. *Ordeal*, the so-called "final challenge" game show, actually prides itself on the high casualty rate among its competitors. Rumors also abound that some killshows pay top prices for shanghaied "ratings fodder"—people of exceptional skill or beauty who are forced to compete.

Many pirate stations, however, only broadcast programming that does not sit well with the government and the corps. *The Dart Board*, now in its fourth year of investigative reporting, is available on six satellite signals, as well as being re-transmitted over local trid systems in cities all across the UCAS. So far, Vic Dart has scored the political scalps of three Senators, a dozen Congressthings, and any number of local officials so corrupt that his revelations forced their fellow oppressors to sacrifice the exposéd on the altar of public opinion. Dart may be trying to scoop back the ocean's waves with a teaspoon, but he does it with style. The latest word on the street puts the bounty for his head in the $100,000 range.

The equipment needed to inject a pirate signal into a satellite link or to piggyback it into a trid network is compact enough to fit into a small van. With the services of a competent decker to bypass the security on these systems, the signal can be brought online in minutes. So when that slick broadcast on your screen gets replaced by

**FDC SPORTS TEAMS**

**National Football League:** Washington Chieftains
**National League Baseball (Augmented):** FDC Senators
**AAA Baseball (Non-augmented):** Fairfax Monuments, Howard Columbians
**National Hockey League:** Washington Capitals
**National Basketball Association:** DC Bullets
**Combat Bike:** DeeCee Shurikens
**Urban Brawl:** PG Demolishers

a fuzzy piece of obviously amateur trid, don't change the circuit selector too quickly. You may miss something interesting!

### HARDCOPY

The old line that claims "print is dead" is not entirely true, but print is definitely not in the best of health, at least not in the FDC. Most trids are equipped with printers that can crank out hardcopy at a rate of a few seconds per page. The *Washington Post*, DeeCee's most venerable news organization, maintains a hardcopy option on its newsnet service, one every bit as stimulating and balanced as its electronic programming. Which is to say, not at all. Print media is mostly an affectation assumed by self-proclaimed intellectuals and the odd archaist who longs loudly for the "good old days."

Of course, the policlubs, gangs, terrorists, and yes, even a few neo-anarchists, favor print media. Distribution can be decentralized and is electronically untraceable. What it is *not*, is effective. Handing subversive literature to the average member of the underclass is slightly less effective than just burning it. At least burning it might keep one warm. The man in the street takes one look at printed material, and if he sees no pictures, he drops it. Pictures might hold his attention until his mind rebels at absorbing printed words, and then he drops it. Pictures of naked people copulating might keep the sheets in his hands for a little longer, but the reader would tend to miss the content, focusing solely on the form.

Maybe one person in a hundred, or a thousand, actually responds to the sea of handbills, leaflets, and written diatribes floating through DeeCee. However, it is gratifying to see that our masters *do* know how to read. A well-timed pamphlet promising doom and destruction to the powers that be can usually be depended on to spark a frantic scurrying in the Government Zone and its many satellites. And how often can one enjoy that kind of comedy for such a reasonable price?

## GOOD TIMES BETWEEN CRIMES

### by Mimosa Boy

You've just finished a shadowrun that turned your hair gray. What's next? Well, first see your follicle restoration therapist to get that nasty hair back to its original lustrous color. Now, where do we little shadow types go to unwind in DeeCee? Follow M-boy, children, and you shall see.

### HIGH END

These places are for the well-heeled who walk in the sunlight or the shadows. But don't even walk *by* any place on this list unless you can put your credstick on autofire for the evening.

**Aleister's (1)**

Night Club Archetype/Wisconsin Avenue and K Street NW (Washington)/Tommy Hall, Owner/No Racial Bias/ LTG# 4202 (61-9054)

Aleister's is currently at the top of the heap of the clubs that come and go in Georgetown. Macroflash and mucho dinero are the entry requirements. A taste for syntho-booze at premium prices also makes your evening easier, but the sounds, my dears, make up for a multitude of sins. Tommy has managed to get club dates from all the best people, including Maria Mercurial, ME-109, and Savage Spirit. Every so often the rumor floats that he's bagged the big one, and Concrete Dreams will be playing Aleister's. So far, this hasn't panned out, but hope springs eternal…

**Kingdom Seven (not on map)**

Night Club (2 floors), Large Restaurant (2 floors), and Casino Archetypes/Columbia Tower, Columbia (Howard)/ Farrell Schorr, Owner/Bias Against Seedy Dressers/LTG# 1301 (98-1630)

In the top seven floors of the 80-story Columbia Tower, Farrell the Barrel (my dears, have you ever seen the man? Even for an ork, he is positively obese!) has created a glittering den of vice unrelieved by a single smidgin of taste. Food is overcooked and overspiced to blahness, and the night club acts guarantee that even the terminally dull will be pleading for mercy in minutes. All this in a setting that makes old Las Vegas look like the epitome of elegance and refinement.

Farrell has managed to open the only legal casino in the sprawl in plain sight of God and everybody. In fact, almost everybody but God comes to play there, if they have the credit to spend. Rumors that the Barrel-man is the heart, soul, and bank account of DeeCee's Neighborhood Decency League Against Legalized Gambling are too cruel to be true. It is not as if legalization would eat into his profits *too* badly, hmmm?

Strictly speaking, you are on Kingdom Seven soil as soon as you set foot in Columbia Tower. The whole tower is extraterritorial. Because Kingdom Seven Enterprises is hardly in the same league as the companies that usually pull this off, the rumor mill constantly churns out delicate little guesses as to who pulls Farrell's strings.

### Nexus (2)

Six Night Club Archetypes linked by tunnels (add 1D6 shadowrunner archetypes to typical clientele)/Dupont Circle NW (Washington)/Yuri Korsakov, Owner/No Racial Bias/LTG# 6202 (36-4561)

This charming little catacomb is under Dupont Circle, extending out from assorted abandoned steam pipes and the old streetcar tunnels into a series of chambers where the elite can shadowmeet. Ten seconds after you leave, no one remembers that you've been there, and the interior surveillance countermeasures are maintained by the most paranoid techies in captivity. Add in Mr. Stone, who acts as mâitré d, bouncer, and freelance SWAT team, and you have just the place to contract the highly talented and highly paid. Imposing even for a troll, Mr. Stone is rumored to be a veteran of many Germanic states brushfire wars. Don't mess with him, because word is he can erase old-style computer disks just by looking at them.

The Stone experience alone would be worth the prices, but darling Yuri also has the best blini, stroganoff, and other Slavic dainties you've ever tasted. The bar is stocked with rarities worth their weight in rubies. Add some of the best jazz in the UCAS and you have the perfect place for the well-heeled shadowfolk to get away from it all.

### Trianon (3)

Mid-Size Restaurant Archetype/Pennsylvania Avenue and 22nd Street NW (Washington)/Andre Santiago, Owner/Bias Against Non-Corporate Types/LTG# 3202 (49-7692)

*The* power restaurant in the Government Zone. Senators, cabinet members, and top-ranked suits from the corporate lobbies frequent this establishment. The average tab in Trianon is $250 per person, *not* counting the wine. Trianon features French cuisine, and five-star at that. Reservations are a must (and almost impossible to get unless you fit into one of the aforementioned categories).

Do be aware that troublesome diners not only have to deal with the restaurant staff, but that most guests are attended by their personal security, including Secret Service, bodyguards, corporate police, and such.

## LOW END

There are hundreds of spots around DeeCee where you can get a nice little meal or a few hours boozing time for a reasonable price, and they are all very much alike. The little gems listed here stand out from the rest enough to earn the Mimosa Boy Seal of *Je ne sais quoi.*

### Blues Heaven (not on map)

Night Club and Bar Archetypes/Wisconsin Avenue and Macomb Street NW (Washington)/Brother Zebra, Owner/Bias Against the Tone Deaf/LTG# 7202 (36-2453)

Jazz is the name of the game. Best in town. Enough said.

### Circle Hands (not on map)

Mid-Size Restaurant and Bar Archetypes/Henderson and Clifton Roads (Fairfax)/Pours-Large-Drinks, Owner/No Racial Bias/LTG# 9703 (73-5729)

Circle Hands gets its name from the Native American sign language gesture meaning "all of us." It is a strangely peaceful place tucked into the middle of a dozen acres of woodland near the border between Fairfax and Northern Virginia, an undeveloped part of the sprawl. Even a wicked child of the city like Mimosa Boy finds it a refreshing place to visit.

It is a favored watering hole for the shamans among us, dearies. Don't go expecting the clientele to exhaust themselves putting on little shows for us mundanes, though. Most magicians' clubs have no patience with such goings-on. Try Mr. Henry's Astral in Upper Northwest, or, if you can foot the bill and simply must have a little magic with your meal, go to Periapt in Foggy Bottom. Half their clientele actually are paid by the management to "enliven" the evening.

This is not to say that the lucky visitor to Circle Hands won't stumble into an occasional drumming circle when Pours-Large-Drinks, a Bear Shaman, is in the mood. Though he does not rouse himself from his gruff-and-grumble act too often, when he does the intensity is almost un-*bear*-able. (M-boy is sorry. He just could *not* resist.)

### Locus Spiritus (not on map)

Night Club Archetype/Georgia Avenue and Randolph Road (Montgomery)/Ash Russell, Owner/Subtle Bias Against Non-Magicians/LTG# 9301 (61-3474)

As the name suggests, Locus Spiritus caters to magicians. The decor, like the clientele, is mostly hermetic. Ash is a magician himself and once told M-boy that people asking him to "show them something" while he was out on the town used to drive him absolutely psycho in his days of flash and fame. Only magicians and their guests are welcome at Locus Spiritus. Mondo no mundane-o, darlings.

The food is plentiful, the beer is world-class, and the prices are low. The most astonishing little mix of bands can be heard here. Monday's jazz combo may be followed on Tuesday by a string quintet and some ear-searing Novasynth rockers on Wednesday. Eclectic Ash says it helps keep the spheres in harmony. Don't you hate it when magicians talk that way?

Shadowside, this is the best place in town for making magical contacts. You name it, it's here—magicians for hire, rare goods, help finding ritual workplaces, and more.

### Thunderheads (not on map)

Night Club Archetype/Benning Road and East Capitol Street NE (Washington)/Michael Freeman, Owner/No Racial Bias/LTG# 8202 (15-4391)

A rock club where you get more than the usual dreary little wanna-be bands synthing the top ten songs through their consoles. Michael Freeman only books those who play, sing, or synth music they have written themselves. Result: an awful lot of weird music and a lot of young musicians worth hearing. Thunderheads is on the northern fringes of the Anacostia Barrens, near the Benning Road Metro station. Mimosa Boy suggests proper attire and appropriate firepower when visiting, but would point out that the zone is controlled by the Sables, and the club is under their protection.

### War Zone (4)

Night Club and Mid-Size Restaurant Archetypes/ 14th and T Streets NW (Washington)/Unknown Owner/ No Racial Bias/LTG# 3202 (63-5377)

Danger to the max, darlings. This club in Shaw is favored by the Type-A personalities among DeeCee's samurai population. Most nights the atmosphere is a simply palpable mix of biz, adrenalin, and whatever high-tension killmusic the band is cranking out. If you're one of those dreary dearies who worries about losing your precious "edge," then by all means drop by War Zone. They're your kind of people.

## BITTER END

Down and out, sweetums? Last run was a dump? Places offering cheap thrills abound.

### Chainsaw (not on map)

Night Club Archetype/Rhode Island and Eastern Avenues NE (Washington)/Red Arkisian, Owner/No Racial Bias/LTG# 2202 (42-6015)

Chainsaw features a very kicky post-industrial decor that—oh drek, it's an old warehouse in a Mount Rainier neighborhood. When crime in the area started to go ballistic, the residents took up a collection to maintain a group of samurai to keep their streets safe. The samurai took over this site as a headquarters-cum-hangout, and it grew. Would-be samurai or established fighters down on their luck can see about joining up with Red and his guys, but this is comfortable subsistence here, not big nuyen.

The bands at Chainsaw are rarely famous, and even more rarely skilled. They are, however, *loud.*

### Eskimo Nell's (not on map)

Night Club and Bar Archetypes/Old Courthouse Road and Maple Avenue (Fairfax)/Charley Crick, Owner/No Racial Bias/LTG# 4703 (36-6375)

This is a rich man's folly providing good times for the rest of us. From what Mimosa Boy can see, Mr. Crick runs the place at a loss, but ever since Crick racked up megayen in some *mysterious* endeavor some years ago, he seems to regard his losses as money well-spent on a hobby. Given that some of the local clever-boys have reported getting blown out of Eskimo Nell's computer with their little cybernetic tails on fire, one suspects, children, that Crick has done some high-level bit-bashing of his own in days gone by.

A number of local deckers have embraced the club, and the discerning recruiter can find reasonably priced talent here on most nights.

### The Pit (not on map)

Casino (1 floor) and Night Club Archetype/Exit 13 on I-295 (Washington)/Unknown Owner/No Racial Bias/LTG# 3202 (26-0142)

In the middle of the Anacostia Barrens sits The Pit. It boasts nightly fights, and honest ones at that. (They surprised even me with that, for nobody can dig up dirt like Mimosa Boy, darlings.) Categories include augmented and non-augmented, and armed and unarmed, with bouts theoretically fought on points. Right. Still, the management, whoever they may be, does keep some decent biotechs on hand, keeping fatalities to a couple per week.

Purses are low, around $1,000, but the betting runs in the hundreds of thousands each night. If you like cheap nutrisoy and raw synth-alk, you can load up for a few dollars (contestants eat free). If your tastes are a tad less sanguinary, The Pit also offers more conventional forms of gambling. Illegal, of course, but then aren't we all?

## CYBER-RESTRAINTS

### Containment Manacles
#### Cost: $2,500 (restricted)
Designed for the wrists and ankles, these act as heavy wrist- or leg-irons. They use a mechanism designed to clamp down with agonizing pressure on tendon and bone if razors, spurs, or similar cybermods are extended. Each turn that the cybermod is extended, the user must resist 5S2 damage to the limb. Damage is "physical," but only affects the use of the limb, not the entire body. The wearer must also resist 4M1 Stun damage each turn the manacles are clamping down, due to pain.

### Headjammer
#### Cost: $1,200 x Rating
A headset that can be equipped with straps to "lock" onto the victim's head, the headjammer jams signals from implanted cellular phone or radio links. It also heterodynes feedback to such implants, causing (Rating)S1 Stun damage each time the wearer tries to use the implants.

### Jackstopper
#### Cost: $100
This is a dummy plug, formatted to fit into a chipjack or datajack, that injects the jack with a quick-bonding epoxy on insertion. Jackstoppers are often used on captured deckers.

It takes the attention of a biotech and a dose of resin solvent ($10 in most hardware or convenience stores) to clear the jack. Make a Biotech Test, Target Number 6, base time of 90 minutes. Divide time by successes to see how long it will take to clear the jackstopper.

### Magemask
#### Cost: $200
A simple plastic hood, easily fitted over a prisoner's head, the magemask blocks vision, and is equipped with a gag-tube that can be shoved into the magician's mouth, allowing him to breathe but not speak. The nostrils are left uncovered for breathing as well. The mask is also equipped with a white-noise generator that can be cranked up to deliver as much as 90 dB to the wearer's ears. This serves as a major distraction for the victim.

### Skilltwitcher
#### Cost: $2,000 (restricted)
Formatted like a standard skillsoft, a skilltwitcher inserts a jamming signal into skillwires, imposing a penalty to *all* active skill use (whether it is from a skillsoft or not) equal to the victim's Skillwire Rating. The jamming lasts only as long as the skilltwitcher's soft is plugged in, but can be combined with a jackstopper (see above) to make removal difficult.

# CRIME AND PUNISHMENT

by T.

Drek! I don't know how I let the Prof talk me into this. I'm no policlub yutz like these Neo-A's. I'm just a poor, dishonest elf trying to make a bundle so I can retire to a life of unbridled consumerism. If I didn't owe that old poot for …well, this makes us quits, Prof, you hear me!

Right. Pay close attention chummers, because I'm here with the latest data on the cops-and-robbers scene in DeeCee. No quiz after class. This one you flunk by getting very dead if you irritate the wrong big boys.

DeeCee law is *tight* in some quarters. You *don't* go purse-snatching outside the White House Entrance Barrier, for example. The Secret Service detachment there will shoot you for spitting on the sidewalk; walking by is often regarded with deep suspicion. The Capitol Enclosure has equally tight security. Other parts of the Government Zone and the home-zones for the mega-suits are almost as secure.

The rest of DeeCee ranges from heavy FedPol private cop coverage to the law you carry in your holster, just like any other sprawl.

Runners in DeeCee have it good and bad. On the one hand, we're in demand. This town's biggest growth industry is secrets. Sometimes I think everyone in DeeCee needs some shadowrun done. On the other hand, this is not a town for frag-ups. They're gone once FedPol or some other gummint crowd gets on their case. Not to mention what happens if you honk off the Maf or Yak!

## THE FEDPOLS

When the virus fried the computers back in '29, the job it did on food, power, and comm turned DeeCee into…well, I was here for the Collapse. It was not pretty. Whole zones got pounded into rubble. DeeCee was a compact war zone from mid-2029 until 2031.

The local cops folded early. They weren't set up for that kind of fracas. The Army cordoned off the G-zone and pushed control back out from there. That's when they built the barriers around the White House and Capitol.

In '31, the UCAS Congress set up the FedPols to keep DeeCee supplied with heat. The "Federal Capital Police" run the law-and-order-show for the whole sprawl. A lot of zones keep private heat on tap, so they're not the only police outfit here, but the FedPols have jurisdiction everywhere in DeeCee. No other organization operates without their say-so. A FedPol liaison watches all the cop-shops and rent-a-guards in the sprawl. He can shut them down any time he wants if he decides they are not maintaining the standards set by Sister Cindy, the Chief of FedPol.

In the Government Zone, the FedPols are the only local law enforcement, but remember you have the Secret Service, FBI, and other spooks running around loose down there, too. About the only turf in DeeCee the FedPols can't get into anytime they want is the extraterritorial corporate and diplomatic enclaves. Even they have to be invited in. Hitting a place like that without an invitation is messy, and the Justice, State, or Business Departments usually end up playing lots of bureaucratic footsie to cover their butts. FBI or Secret Service agents are the troops of choice in these raids, not the FedPols.

## LOCAL LAW ENFORCEMENT

Outside the zones on the FedPols' beat are the private police companies. Knight-Errant Security is currently the leader of the pack, with Lone Star running a close second, working the better-off neighborhoods. UCASPro (UCAS Protective Services) is a local operation, and they try hard, but they're not in the big leagues yet. As in other sprawls, poor zones either do without or hire a few samurai to cover their turf. In a lot of places, the local gangers are the only protection. Some, like the Sabies, do a good job. Other gangers are just wolves wearing sheep dog clothing.

## NATIONAL GUARD AND URBAN MILITIA

Prexy and the Congress aren't too excited about the Urban Militia in DeeCee. Too many cits with guns seem to make them nervous. The Militia is only allowed in zones full of nice, trustworthy salarymen, so the places that need extra protection the least are where it's at. You've got macho suits with very large guns out to protect hearth and home from anyone who walks into their sights.

The Militia are part of the FDC National Guard. The Guard is outside the FedPol chain of command, receiving their orders directly from Chief Commissioner Ericson. This means the FedPols and the Guard have a lot of jurisdiction fights, particularly when dealing with civil disorders. Unfortunately, they only shoot each other every now and then.

## MAFIA

DeeCee has two Maf operations in town (lucky us). Victor Marconi, a fifth generation *mafioso*, age 52, proclaims himself as "the Ambassador from the Cosa Nostra." He fronts as a big-deal lobbyist, throwing parties the suits will kill to get into. Literally. Don Victor has not dirtied his hands with mob work since 2009, when he was just a young man with a future in San Diego. At that time, the Torricelli Family was getting edged out of San Diego by a bunch of hot young thrill gangs. Don Victor married Don Howard Torricelli's daughter after her father was gunned down, then proceeded to turn the family fortunes around in a five-year campaign that obliterated the local competition.

The only reason knowing all this doesn't scare me half to death is that I can't prove diddly. If I had documentation, I'd probably have joined the ranks of people Don Victor has sent to the Big Beyond. This is graveyard secret stuff, you catch?

Marconi is not the "working" Don of DeeCee. He's the top go-between for the Commissione and the UCAS government, not a mobster.

The Mafia crime boss in the Sprawl is Franco Mueller. A big guy in his mid-forties, Don Franco came to power in DeeCee about 20 years ago. His boss took his finger off the number, and got nailed by the Chong-Pak-*Pa*, a Yak bunch. Mueller, a "made man" fresh out of a hitch as a corporate mercenary, duelled the Chong-Pak to a standstill. He impressed the Commissione, who gave him financial assistance and the go-ahead to rebuild Maf operations in DeeCee. He became a member of the Commissione in 2043.

The Maf controls numbers-running and other gambling, loan-sharking, vice, and drugs, including BTLs. They concentrate on Montgomery and Washington, but also operate *regimes* in the other regions. Mueller is not subtle—gang wars in this town sound like instant replays of the good old days in Chicago. There's only one rule: no wetwork allowed in FedPol zones.

## YAKUZA

DeeCee has seven active Yakuza organizations.

The Saidoh-*gumi* are part of the Yamaguchi-*gumi*. People say that *gumi* means "family," but it actually translates closer to "syndicate." The Yak don't have a central bunch of bosses like the Mafia's Commissione. There's no *oyabun-no-oyabun* the way the Maf has a *capo di tutti capi*. But I have to say the Yamaguchi are powerful enough, and feared enough, to come close to filling those roles.

Serving a function similar to Don Victor's, the Saidoh are the spokesmen to the UCAS government for Yamaguchi interests. They also represent other Yak organizations for heavy compensation, when this does not conflict with their obligation to the Yamaguchi-*gumi*. As a sideline, the Saidoh also act as mediators in disputes between UCAS-based Yak gangs. The Saidoh operate out of several "consulting" firms they've set up as fronts.

Four of the other gangs are pretty typical Yak operations: the Matsui-*gumi* ; the Fudo-*rengo* (Immovable League); the Sessho-*gumi*; and the Chong-Pak-*Pa*, who are mostly Korean and getting pretty antsy as other gangs get more and more into Japanese purity.

These gangs get into turf fights with each other or the Maf every few months. Lots of ammo, swords, and spurs are used, then things quiet down again. All the gangs I've mentioned so far are big on Yakuza tradition, so violence in these clashes is mostly restricted to other Yak, the Mafia competition, or local gangs who frag with the syndicate. Folks who don't mix into Yak business are usually off limits.

The Mizugumo-*rengo* (Water-Spider League) also operate in DeeCee. They specialize in industrial espionage and other spook operations in the realm of corporate subversion. They don't get into the street-nasty stuff, but they do have some incredibly hot deckers on the payroll, loaded with the latest Matrix toys. The deckers are for hire if you can afford the very best.

The Shonen-*gireina* (Pretty Boys) are newcomers. Most of them are young and have been kicked out of established gangs. They come to the UCAS hoping to make it big. Like a lot of splinter Yak gangs, they are supported by Japan-based neofascist policlubs.

The Shonen-*gireina* are carving a niche for themselves in DeeCee street crime. They don't care who they kill as long as they get what they want; other gangs handle them like rabid animals. They are borderline psychos, so avoid them unless you are ready to pass on.

## DISORGANIZED CRIME

These days, the freelancers haven't got enough trouble just staying on the right side of the Big Boys I've been talking about. Seems like every street corner in town sprouts ten-yen thrill gangs the way drek sprouts mushrooms. Each region has one or more major gangs that can put more than a hundred guns on the street, some with mil-spec bang-bang. Your typical ganger isn't much in a fight, but some of these guys are wired as nasty as any samurai. In addition to the majors, each region has a dozen more good-sized gangs holding turf, and Ghost-only-knows how many gangs roving the sprawl that are nothing more than a dozen clowns and a rented pistol.

Gang politics make the G-zone look tame. Treaties come and go every week. Gangs that were sworn blood-brothers last month are now out on the concrete slicing and dicing each other. Next month, they'll ally to whomp the guys over in the next zone. Kaleidoscopic, is what I mean.

Still, there are some fixed points to steer by. The Princes of the Blood and Thundercross will only bury the hatchet in each other's skulls, for instance. The Sables and the Halfies will never talk peace. Probe are fraggin' weird and likely to stay that way.

Here's some background on the big gangs, the ones who can give the Maf or Yak a run for their money.

### Halfies

A go-gang with mixed membership, their current leader is Mace, an ork with heavy cybermods. They hate the Sables, and the feeling is mutual.

**Colors:** Skin job: the face is done in black and white, the pattern is up to the ganger.

**Allies:** None.

**Enemies:** Sables.

**Turf:** I-295, right through the middle of Anacostia (Washington).

### Princes of the Blood

All elf, the kind who make me wish my ears weren't pointed. The Princes are trying to move up to big-time crime. They distribute about 15 percent of the BTLs and other controlled substances in DeeCee, supplying pushers all over the sprawl. They take a cut on the joyfolk action in several areas, either running strings directly or skimming a piece of the take from the pimps, who just up their cut from the joyboys and joygirls in their stable. The Princes also do flat-out extortion. They call it "protection," but you won't see a shop showing Prince colors to keep the other goons away. The Princes don't care what happens to the poor fraggers as long as they get their cred each week.

The Princes do the same *Alfheim, Alfheim über alles* thing that you find in Tir Tairngire, but with a nasty, street-smart beat to it. When they start with the three-level puns in Sperethiel (that's elvish, for you non-Speech types out there) or do the fake knights-and-maidens talk, find a comfy bunker, 'cause drek is about to fly.

**Colors:** Red, black, and silver.

**Allies:** You're kidding me, right? They keep a few rich-kid thrill gangs full of elf wannabees on their leash, as a wedge into shaikujin turf, where the money lives, but that's as close as they come.

**Enemies:** Thundercross, Young Senators.

**Turf:** Montgomery, but the Princes have half a dozen small hangouts across the sprawl.

### Probe

Of mixed racial membership, almost all are deckers, riggers, techs, or samurai with enough chrome to decorate God's own limousine. Probe are technofetishist-terrorists, doing Matrix black magic to push a neo-dada-anarchy kick. For hire, they supply most of the street cyber in the sprawl.

Probe are big on the "group mind of the Matrix." One Probe are all Probe, they say. Using the singular to refer to a Probe is a quick invite for a cyberstrike on your bank account, or some esoteric neurotoxin in your soykaf.

**Colors:** Dazzle suits made of Neolux fiber capable of 5,000 candlepower of mindblowing patterns.

**Allies:** None.

**Enemies:** None—nobody wants their cred shredded in the Matrix.

**Turf:** No fixed abode. Mostly decentralized, they sometimes claim the DeeCee Matrix as their turf.

### Sables

The Sables have a mixed membership of norms and metas, but all members are of African-American descent. They started as a typical street-corner gang in the middle of the Anacostia Barrens. As the Barrens slid to the bottom of the old socio-economic food chain, the Sables started moving to the top. They don't exactly run the Barrens, but no other gang there can take them on single-handedly and survive.

The Sables run dope, gambling, and protection, and their protection is for real. Anyone hitting a place with the Sable colors on it better move fast or these guys will knit socks out of your insides.

**Colors:** Black and green, with a gold lion's-head patch.

**Allies:** Turkeys. Treaties with smaller Barrens gangs come and go.

**Enemies:** Halfies and most other Anacostia gangs who aren't allies.

**Turf:** Anacostia (Washington).

### Thundercross

For normals only, and I mean only, these delightful young anti-meta fascists wear urban camo, buzz cuts, and moderate cybermods. Mostly rich kids from Northwest, these gangers have access to "surplused" Militia weapons from daddy's collection. Rumor has it that Thundercross

is backed by Humanis—what a surprise. Hunting metas, not crime, is their thing, though some profitable arson recently in poor zones may have been their work. The buildings were mostly meta squats, natch.

**Colors:** Black, gray, and white urban camo, with a patch or badge of a cross shooting lightning.

**Allies:** None.

**Enemies:** Mainly the Princes and Turkeys, but every meta gang in DeeCee would like a piece of them.

**Turf:** Upper Northwest (Washington).

### Triples

This is actually an alliance between three gangs: the Rebels (go-gang, human, Fairfax), the Brick Hogs (go-gang, ork/troll, Prince Georges), and the Moccasins. The Moccasins are a mixed-race, water-based go-gang, and all their members are from watermen families on the river and Chesapeake Bay. The Triples have smuggling routes running from the Bay up the US-301 or I-95 corridors from the CAS. They also dabble in hijacking. They are more into biz than gratuitous violence, but have a nasty war brewing with the Young Senators, who are starting to cut in on Triple's smuggling traffic.

**Colors:** Rebels: CAS flag colors. Brick Hogs: red, brown, and green. Moccasins: blue and copper.

**Allies:** They've got each other.

**Enemies:** Young Senators.

**Turf:** See above.

### Turkeys

This gang has an ork/troll membership only. A pretty standard street gang in northeast Washington, they sell a lot of vice and dope to the nice boys and girls at the universities. Several hot riggers stand out in this crowd, and the gang is rumored to run the fastest chop shop on the East Coast. A stolen car can be parts before it finishes rolling in the door.

**Colors:** Red and gray.

**Allies:** Sables.

**Enemies:** Thundercross, Young Senators.

**Turf:** Northeast (Washington).

### Young Senators

The Young Senators are playing catch-up with the Princes. Rumored to be backed by the Maf, this mixed-membership gang does a lot of street crime and pushing in the southeast part of Washington, along the river, and in Fairfax and Arlington.

**Colors:** UCAS red, white, and blue.

**Allies:** Many smaller gangs on both sides of the Potomac.

**Enemies:** Princes of the Blood, Triples.

**Turf:** Waterfront (Washington) and Arlington.

## LEGAL AID

If you are a paying customer, the phone databases for lawyers give you several meg of entries to choose from.

If you get busted and the credstick won't stretch to a private mouth (that's a lawyer, for you nice shaikujin reading this), DeeCee is hip-deep in bright-eyed idealists looking for oppressed victims of the system to defend.

FDCPDO (Federal District of Columbia Public Defender's Office) is paid for partly by the Feds and the District Commission and partly by the local lawyers piling up brownie points for *pro bono* work. Most of them couldn't get a saint off on a jaywalking charge, but can usually help you make bail on minor busts or cut a plea bargain on the middle-range felonies. If you don't have your own mouth, a PD will show up within 24 hours after you're booked, usually with easily ten minutes to spare before your arraignment.

Metas can contact the headquarters of MRCC (Metahuman Rights Coordinating Council), a UCAS lobby backed by a half dozen policlubs and other pro-meta groups, for free legal aid. Call them at LTG# 2301 (40-5638).

The NACLU (North American Civil Liberties Union), which claims to represent legal rights for SINless and other disadvantaged types all over the continent, have their UCAS headquarters in DeeCee, natch. They are not popular in DeeCee, because they claim to transcend national boundaries, but they tend to have better-than-average shysters on their side. LTG # 7202 (65-3333).

The homegrown version of NACLU, the ULRA (UCAS Legal Rights Association) has a better relationship with the powers-that-be. They can keep you from getting slammed real hard if they lose on minor charges, because the judge won't have as big an axe to grind as he might with NACLU. They are, however, less together than the NACLU mouths. LTG # 2703 (45-6195).

NAN cits who find themselves on the short end of DeeCee law can contact their tribal embassy for legal assistance.

## PRISON SYSTEM

If you get hauled in, you'll probably sample the hospitality at the regional FedPol HQ. You can only be held in the pens here for 24 to 48 hours, after which you get transferred to the FDC jail complex, in Northeast. Built in 2027 and expanded on several occasions since, this dump is a tad overcrowded—only five inmates to a cell. The screws are amenable to most reasonable business offers. You will abide in this enchanted little hideaway until trial, and if you receive a short-haul sentence or minimum security time, you'll probably stay there afterward.

The Big House proper is in Lorton. Long before the sprawl was the true-blue, one-and-only FDC, this was the city prison. Congress took over Fairfax as part of its landgrab in '24, and declared domain over the whole area around the existing prison. The whole zone is now slammer city.

Fairfax features minimum security, maximum security, work camps, rehab centers, and death row under guns on the ground and in the air. Just you and 12,000 of your fellow convicts living in luxurious facilities capable of handling, oh, maybe half that number. The Twelfth Urban Response Infantry keeps everything nice and cozy.

With luck, you'll stay in the DeeCee slammers. If your case has honked off the big boys sufficiently, you may find yourself hauled off to one of the Omega-class hellholes. The feds contracted private "rehabilitation engineering" corps to run their maximum security prisons, granting them full extraterritorial rights, and doing hard time has never been harder. The average survival rate inside makes five years about right for a life sentence. The UCAS has two known Omega-dumps. Inferno, or The Ex-Urban Reclamation Project, as it is quaintly called in the official records, is an open-air vacation spot in the toxic zones of New Jersey. Leavenworth, in Kansas, is fitted with all the latest in social readjustment gear: experimental neuro-modification labs, cyber-monitor implant facilities, row upon row of sensory-deprivation units, and a pharmacy boasting most of the behavior-altering substances known to man. Ain't progress grand?

# CHICAGO

**Compiled by Defcon 1**

## THE CITY THAT WORKS...FOR THE CORPORATIONS, THE GOVERNMENT, AND THE MOB

Here's the game, brothers and sisters: I know Chicago better than the rest of the UCAS, but I don't think I'm wrong in saying this town has got to be one of the best examples of why we've got to burn the old contracts and come up with a new set of rules for running the world. This city is split between the haves and the have-nots—and the haves are winning big-time. Not only do they practically starve the working class, but they've fixed it so that the poor are burning out their gray matter in straight simsense chips and BTLs coming from City Hall, the corps, and the mob. These guys sit around making fragging profits off the despair of the poor!

Things may be starting to turn around, though. We (the neo-anarchists of Chicago, that is) have gotten a few grassroots organizations going. We're working hard on the Northside, which has become a breeding ground for violence. We've set it up so that the workers who want to fight for change collect money to hire shadowrunners. It's

true the runs don't pay great, but so many runners around here are so fed up with the situation in Wind City that they do part of the job as charity. Hooding, it's called, stealing from the rich to give to the poor. They also get dirt sometimes for the aldermen who are almost on the straight and narrow.

All the stuff you don't want to hear about and can't quite believe, it's happening right here. For better or for worse, this city is rockin' and rollin'.

## BASIC INFORMATION

### CLIMATE

Here's what they say about the weather in Chicago: "If you don't like it, just wait five minutes and it'll change." And that's no lie, chummers. Show up and take your chances. Some of the "mages" down in Little Earth say that the free air and water elementals along Lake Michigan are an especially mischievous lot who have been hassling the city for centuries. That's about as good an explanation as any for this city's crazy weather.

You do need to be prepared for the blizzards. Snow drifts can pile up to three and a half meters or more, and traffic grinds to a halt. Plan your winter runs with an eye to the sky.

### TRAVELING TO CHICAGO

There are plenty of ways of getting to Wind City. Which one you take depends on what you're trying to hide.

**Plane**

O'Hare International Airport is the busiest airport in the world, handling flights from all over the globe. It also serves as *the* hub of people and cargo transport for North America. The place is so busy, in fact, that the O'Hare Sub-Sprawl has developed in the middle of Chicago. (The Sub-Sprawl is covered later on. For the moment, all you need to remember is that, armed with a visa and nuyen, you can travel by plane from anywhere in the world to Chicago. The reverse is just as easy.)

Domestic flights cost $100 to $500, depending on ticket class, time of year, city of origin, and time of day of travel. The price could also change if the airlines are in the mood to try a free-market economy instead of depending on fixed prices. Multiply these prices by 100 to 500 percent for international flights.

Security used to be really tight in the O'Hare Sub-Sprawl. Since the assassination of the Chancellor of either North or South Germany last year (don't ask me which one) it's *really tight*. Security requires that all guns be checked through, but they usually discover someone trying to slip one by. The search always turns up some BTLs, too. If the old dreks up at City Hall don't want something in the city, I'd think twice about trying to smuggle it through the airport.

Midway International Airport is almost exclusively for use by the corporations in the Elevated. Security is just as tight as at O'Hare (AAA), but they're much nicer about it. I went through once, posing as a wage slave for Ares, and I couldn't believe how fraggin' polite security was. It's a different world down in the Elevated.

### Automobile or Bus

The roads aren't great in the Midwest, but you can get into Chicago by car and bus. This is your best bet if you need to import something illegal. Bus tickets run about $150 to $250, depending on your point of departure. For the money, you're getting a secure, reliable service.

### Train

Amtrak Inc. handles the passenger-train travel in and out of the city to most points in the UCAS. Amtrak's security is fairly tight for weapons (A) but lax on contraband. They only make spot checks, so you can slip almost anything small on board if you're careful. Travel in Illinois ranges from $20 to $50 within the state and runs $50 to $300 from other states. The travel schedule also changes with destination and departure points. Tickets are either first class, second class, or tourist.

## LODGING

Hotels on the Northside are about $30 a night, becoming more expensive the further south you go. The YM/WCAs can put you up for $2 to $5 a night, and metahuman hostels run about the same. Lately, a lot of the hostels have been getting shot up in the middle of the night. No word on the perps yet, but we're going to nail their scalps to the wall when we catch them.

If you're looking for a place whose security is really tight, try a hotel in the Noose. The prices are steep for the quality ($100 a night for a mattress and a bare bulb), but the security is top-notch and the staffs never snitch.

## GETTING AROUND

### "L" Trains

Two elevated lines currently run through Chicago. Metrorail serves the Northside down to the Noose, and Skytrack handles the downtown area known as the Elevated. The trains of both lines run 24 hours a day, each handling a good chunk of the rush-hour crunch.

Though each line of Metrorail passes over or under the Noose, Metrorail officials have closed and sealed all the stations there.

The security rating on Metrorail is B. Each train normally has two guards on board. Extra guards are available for each train making its round through the Noose; two additional guards board every train at the stop before the Noose and get off when the run through the Noose is completed.

Skytrack began developing a monorail system for the Southside in 2025. Using cash earned in the trideo boom of 2026, the company expanded its original design to create something more like an amusement park than a transit system. Skytrack is supported by sturdy pillars seven stories high. At night the lights of the Skytrack system make the Southside sparkle like a simsense fantasy.

Security on the trains and at the stations is A, contracted from Eagle Security.

A single trip on Metrorail or Skytrack is $2. A monthly pass is $75.

### Bus

Wind Transit won the contract for the city's ground-based mass transit a decade ago. What can I tell you? South of the Noose, the buses are clean and efficient. North of the Noose, the buses and service are dirty and undependable. Northside drivers are protected by bulletproof booths, but won't do anything to stop a mugging in their own vehicle. They've even been known to tear through other vehicles and pedestrians when rushing through a nast neighborhood.

Fare throughout the city is $1. The security rating depends on the neighborhood through which the bus is traveling.

### Boats

A ferry service runs from Business Village to the Southside, giving the business-school students a way to get downtown without having to get dirty. The ferry docks at the University of Chicago Pier, making the round trip three times a day. The service can be cancelled in inclement weather. The fare is $7.

### Choppers

For just over $100, you can travel between any of the Southside's major buildings (governmental, offices, shopping malls) via Federated Boeing's local air service. All key buildings have heliports.

### LEGAL AID

The North American Civil Liberties Union is pretty competent in Chicago and can usually put you in touch with someone who knows what's what. However, unless the charges against you are really lame, the ties between the mob, City Hall, and corps are so tight that you can count on doing time no matter who defends you. The only way to avoid all that trouble is not getting caught. This was kindly pointed out to me by a cop who busted me back when I was just a punk.

## HISTORY

The town of Chicago was incorporated in 1833 with less than 100 inhabitants. A portage site for fur traders, it developed into a major crossroads for trade during the early years of stealing North America from the Indians. The city has remained a hub of commerce as well as a cauldron of racial unrest.

Two key events in this century have shaped Chicago. The first was the discovery of ASIST technology by Dr. Hosato Hikita of ESP Systems, Inc. The second was an act of terrorism unequalled by any that followed.

As soon as ESP Systems "leaked" their ASIST concept, the company was snapped up by maverick financier Dan Truman. Truman had the bucks to back the development of the ASIST technology, turning Chicago into the capital of ASIST and simsense research. According to Truman, "[Chicago is] never going to be Hollywood, but by God, those people are going to stop calling us the fly-by city!" Rumor has it that Truman got ESP only after offering its two founders a "permanent vacation."

ESP became a subsidiary of Truman Technologies, but was absorbed into the parent company after TT lost the suit it brought against Fuchi on ESP's behalf, charging that Fuchi had stolen ESP's ASIST technology. Truman still wants revenge against Fuchi, which has set up an unhealthy competition between the two companies. They constantly try to steal top scientists away from each other.

Within seven years, Truman Technologies was rich enough from simsense entertainment profits to begin revitalizing Chicago's south side. Contracts were signed, cheap land bought, and neighborhood folks were tossed into the streets. The now-homeless were bought off with simsense prototypes presented as "market surveys."

Chicago, traditionally known as a city of neighborhoods, became a magnet for the Awakened. Many of the metahumans headed for Chicago's Southside, where a strong back often compensated for green skin, especially in the factories. The numerous districts of the city provided conclaves where orks, trolls, dwarfs, and elves could gather together in safety, but it reinforced the old ghetto mentality. Each racial group had a place where they could feel at home, but they were separated from the rest of the city. A corper feels like he's part of Chicago, but a ghetto-dweller identifies with the six-by-four-block area he must call home. Soon even these areas no longer belonged to the metahumans.

When the Loop expanded, it headed south and west, driving up real estate prices in areas where metahumans had recently settled. Truman's land development deals displaced much of this working class to the fringes of the city. The situation got worse when office workers from the northern suburbs moved south to avoid a three-and-a-half hour commute to the relocated business district.

When the business district moved, metahumans and other racial minorities had to find new places to live. Members of the suburban communities circling the city

forced acceptance of the metahumans into their own neighborhoods for economic and other reasons, creating balanced, racially integrated areas. Unfortunately, these neighborhoods were also absorbed into the city, collapsing as the corporations moved south and southwest. Once again the metahumans and their working-class neighbors were forced to move.

In 2029, the waves of anti-metahuman violence set off by Seattle's Night of Rage swept through the country. It was widely believed that the most radical arm of Alamos 20,000, the Hand of Five, was responsible for the warehouse fires that caused the tragic deaths of hundreds of Seattle's metahuman population on that night. The terrorism continued all over the world in the days that followed.

Three days after the Night of Rage, members of Alamos 20,000 committed the most outrageous act of terrorism yet, the second major event affecting Chicago. IBM had acquired the Sears Tower years earlier. From the beginning of the Awakening, the computer company supported an equal-opportunity program. Just when it seemed as if people could begin to pick up their lives and go on in the wake of the Night of Rage, the terrorists of Alamos 20K, with a combination of magic and explosives, destroyed the balance of the nine units making up the Sears Tower, sending the building down to the street during a weekday lunch hour.

The falling debris destroyed blocks worth of buildings, streets, and sidewalks. Thousands were crushed to death, but it was still not over. When gas lines were ruptured, the whole Loop area went up in flames. A second Chicago Fire was narrowly averted by mages who managed to contain the blaze in less than an hour. The damage was still severe, with the death toll reaching nearly 26,000.

The physical damage was not the worst part of the incident. Alamos 20K made the destruction of the Tower look like metahuman retaliation for the Night of Rage. The corporations responded by immediately sealing the metahuman and poor (currently lumped together as one group) out of their neighborhoods. City Hall and the corps built projects on the Northside to house the metahumans and keep them separated from the rest of the city. They also built factories in the same area to serve as work camps, and the official tongue-wagging says the situation is "under control."

The areas crushed by the Sears Tower are known as the Shattergraves. All forms of human and inhuman creatures, as well as the ghosts of those killed in the building's fall and aftermath, are said to roam the mazes of steel and concrete. The rest of the Loop, left to rot by the corporations and government, is under the thumb of Chicago's underworld, which is why it's known as the Noose. In the eleven years since the fall of the Tower, the Noose has expanded its boundaries as far as Western Avenue.

## CHICAGO DISTRICTS

Chicago is divided into six broad sections: the Elevated, the O'Hare Sub-Sprawl, the Noose, the Northside, the Westside, and the Southside. These sections have no political basis, but have developed along economic lines.

## THE ELEVATED DOWNTOWN, OR THE CORE OF THE WASTE

**District Size:** Approximately 676 square kilometers
**Population:** 610,040
    Human: 77%
    Elf: 14%
    Dwarf: 4%
    Ork: 2%
    Troll: 2%
    Other: 1%
**Population Density:** 902 per square kilometer
**Per Capita Income:** $500,000
**Below Poverty Level:** 0%
**On Fortune's Active Traders List:** 3%
**Corporate Affiliation:** 95%
**Wards:** 17
**Education:**
    <12 years: 1%
    High School: 5%
    College Degree: 65%
    Graduate Degree: 29%
**Hospitals and Clinics:** 14
**LTG Access Numbers:** 1312 and 2312

## GEOGRAPHY AND DEMOGRAPHICS

The Elevated includes the area of Chicago encircled by Skytrack's cloverleaf, and the lands just outside the tracks. The cloverleaf stretches from 71st Street on the north down to 159th Street, and from the lake out to Route 43. The center of the cloverleaf is known as the Core—a 15 square-block area formed by the monorail tracks as they come in off one leaf and head out on another.

Suburban-style living dominates the Core and the land immediately surrounding it. Almost all the units are owned by corporations for use by their own employees, or are rented out to other companies. The rest of the Elevated is made up of sleek cement-and-glass office buildings, condos, and shopping centers. The destruction of the Sears Tower did little to dissuade people from raising their own phallic symbols.

## NEIGHBORHOODS

### The Core

The Core consists of the 15 square-block area created by the Skytrack, and the ten blocks immediately outside the square. Easy access to the Skytrack makes this prime real estate. The biggest corporations and the tallest skyscrapers rise out of the heart of the cloverleaf. Key companies have buildings in the Core, including Truman Tech, the Chicago Board of Trade, Ares Macrotechnology, IBM, Federated Boeing, UCAS Steel & Manufacturing, and Fuchi-America. Truman Tower is intersected by Skytrack, with one of the stations located inside the building.

The Core is where most of the art looted by the execs from Chicago's museums is now stored. Oh, you didn't hear about that? Well, after the Sears Tower went down, insurance companies refused to cover art in the Institute and other museums. The sararimen picked it up, convincing the owners that it was better to keep the art in Chicago, even if it was no longer public property, than to transfer it somewhere else. Wanna see some oil paintings? Become a wage slave. The funny thing is, some of the paintings have been stolen from the corps, and now the corps want to get them back. I guess they're not as hyped on the public good as they say. From what I hear, the paintings and statues are part of an "illegal museum" (strange words for strange times) on the Northside. The parents are trying to get their kids off on paintings rather than dreamchips. More power to 'em.

Real estate in the Elevated is expensive, but the corps like the fact that the area is rated AAA with Eagle Security.

### Malony Government Complex

Named after the Mayor who got Chicago's political machine back in working order just in time to stop the corps from controlling the city, the Complex is located at the southern edge of Skytrack's northwest leaf. There is a central plaza surrounded by City Hall (where the mayor usually hides with his officially appointed lackeys), the Council Building, where the alderman gather to debate important issues and decide who's picking up the the

profits from organized crime this month, the Midwest FBI Division, the Postal Building, and the Cook County Circuit Court Building.

### University of Chicago/Little Earth

The U of C's campus has grown steadily over the years. It is now located just outside Skytrack's northeast leaf.

Magical studies were incorporated into the University of Chicago's philosophy department in 2028. Less flashy than the programs at Texas A & M and MIT & T because of the lack of industrial, or "practical," application, the program is actually more important because it incorporates magic into our view of the universe.

Shortly after the CAS formed, the Atlantean Foundation donated funds to the U of C to develop a research park out on Lake Michigan. It seems the lakefront area is alive with free air and water spirits. The research park was viewed as a boon to students studying detection and illusion, concentrations of magic important to the Atlantean Foundation. Other corporations kicked in, and Elemental Hall was floating off the shore of Lake Michigan by 2034. Magician philosophers quickly assembled, giving the program a reputation for producing some of the subtlest, if laziest, magical theorists around.

Elemental Hall is located half a kilometer off the shore of Lake Michigan. The four-story building sits atop a concrete foundation set in the bottom of the lake. The building has a courtyard in its center, and a ten-by-ten meter section of the courtyard has been cut out for access to the lake. The pool is heated in the winter so that the lake is always available for study. The Hall has 30 students and 12 professors as permanent residents, and other students sail out for classes and research. I don't know much about this stuff, but last I heard, the Hall's library was considered the best magical research library in the midwest.

The University has also become a mecca for the fringe elements of the magical world. Those who don't make the cut for the U, or who just want to gather with others who share their particular point of view, have taken over an area near the campus. It's called Little Earth, a term taken from the Middle Earth books by Tolkien. (I hear the U of C still gets flak about that from the local metahuman rights groups.) Any theory you've got about magic will find a sympathetic ear in this neighborhood. A fair share of artisans and anti-tech policlubs have also settled here.

The U of C's security rating is AA. Little Earth's is B.

### Residential Areas

The Elevated combines two types of residential neighborhoods, suburban and high-rise.

The suburban style features single-story and two-story houses set along tree-lined streets. Kids can play in the streets without their parents worrying. Illegal chip use is low among the juvies, and there's little crime. Humans make up the majority here, though there is one neighborhood called Elfhome, which is simply a bunch of pointy-ears keeping up with the Joneses.

The high-rises are condo units stacked on top of one another. They're usually filled with younger wageslavers who haven't begun their own families.

The burbs and illegal chips seem to share a symbiotic relationship. Zealous execs looking to turn a profit on simsense and BTLs at every opportunity are waging a strange sort of war. Corps invest money to rout illegal chip use from their own communities, while doing their best to shove chips down the throats of their neighbors. Truman and Fuchi seem to be the leading factions in this war.

The tax base on land around the Elevated is higher than anywhere else, but the city also dumps most of its money for security and city services here.

The residential neighborhoods are middle- to upper-class and have a security rating of B to AA.

## O'HARE SUB-SPRAWL

**District Size:** Approximately 169 square kilometers
**Population:** 172,800
    Human: 60%
    Elf: 12%
    Dwarf: 14%
    Ork: 8%
    Troll: 5%
    Other: 1%
**Population Density:** 1,022 per square kilometer*
**Per Capita Income:** $250,000
**Below Poverty Level:** 1%
**On Fortune's Active Traders List:** 3%
**Corporate Affiliation:** 98%
**Wards**: 5
**Education:** (Unconfirmed)
    <12 years: 2%
    High School: 8%
    College Degree: 68%
    Graduate Degree: 22%
**Hospitals and Clinics**: 3
**LTG Access Number:** 3312

*This high density is even higher for the working class, who are crowded into so little residential space.

### GEOGRAPHY AND DEMOGRAPHICS

The Sub-Sprawl is a vast recreational and tourist complex surrounding O'Hare International Airport. The Sub-Sprawl's permanent population works the facilities (tourist and airport) 'round the clock. During the day, when the crunch is on, 15,000 commuters make sure the "Hub of the UCAS" keeps the flights moving and the travelers entertained.

Most of the area immediately outside the airport is what passes for class these days—chrome and glass. There's not much greenery, but the tourists are too full of alcohol to care. Various corporations and nations supply the services, making sure their employees and citizens have the chance to give cash back to the corps when visiting. Proper ID is required to enter these areas, but you

can get a visitor's day pass for $25 to $50 and a security check. The area beyond the visitors' section is middle- to lower-class residential. Most of these areas are shabbily genteel, rundown buildings that have been patched and repainted over many decades.

The airport is the only game in this town; if you work, you work for the airport. Dwarfs repair the planes, orks and trolls take care of building maintenance and security, and the humans and elves sell tickets, serve drinks, and keep the overstimulated tourists "happy." Exploitation figures heavily in the long list of activities they supply, but where the responsibility falls is up for grabs. Much is made locally of the apparent stereotyping of jobs and workers. Pressure groups have been trying to prove that a hiring bias exists, but the corporations deny the charges, producing their personnel files as proof of their equal-opportunity policies.

The city makes money off the airport, and it's the hundreds of thousands of airport employees who ensure that profit. Do these workers see benefits from the city? Nope. The profits are dumped either into more tourist facilities or into the Elevated to court more business.

### NEIGHBORHOODS

**O'Hare**
Though not officially a neighborhood, the airport deserves a special mention for its AAA security rating.
**National and Corporate Enclaves**
The CAS, Aztlan, California Free State, Aztechnology, Ares Macrotechnology, Truman Technologies, Federated Boeing, Fuchi Industrial, and England all own large sections of land around the airport which they use to entertain visitors. Some of this land, as in the case of Fuchi, amounts to little more than a hotel with several floors set aside for employees. In other cases, several blocks are set aside, complete with restaurants, bars, theaters, and other amenities. By creating a mini-environment right at the airport, the enclaves act as tourist traps for visitors on stop-overs at O'Hare.

Each enclave is walled off from its neighbor. Security is provided by each nation or corporation (AAA), but per a deal with City Hall, all other jobs are filled by Chicagoans. Applicants for work at an enclave are thoroughly screened. Because almost every service is available right at O'Hare, Chicago's embassy ghetto is at the airport.
**Labor Neighborhoods**
Most of the lower-income employees of the airlines, airport, and enclave facilities live in middle- to lower-class neighborhoods, with security ratings from A to C. Overcrowding makes the labor neighborhoods the most depressing areas in Chicago. Disease is a huge problem in the area around the airport, though you'd be hard-pressed to find a published study from City Hall to that effect.

### Luxury Neighborhoods

Elk Grove, Elm Park, and Spring Heights are the three well-to-do areas in the Sub-Sprawl. Airport and airline execs live out here, as well as some of the folks who bring sex, drugs, and illegal chips to the weary traveler. In fact, Madame Wings in Spring Heights is reputed to be the classiest brothel in Chicago.

The security rating is AA for all three neighborhoods. Spring Heights has almost no crime because so many members of the Mafia live there.

## NOOSE

**District Size**: Approximately 60 square kilometers
**Population**: 60,000
    Human: 40%
    Elf: 8%
    Dwarf: 12%
    Ork: 19%
    Troll: 20%
    Other: 1%
**Population Density**: 1,000 per square kilometer
**Per Capita Income**: Who knows?
**Below Poverty Level**: 70%
**On Fortune's Active Traders List**: Not likely.
**Corporate Affiliation**: 0%
**Wards**: 0*
**Education**:
    <12 years: 72%
    High School: 5%
    College Degree: 16%
    Graduate Degree: 4%
**Hospitals and Clinics**: 1
**LTG Access Number**: X312**

*City Hall refuses to acknowledge the "illegal" inhabitants of the Noose.

**The LTG was rigged by hackers who wanted to work out of the Noose. It's not on the city's phone lines. Security is Orange 3.

### GEOGRAPHY AND DEMOGRAPHICS

The Noose covers Chicago's old Loop area and then some. It now stretches from the lake to Western Avenue and from North Avenue down to Cermak Road. The area emptied out after the Sears Tower went down and the corps took their business to the Southside. That left a lot of available space, and those with small "business operations" found a cheap place to set up shop. The area quickly became a red-light district, and then the squatters started moving in. Actual living quarters were scarce, so inadequate, makeshift bathroom facilities were built. That's the reason the Noose stinks so bad.

Two types of people live in the Noose: the dirt-poor who have nowhere else to go and criminals looking for a place to start a career. Both types are going to want something from you, so be careful if you go in.

And there are reasons to go to the Noose. It's the nexus of black-market weaponry in the city, a great place to fence goods, and the home base of street contacts and rumor-mongers. You can hire muscle, deckers, and mages, and they're all hungry. If there's a black hole in the UCAS, this is it.

Why doesn't City Hall clean it up? For three main reasons. First, it's a kind of ready-made housing project that requires nothing from the Hall. The Noose is a collection of buildings that people have taken over unofficially, a ruined area with ruptured water pipes and destroyed power lines. The city isn't responsible for doing any repairs.

This leads right into the second reason. City Hall has always taken the attitude "Let them eat each other." If the poor have to destroy one another to stay alive, that's fine as long as it doesn't bother the folks down in the Elevated.

Third, there's currently enough firepower in the Noose to fight a full-scale war. Eagle Security prefers to patrol the perimeter rather than actually wade into the mess. Frankly, I can't blame them.

Chaos in the streets is prevented by the strength of the Murphey's Law gang, currently ruled by "Alderman" Jack Strong. In addition to being boss of the Noose's biggest protection racket, Strong has declared himself arbiter and judge in the Noose. In the rare instance when two parties want to settle a dispute without gunning each other down, they take the case to Strong at the old Circuit Court Building. If you don't agree with his decision, you get your legs snapped by his goons.

The Noose also has the Shattergraves, but it's hardly a tourist attraction.

When Alamos 20K destroyed the Sears Tower, the nine smaller towers making up the building fell away from each other, crushing other buildings and the people in them for four blocks. The remaining piles of rubble have become known as the Shattergraves. The area is a four-block circle around the former site of the Tower. Some portions of the Shattergraves are simply rubble, huge piles of concrete and steel. In other places, large sections of office buildings still stand.

It quickly became apparent that the area was inhabited by the ghosts of those killed in the disaster (one of the reasons the area was never cleaned up), with estimates of over a thousand apparitions and specters. Though rescue crews removed as many of the bodies as possible as quickly as possible, the area became a feeding and breeding ground for Chicago's ghouls, drawn to the thousands of corpses left there. The ghouls have stayed, having worked out an unspoken deal with the living inhabitants of the Noose. The ghouls keep away from the living, and the living let them have their inconvenient and troublesome dead.

Lone Star rates the Noose as Z. Except for a few really nice hideaways, the Noose qualifies as a slum.

# NORTHSIDE

**District Size**: Approximately 1,080 square kilometers
**Population**: 1,274,400
    Human: 38%
    Elf: 11%
    Dwarf: 17%
    Ork: 16%
    Troll: 17%
    Other: 1%
**Population Density**: 1,180 per square kilometer
**Per Capita Income**: Low
**Below Poverty Level**: 15%
**On Fortune's Active Traders List**: 0%
**Corporate Affiliation**: 1%
**Wards**: 37
**Education**:
    < 12 years: 12%
    High School: 44%
    College Degree: 32%
    Graduate Degree: 12%
**Hospitals and Clinics**: 23
**LTG Access Numbers**: 7312, 1708, 2708

## GEOGRAPHY AND DEMOGRAPHICS

The Northside is a vast stretch of urban blight that crawls north along the lake from the Noose up to where Route 60 crosses Interstate 94, and from the lake over to just past Interstate 290. The average worker's family is crowded into a small apartment in a towering building with broken elevators, flickering electrical systems, and faulty water delivery. Both parents have to work to feed their children. The kids are herded into schools that teach them nothing more than to sit still for 20 minutes at a time. At least 80 percent of the Northside's population, both adults and children, indulge in alcohol or dreamchips.

The plastics factories and metalwork centers belch black soot into the sky, and the snow is dirty before it hits the ground. The lakeshore is littered with garbage from the factories. People visit the lake in the summer, but they do so at their own risk.

Poverty and despair have made this area the hotbed of racial unrest in the city. Though the metahuman population outnumbers the human population, the metahuman factions distrust one another as much as they distrust the humans. Each neighborhood is a ghetto for a single race.

## ECONOMY

Most of the residents of the Northside work in factories that produce synthetics and chemicals or steel. The slaughterhouses, which ship meat across the UCAS, are also located here. Unions are effectively busted. The unemployed population is made up mostly of people who went on strike to get decent wages. They remain unemployed until they're ready to take *any* job over fair treatment.

At least once a year a strike turns nasty. These strikes unite the races, then Eagle Security comes in, some workers are killed, and it's business as usual. A new simsense intended to placate people invariably hits the streets just after the murders.

## NEIGHBORHOODS
### Blood Town

Blood Town is representative of the neighborhoods on the Northside. It is made up almost completely of orks and trolls who work at the huge Fast-Flesh slaughterhouse just east of 94. The stock, most it from up north, is brought down the train line, unloaded, killed, packaged, and sent off to the old states.

I spent some time in Blood Town, and I've never seen such docile orks and trolls. The big guys were actually gentle with the animals. One of the foremen explained that most of the workers had been herded from one camp to another when they were children, so they shared a certain empathy with the beasts being led to slaughter. Not that they consider themselves animals, but they share the prospect of dead-end lives.

Most of the workers live with their families in housing projects built by Fast-Flesh. Doorways and furniture are scaled to fit them comfortably. I'd like to think this shows consideration on the corp's part, but that's not likely.

Rather, it probably means they think this is where the metahumans belong, living in dirty apartments that will smell of blood forever.

Most of the inhabitants of Blood Town want out pretty desperately. Most are also in debt to loan sharks of the Skarz Mob, a big-time Northside underworld operation. They use the money to buy up dreamchips for resale at a profit. The problem is that the poor suckers can never catch up on their payments, and end up further and further in debt. So where does the mob keep getting its expendable muscle? It calls on Northside workers who owe money and want to protect their families.

Blood Town is rated B. The neighborhoods of the Northside get B through Z ratings from Eagle.

### Business Village (Evanston)

Where do all the execs come from who run the factories on the Northside? From the area known as Business Village, and locally as just the Village.

The Village is an armed camp (AAA) complete with walls and barbed wire. Once upon a time, it was the city of Evanston (LTG# 1708). When the Northside turned sour, the town of Evanston bottomed out. Northwestern University, embedded like a splinter in the city's side for years, eventually bought up the whole town, destroyed the tax base that had been so hotly contested for years, and made out like bandits.

The cash really started flowing into N.U. after the Kellog Business School's Dean Tarkton instituted the Terror Principle, still in use today. In case you don't know, the Terror Principle is designed to train young execs for the real world. All of the students' income, living expense funds, and gifts are kept in accounts controlled by the school. The students receive a weekly allowance based on their biweekly grade-point-average postings. The higher the rating, the larger the allowance. The fun part is that the whole system is set on a curve, so each grade is limited to a certain number. It's basically a proving ground for academic Darwinism.

Kellog, always well-respected as a business school, became a mecca for those who wanted a Master of Business Atrocities. When the corporate draft picks come up, Kellog is always first. In fact, it's not uncommon to see shadowrunners hanging out in the bleachers of graduation ceremonies to ensure that corporate investments get delivered safely to their first day of work.

A lot of the Kellog grads cut deals with the future deckers from the Tech school to get dirt on their companies in the Elevated. This way they can up their salaries even before they start pushing pencils. The situation benefits both sides. The deckers manage to pull in pretty hot stuff using clues provided by the Kellog kids. They should really inform the feds or my neo-anarchists instead of keeping it all in the family.

The streets of the Village are clean and safe, with plenty of nice shops and movie theaters. The only time something bad happens is when kids from the adjoining neighborhoods get wasted trying to slip over the walls to pick up some extra cash.

## WESTSIDE

**District Size**: Approximately 1,440 square kilometers
**Population**: 1,090,380
  Human: 43%
  Elf: 26%
  Dwarf: 16%
  Ork: 8%
  Troll: 6%
  Other: 1%
**Population Density**: 757 per square kilometer
**Per Capita Income:** Middle to High
**Below Poverty Level**: 14%
**On Fortune's Active Traders List**: 1%
**Corporate Affiliation**: 30%
**Wards**: 32
**Education:**
  <12 years: 3%
  High School: 12%
  College Degree: 70%
  Graduate Degree: 15%
**Hospitals and Clinics**: 27
**LTG Access Number:** 5312

### GEOGRAPHY AND DEMOGRAPHICS

The Westside is huge and varied. Most of the people living here are commuters to the Elevated or well-off employees of the Sub-Sprawl. Stretching from the Noose to Route 59 and from under O'Hare to down along 55, the Westside neighborhoods get better the further west and south you go.

### ECONOMY

The residents are mostly white-collar and service-industry. Ares, Truman, and Mitsuhama all have research parks out here in large, cleared areas, safe from prying eyes. Most of the employees live nearby.

If the Yak have a base in Chicago, this is HQ. They're quiet about it, hiding behind the white-bread citizens of our fair city, but this is their command center. I've no doubt that several of the warehouses at the Mitsuhama park are stuffed full of Japanese black-market goods.

Fifteen "clean" computer factories, most of them part of the Truman Technologies simsense facility, drive a large part of the Westside economy. Many of the execs from various companies live out here, and somehow most of these factories follow federal guidelines enough to keep pollution to a minimum. Go figure.

Dream Town, located in the heart of the Westside, covers the largest area. Truman knew from the beginning that programmers wouldn't be the key to creating the fantasies that would sell dreamchips. Twenty years ago, he began building up a colony of writers, painters, and hallucinogenic experts to create the concepts for his chips. Unlike the other early creators of simsense chips, who thought the technology best suited for travelogues, the Chicago folks knew immediately that over-stimulation was simsense's true destiny. Dream Town is like Hollywood used to be—sprawling, demanding, and filled with folks having too much fun for their own good.

The three major studios in Chicago are Fox, Brilliant Genesis, and Living Life. All three work independently of Truman, but distribute their simsense through Truman Technologies. TT makes money on distribution as well as by selling the studios new developments from their research park. This leaves the studios free to work up new thrills for the masses.

The studio people are well paid, and they spend lots of money in the area, be it on research for fantasies or on expensive nights out. They are a boon to the economy, even if it's true that they ruin the minds of people who shouldn't be wasting their time plugged into chips. Most people don't realize just how competitive the simsense and dream-creation industry is or how fiercely companies protect their stars. The defection of Witt Lipton and Honey Brighton from MegaMedia to Brilliant Genesis proves that the stakes in the entertainment industry are now high enough to attract major attention.

### NEIGHBORHOODS

Most of the Westside was incorporated into Chicago in the last 20 years, and is still searching for an identity. It's a sprawling patchwork of economic levels and races lumped together only because no single area is large enough or unique enough to stand out.

The Westside will eventually subdivide (I expect to see a really souped-up computer ghetto in another five years), but until it does, it's just two million hard-working people. Tenement ghettos (slums), re-landscaped areas with mansions and barbed wire fences (upper-class), and every other lifestyle exist here side by side. Security ratings range from AA to D.

## SOUTHSIDE

**District Size**: Approximately 864 square kilometers
**Population**: 980,430
  Human: 44%
  Elf: 11%
  Dwarf: 12%
  Ork: 15%
  Troll: 17%
  Other: 1%
**Population Density**: 1,134 per square kilometer
**Per Capita Income**: Middle to Low
**Below Poverty Level**: 15%
**On Fortune's Active Traders List**: 0%
**Corporate Affiliation**: 1%
**Wards**: 28
**Education**:
  <12 years: 6%
  High School: 44%
  College Degree: 20%
  Graduate Degree: 30%
**Hospitals and Clinics**: 25
**LTG Access Number**: 9312

## GEOGRAPHY AND DEMOGRAPHICS

The Southside of Chicago runs from 294 over to the Indiana border. The Chicago sprawl actually extends into Gary, Indiana, which Chicago wants to swallow up to increase its size and to qualify for more federal aid. It's only a matter of time.

## ECONOMICS

The majority of jobs on the Southside are in the steelworks and factories. The city's power plants are also located down here. The neighborhoods run by UCAS Steel are the best.

## NEIGHBORHOODS

The neighborhoods range from slums to middle class. Security is rated from C to A, but the A ratings are only given near the Elevated.

## GOVERNMENT

Chicago is divided into 124 wards, each ruled by an alderman. In theory, the aldermen are responsive to the needs of their constituents. In fact, ballot-box stuffing by the corps is quite common in poor neighborhoods. If someone not on a corporate payroll accidentally ends up in the Hall, he is usually bought off or killed off. What does an alderman do? He lines his pockets and the pockets of those who keep his ward's illegal proceedings moving along smoothly.

An alderman has to listen to his constituents enough to prevent riots in his ward. Every once in a while, he's forced to use the money earmarked for repairing street lights and potholes for exactly those purposes. He doesn't really want to give up the money, however, so he often steals supplies and money from neighboring aldermen, who are in turn stealing from other aldermen, using street thugs for the dirty work. The "Aldermen Wars" are the largest-scale gang wars in the country. Anyone too closely associated with a hostile ward takes a big risk walking into an enemy ward.

The aldermen make up the City Council, which is presided over by the mayor. Each office is up for grabs every four years, but 72 percent of the incumbents retain their position each year. Because the aldermen are drawn from the neighborhoods, metahumans make up 12 percent of the Council. Most of the orks and trolls are on the take. The elves are doing all right for themselves and simply want to keep what they have—even if it means beating out the city's other needy groups for funds.

Jerome Standish is the current mayor. He's a thin, creepy guy rumored to have tapped into some weird voodoo juju while with some merc unit down in the Caribbean League. He's just finishing up his first term, and word on the streets is that the Elevated has picked him to win again. Little Earth says His Honor is jammed with some bad voodoo and is some kind of undead. No one suggests who might be pulling his strings.

Honorable aldermen include Barbara Edwards, Bruce Gorden, and Finch "Teeth" Stump. Edwards, a beautiful human from the Elevated, keeps eking what she can out of City Hall for the city's downtrodden. Gorden is from a Southside family of steelworkers, knows how corps can take advantage of the working class, and does what he can to keep the unions intact. Most of his efforts are focused on the Southside, where the unions are still respected.

Teeth, one of the more personable orks I've ever met, hails from the Northside. He tells me he's received bribe offers and threats from Truman, Ares, and Perfecto Polymers. He's willing to die for his people, both metahuman and human, despite the complaints of his ork constituents that he should only deal with ork needs. Every week he shows up at the Council meeting prepared to shove another obscure federal statute dealing with municipal housing requirements in the Council's face. He makes it impossible for the Council to ignore the housing problems in his ward.

Each of these aldermen has been on the Council for just over a decade. They started out quietly, gathering dirt on their fellow aldermen and on Chicago's corporations, then started asking for little favors. Those who didn't play the game were suddenly busted by federal investigators. The trio, independently of one another, attained folk-hero status, and were targeted for assassination. All attempts on their lives failed. This is because Teeth has managed to get orks and trolls to donate time as bodyguards for the three aldermen, and because Edwards has secured shadowrunners known as Hooders to enter the Matrix and keep tabs on the files the corps keep on her, Gorden, and Teeth.

Anyone who wants to donate Hooding time should talk to Edwards. The pay isn't always as good as a straight run, but it'll make you feel all warm and gooey inside.

## THE HALL, THE CORPS, AND THE MAFIA

Chicago is one of the few cities where the government still exerts as much authority over the populace as do the corporations. There's nothing particularly cheery about this picture, however. City Hall still has power because it uses the Mafia as a lever against the corporations. In effect, City Hall acts as the fulcrum between organized crime and criminally organized business.

The Hall's traditional alliance with the mob goes way back, but it became a permanent fixture in the city's politics during the 2030s. During the Awakening, Mayor Malony cut a secret deal with the newly installed Don, Patrick Murphey, to get black-market medical supplies and food to the city during the worst of the chaos. The mayor knew that the Mafia was personally involved in the city in a way the corps were not, so he split the effort to keep Chicago alive between the two sides.

His illegal dealings seem to have paid off. The corps and the mob have equal money and manpower. Over the years, City Hall has mediated between the two parties to help them act together for the benefit of the city.

## ECONOMY

Chicago is currently prospering at an incredible rate. Here's how the rich are getting richer.

The city has always been well-placed to handle trade. Since the breakup of the United States, new nations have begun specialized production of certain goods, and have increased imports and exports. This means tariffs, and O'Hare gets a piece of all the money changing hands. Chicago also serves as the hub for all the train lines in North America. Chicago's simsense hardware and software, cattle, chemical goods, and steel products are now shipped across the continent.

Speaking of simsense, no company is currently doing better than Truman in the mid-scale market. The products are lower quality than Fuchi's, but these people can really market their technology. Close ties to Fox Simsense, Brilliant Genesis, and Living Life Productions give them plenty of software to support their systems.

Dream Town is making a big name for itself. The employees there are quickly getting rich off their residuals, and more and more writers, actors, directors, and engineers are flocking to the Westside to get in while the boom is on. Just as Hollywood was synonymous with movies in the past, Chicago is becoming *the* production town for simsense (and BTLs). Information from other parts of the world indicates that simply having the name Chicago on a simsense chip marks it as a quality product.

The meat market is thriving here, but retail prices are so high locally and throughout UCAS that most Chicagoans can't afford to put meat on their tables. The prices of other natural foods are jacked up as soon as the trains come into the city. Like other major cities, Chicago has had its share of food riots. People who can afford a good meal every night are those who have money to burn.

Cyberware is also a bit more expensive in Chicago, due mostly to a hefty city tax imposed to generate income. Most cyberware runs 5 to 10 percent higher than standard catalog prices.

## MAJOR CORPORATIONS

### BRILLIANT GENESIS STUDIOS
**Home Office Location**: Chicago, Illinois, UCAS
**President/CEO**: Victor Marquette
**Chief Products/Services**: Simsense scenarios
**Business Profile:**
Brilliant Genesis was the first studio devoted exclusively to simsense scenario production. Though they've maintained a streamlined budget in the past, they're currently pouring major money into new talent. Word is that the Mafia just bought a controlling interest in the company.
**Security/Military Forces:**
Brilliant Genesis has just upgraded to Knight-Errant Securities.

### FAST-FLESH ENTERPRISES
**Home Office Location:** Chicago, Illinois, UCAS
**President/CEO**: Virginia Kidd
**Principal Divisions**
  **Division Name:** Fast-Flesh Processing
  **Division Head:** Evan Gore
  **Chief Products/Services:** Slaughtering and processing of cattle and livestock.
**Business Profile:**
Fast-Flesh made a killing on secret, patented, FDA-approved steroids and growth stimulants. Livestock is reported to reach full growth in just over a month. Rumors abound that the FDA was paid off for approval of the company's chemicals. Studies that question the safety of Johnson's Old Fashioned Meats (Fast-Flesh's retail name) are quickly buried under a pile of counter-studies. I've also heard that some of these drugs might be out on the streets pumping up goons, and that the corp's R&D division might be experimenting with illegal "super-soldier" serums.
**Security/Military Forces:**
Fast-Flesh maintains standard security forces.

### LIVING LIFE PRODUCTIONS
**Home Office Location**: Chicago, Illinois, UCAS
**President/CEO**: Charna Halpburn
  **Chief Products/Services**: Simsense scenarios
**Business Profile:**
Living Life has made a name for itself with its action/adventure line. Rumor has it they are able to turn their scenarios out quickly by adding the hero's adrenaline in post-production, as well as by creating the more spectacular stunt sequences with computer animation rather than putting an actor through the paces.
**Security/Military Forces:**
Living Life Productions has just upgraded to Knight-Errant Securities.

### TRUMAN TECHNOLOGIES
**Home Office Location**: Chicago, Illinois, UCAS
**President/CEO**: Dan Truman
**Principal Divisions**
  **Division Name:** Simsense Systems
  **Division Head**: Mike Malony
  **Chief Products/Services:** Primarily simsense hardware, with a small output of low-end cyberdeck equipment
  **Division Name:** Truman Distribution Network
  **Division Head:** Julie Miller
  **Chief Products/Services:** Distribution of simsense chips
**Business Profile:**
Truman, now in his sixties, is just as arrogant and driven as he was when he made ESP Systems of Chicago into a multi-billion dollar business. His company manufactures its own simsense hardware and distributes software designed by several studios on the Westside. There is no doubt in my mind that there is a division of the company producing BTLs and other illegal chips.

When the independent studios make a simsense scenario, they need to get it to the people who own input jacks. Rather than investing capital to distribute the chips themselves, they sell the scenarios to TT, which prints the chips and sells them across the country. This way, both the studios and TT make a profit.

**Security Profile:**

Truman Technologies maintains standard security forces, though the research park on the Westside appears to be fairly paramilitary in nature.

## UCAS STEEL AND MANUFACTURING

**Home Office Location:** Chicago, Illinois, UCAS
**President/CEO:** Linda Jenkins
**Chief Products/Services:** Steel processing, manufacturing, and distribution

**Business Profile:**

Jenkins is a powerful, rich woman. Like many 20th-century corpers, she is intrigued by the entertainment industry. She is rumored to have her eye on one of Chicago's independent simsense studios. It's well known that there's no love lost between Truman and Jenkins (or, apparently, there was). She'd probably take the studio to Fuchi for distribution, depriving TT of a cash crop.

**Security Profile:**

UCAS Steel and Manufacturing maintains standard security forces.

## CRIME

A disgruntled FBI agent on assignment in Chicago once said, "Crime? What crime? To have crime you need good guys and bad guys. Around here it's impossible to tell where City Hall ends and the Mafia begins!"

## YAKUZA

The Yakuza are slowly making inroads into Chicago. They've set up gambling parlors and prostitution rings near Dream Town to pick up some of the new money, but are finding it hard to get a foothold in the more established sections of town. The Mafia is backing racism against all Orientals in an attempt to prevent the Yaks from becoming accepted. This effort will probably fail, since the Mitsuhama building just opened up in the Elevated last month and a lot of computer factory jobs are being created on the Westside. It's hard to maintain opposition in the face of increased employment. I'm counting on the Yaks to destroy that delicate City Hall/Mafia/corporation balance in the near future.

## MAFIA

Don Jim O'Toole is running the mob now, and it looks like things couldn't be better. City Hall turns a blind eye when his men run Truman's BTLs up to the Northside. In exchange for profits, aldermen leak information about upcoming FBI raids. If a sarariman tries to upset the government, O'Toole's boys ice him.

Only once did a corporation try to move against the mob. Fuchi got cocky back in '45, thinking they had enough clout to buy some land without greasing the palms of the aldermen in charge. When the aldermen refused the sale, Fuchi brought some pressure to bear. The mob backed the two aldermen immediately, and a firefight left most of the mobsters lying on the sidewalk. The suits thought that was the end, but the next day no native Chicagoans showed up for work at Fuchi. None. They were all asked nicely or told roughly not to go to work. And they didn't. And they didn't the next day. And the next. The company threatened to pull out of Chicago. The mayor said, "Fine, boys. We're the second-largest city in the UCAS. Someone will be glad to take your place." They paid off the Hall, 120 lower-class families lost their homes, and the real estate was "developed."

And that's the way it is in the city that works.

# NEW YORK CITY

## FACTS AT YOUR FINGERTIPS

### WHEN TO GO

Any time's a good time to visit Manhattan. Just pack your long coat, a coupla pairs of boxers, and an aspirator with fresh filters and you're set. They used to have something they called seasons way back when. Ask some of the olders; they remember. Now, it's pretty much just warm, and even hotter in summer.

Problem is that ole Manhattan is caught in a nasty atmospheric bind. Nasty air from New Jersey. Nasty air from bits of Pennsylvania. Nasty air from all those wonderful off-shore garbage facilities. (Burn it, pack it, dump it. Pollute the air and water in one shot. Great stuff.)

Most of the year there's enough cold air blowing down from Canada (thanks guys) to keep the nasty air where it's supposed to be. In the summer, however, it all shifts around and dumps itself right on old NY. The air gets

so foul that if they didn't clean it periodically everything would probably rot in a month. How do they clean it? Every night, between 0330 and 0430, the corps seed the cloud-cover. Can we say nasty rain?

O.K., so one month is an exaggeration. Besides, none of Midtown would rot. Ever. They built it that way, with lots of environmental coating and insulation. What about the rest of the place? Don't ask.

### GETTING IN

Are you a resident? Non-resident worker? Resident-worker? Non-resident non-worker? Legal or illegal? Long-term or short-term? Rich or poor? Lots of questions. Plenty o' answers.

The first thing to know about getting in is that Manhattan has got this thing for passes. The three basic types are: Resident, Work, and Temporary. Resident passes are white; solid white for full-time residents, white with a green stripe for part-time residents. Work passes are blue and also come in two types: those with a white stripe indicate that you live and work in NY, and those with a red stripe indicate that you live, but don't work, in the city. Temporary passes are red and are issued on a monthly basis. Occasionally, you might see a black pass. Those guys are permanent guests.

More later about passes, but for now the main thing to remember is that you can't get into the city without one. Most of the access points will issue you a red temp pass almost without a thought. Almost.

There are several access routes into the Manhattan-NYC area. The ones that spill directly into Manhattan are the New Jersey PATH bus routes, the Edward I. Koch Bridge from Long Island City, the Ronald Reagan Bridge (don't ask) from Jersey, and the overland access-ways like the Northern Access connecting the island with New York State, and indirectly back to Jersey through the George Washington Bridge, a short hop up the Hudson River.

There are a couple of PATH lines from Jersey. Most are local, connecting parts of New Jersey and beyond with the NE-Rail network. There is also a direct connection with Newark Airport. All the PATH lines enter Manhattan through Terminal. More on that hell later. Only the unwashed masses use the PATH systems. Nary a white pass to be seen. Costs for riding the PATH system depend on where you get on and where you get off. Short trips are a minimum of 5¥, while long trips across Jersey can cost you as much as 15¥. The direct line from Newark costs 5¥.

The Eddy Koch Bridge is primarily a pedestrian bridge serviced by a small mini-tram that carries peds from the Jersey side to the Koch Customs building. If you've got a vehicle pass (comes with the white card, don't ya know), then you can drive across.

The Ronny Reagan Bridge is really just a copy of the Eddy Koch Bridge, but connects Manhattan with Queens County, more specifically Long Island City. Like the Koch Bridge, it's got a mini-tram connecting both sides and depositing travelers at the Reagan Customs building. Both bridges cost 2¥ for a foot-traveler.

There's another bridge, the old Brooklyn Bridge, that's still standing, but I wouldn't recommend it to anyone but the truly bent. It's a cool place to hang out if you enjoy life on the twisted path: just make sure you're ready for it and that your DocWagon™ account is clean. (Don't expect them to come there for you, though.)

Access by air brings you into either Newark Airport in Jersey or Kennedy International in Queens. Newark is for the masses and handles connections with most of the rest of continental North America. It's also become a rail hub for most of the northeast. Newark also picked up a lot of traffic (like it didn't have enough already) when UCAS seized LaGuardia Airport and turned it into an Air National Guard station.

Kennedy International on the south shore of Long Island is the major UCAS gateway to Europe, and don't let those jokers down DeeCee way tell you otherwise. With three extra-long runways for the various suborbital carriers, Kennedy is the hub of international travel. Airport security is so tight that trying to bypass it would be like trying to sneak a fish through a cat farm. If you gotta bring in something by plane, Newark's the place to do it. If it's split up between a couple of bags and whatever permit you've got seems fairly legal-like, you might not get hassled. Don't even think about taking something through Kennedy unless you've spent some bucks on one of those locked transport cases and your permit is so clean it squeaks.

Kennedy runs a rapid-transit line into Manhattan, via the Reagan, for those on the low-end of the white card spectrum. It also has full tilt- and rotor-craft service to and from the various Midtown aeropads. The rail line will cost you about 10¥ and the air transport about 75¥.

Oh, by the way, those who are wired have another whole set of problems. Without the right permit, forget Kennedy. It's good old Newark that's sometimes lax, and so a couple of tens to the customs boys and girls might get you through. If you do come through Kennedy and you ain't got a Manhattan CBP-107 permit, but do have somebody else's, even a Corp covering your butt, they'll probably slap a real stylish restraint-cuff on you and let you through. You'll notice there's a DocWagon™ station right outside the main terminal for those jokers who figure they can hot-rig the cuffs and pop them once they're clear.

Getting cyberware into Manhattan, Brooklyn, Queens, Staten Island, and what's left of the Bronx is easy. Just take it with you. For Manhattan, the best bet is either down through the Northern Access or through Terminal. The scanners and detectors at those places are ancient enough to pass over any 'ware less than ten years old. In Terminal especially, you can always get an "instant permit" by slipping one of the customs agents the appropriate "fee." Just don't be stingy. You wouldn't want to insult him.

Yes, you can get to Manhattan by water, but only if you're in one of those monstrous city-liners or on a registered private boat. If not, the Port Authority may just mistake you for a smuggler. Whoops.

The same holds for direct entry by air. If you are a scheduled or registered tilt- or rotor-craft, fine. If not, be warned that the Port Authority keeps a couple of dirigibles aloft at all times, packed with enough radar and detection gear to monitor the eastern seaboard. Which is probably what they're doing.

## WHAT IT COSTS

It all depends. To stay/eat/live in Midtown or Times Square costs plenty. Those content to make their homes in any of the lesser neighborhoods pay a lot less.

A hotel that looks safe enough to sleep in is probably more than you can afford. For a ritzy one in Midtown, figure to pay 400¥ to 500¥ a night for a single, nearly 2,000¥ for a suite. One a little less elegant (sorry, no bathroom mints, but maybe a pay-per-view simsense) would probably run you 50¥ tops for a double, per person. They fill up fast, but a couple of sports clubs also have closet space renting for about 12¥ a night. If you're really down on your luck, there are a couple of funeral homes, er, sorry, condensed living accommodation facilities (coffins, chummers), in Terminal and Downtown that go for about 5¥ a night. Don't expect room service, 'cause there ain't no rooms!

At chow time, stay away from the corp or tourist spots, most of which are in either Midtown or Times Square. Figure to drop at least 200¥ for you and a "date" in those areas. Anywhere else—which is where the real New Yorkers eat—will be much cheaper. Figure between 15¥ and 40¥ for a fair to good meal, and higher for better. A pretzel in Midtown will cost you 6¥. Downtown it'll cost you 2¥. Eat with the real people.

Entertainment has a similar swing. If your style is to frolic with the rich and corpy, then expect to pay through an inconvenient orifice. Spend the money in Downtown or Times Square and you'll have a good time. Spend the same amount in Neon City or Soho and not only will you attract a lot of close, personal friends, but you'll have three times the fun. Guaranteed. That is, until those close, personal friends find out you've run out of that money…

If your entertainment interests run to the, um, more exotic, shall we say, then I would recommend connecting with a live cabbie (yes, there are still a few) and have him take you to some of the more interesting places in Soho or Southside. If you've got the bucks, maybe even one of the more custom delights way uptown in East Riverside. Whatever you have to pay, trust me, it's worth it.

The overall cost of living in Manhattan shows a wide

spread, too. A Luxury lifestyle requires about 200,000¥ a month, High about 25,000¥, and Middle about 8,000¥, while Low only needs 850¥ and Squatter about 50¥. Street is still street, though perhaps a tad more physically taxing. Hospitalization is going to run you from 400¥ to 750¥ for basic care, and 1,200¥ to 2,000¥ for intensive care.

## GETTING AROUND

If you're in Manhattan, chances are you ain't got a car. Maybe a bike, if you're lucky, but if the cops catch you, they'll probably nail you. Ever since the "Rebirth," vehicles have been banned from Manhattan Island, unless of course you've got a white card or the right connections. This means that those who can afford it have a car, or two, and those who can't are hoofing it. Bikes fall under the category of vehicle and so, technically, are illegal without that permit. But whether or not the cops will bother you depends on what neighborhood you're in and how fast you're moving at the time.

If you think this puts a damper on the nation's newest favorite pastime, go-ganging, you're wrong. The average pedestrian is probably a little safer in Manhattan than most sprawls these days, but only 'cause the go-heads spend so much time knocking heads with the cops that they leave the common folk alone. Usually.

Transportation around Manhattan and the adjoining areas can get complicated. In the country, outside the city, it's mostly bus and rail for those who can't afford real wheels. If you can find a bus shelter or subway station that still has a readable system map, then getting around is no problem. If you've got the guts, just hop on and see what happens. Great fun.

There's a rail connection across the Ronny Reagan that links up to most of the Queens and Brooklyn bus systems, but that deposits you at the Customs Center, too.

Can't call the Long Island Railroad the Iron Snail anymore, because they finally went mag-lev about ten years ago. If you got the bucks, catch a hotliner from the Midtown terminal that'll get you out to the Hamptons almost faster than you can ask around about which clubs are mainline that weekend. A straight run out to the Hamptons costs about 70¥. A shorter hop to the Mineola Transport Hub, adjacent to Roosevelt Field, the world's largest enclosed shopping mall, costs about 15¥. Anyone visiting NY should make it to the Field. It's a real wizzer, with probably more turned-up noses per square meter than anywhere else on earth. And it's popular even though the place gets hit by a terror-run at least once a month. I guess this is the closest to a real thrill that a lot of people ever get.

On Manhattan itself, you can get around above ground or below on public transportation. One of the above-ground means is the MTA bus system, which is easy to use because most run either north-south or east-west. A single fare is 2¥. A monthly pass runs about 30¥.

Also above-ground is the New El, which runs north-

south along both shores and then heads east-west. This elevated mag-lev system serves mostly Midtown and adjoining areas. It's clean, efficient, and mega-boring. Too much white. A circuit fare costs 3¥, but you can get a monthly pass for 40¥. The cops patrol the system heavily, unlike the buses or the subway.

As for below-ground transport, there's the subway. Much of it caved in during the earthquake, but portions were rebuilt to handle the migration of workers to and from the city each day. The subways primarily service the less-prestigious sections of town. A one-way fare to anywhere on the system is 1.5¥.

Much of the old subway system remains unused and unmaintained, however. For those in the know, this is the Underground, the mainline to everywhere.

Even the parts of the lower Manhattan subway that connect with Brooklyn run through customs check-points. Before crossing the river, all commuters must swap trains and submit to a general weapons and contraband search. The guards are lax enough that you can probably bluff your way through.

The final alternative is one of the licensed cabs that work the streets (mostly north of 32nd Street). The fares are steep, 2¥ a block, but a ride tends to be fairly safe and quick.

## ADJOINING AREAS

### THE COUNTIES

Since 2027, only Manhattan legally has been New York City. In *Manhattan Inc. v. The State of New York*, the city forced the boroughs of Queens, Brooklyn, Staten Island, and the Bronx, all formerly part of NYC, to separate from it. In effect, the suit let Manhattan secede from the rest of NYC, keeping the name and all the prestige. Sort of like my ex-wife.

Realizing that they would be unable to stand alone, the boroughs tried to stick together at first. Typical of their attempt was their inability to agree on a better name than "Quad Counties." Eventually, each went its separate way, all becoming counties of New York State, municipal entities unto themselves again, in 2029.

Many who work in Manhattan live in the counties. Since before the turn of the century, NYC has imposed a moderate "commuter tax" on all non-resident workers. It's been part of city policy not to provide scarce in-city housing for those workers, thereby forcing the tax upon them.

Travel in the counties is relatively sane, with the check-points occurring only when you try to enter Manhattan.

Brooklyn and Queens still walk the line between suburb and sprawl. I'd say they're more sprawl than suburb, but I already have enough enemies. Brooklyn does have the Brooklyn Naval Yards, now reclaimed by the UCAS as a base for much of the country's non-carrier North and Mid-Atlantic fleet. The Coast Guard also bases out of there these days.

Staten Island ranges from dirt poor to filthy rich, sometimes within the space of a few blocks. The place is so hilly, however, that usually neither side of the tracks can see the other. For years, Staten Island wanted out of NYC, and has done a surprisingly good job of running things since they got their wish. Of course, the additional income from the Staten Island Carrier Base, home port of the *Wolverine* Light Carrier Battlegroup, probably doesn't hurt any.

Westchester County, north of Manhattan, was never part of old NYC. Suitville, UCAS, is an incredibly boring place. The only spots of interest are some of the compu-corporate enclaves around Poughkeepsie and White Plains.

The best thing that can be said about the Bronx, which is mostly commercial and residential poor and lower-middle class, is the Villiers Arcology Project. The Arcology, which is under construction on the southern-most tip of the Bronx, adjacent to Harlem River, over the area they used to call Mott Haven, may someday actually be finished. Maybe. It's been under construction for a few more years than the fabled Seattle-Renraku structure, but isn't anywhere near as complete. Plagued by design flaws, accidents, and outright terrorism, the Arcology seems cursed.

## NASSAU COUNTY

Designer living. Chauffeured rotorcraft. Gag. So-stylish-it-makes-you-sick. Nassau's got its cool places, though. Roosevelt Field, the Great Neck almost-arcology, Nassau Coliseum (live skateball), my friend Widow's place in Hempstead, the Inwood Combat Zone (which, being a rocket's flight from Kennedy, makes for great fun), and so on.

You'll find just as wide a swing in background and economics as in Manhattan, but the Nassau PR people work much harder at keeping a it secret. I suspect the whole South Shore is just waiting for a repeat of the '38 riots.

## NEW JERSEY

Need I say more? Actually, except for the urban hells like Newark, Jersey is a decent blend of city and suburb. That is, if you can stomach even the slightest bit of suburb. The monstrous corporate enclaves along Interstate 1 and down the coast have done much to boost the area's economy. To date, they haven't fallen into the socio-economic spiral associated with most corporate-linked communities. Time will tell. (Read: We're working on it!)

If people can get hurt playing it, then the Meadow-lands Sports Sprawl features it. Knock yourself out.

Early last year, the North Jersey ABM system misfired and blew a Euroflot spaceplane to dust as it arced over toward Kennedy. Great fireworks.

## CONNECTICUT

Not really much I can tell ya, having only been there once myself. But it's pure suburban death zone. Zombies everywhere. Maybe even more gray suits per square block than Tokyo. (Nah.) The corporate zones, most of them in places like Hartford, Danbury, and Meriden, are full of wage slaves and *sararimen*, all worshipping at the feet of their respective corporate gods.

Of additional interest is the sub base at New London. This is one of the few the UCAS has left and they guard it like royalty.

## HISTORY

### THE LEVELING

Today, most people would agree that Manhattan's history starts with the quake of 2005. Sure, some old-timers remember how it was before, but what's the point? It's like worrying about world history before 2011. It just doesn't matter.

There'd been talk in NYC about the possibility of a quake since the late 1950s. No one really believed it, even though a couple of faultlines run around and across Manhattan. The major fault runs down the Hudson River to the west of the city, but a couple of smaller ones actually cut through Manhattan Island itself.

At 7:20 A.M. on August 12, 2005, a major earthquake hit Manhattan. The scientists say it was only 5.8 on the Richter, but it seemed higher. Of course, NYC had none of the earthquake protection of cities more prone to them, which made the physical damage greater. Some 200,000 people died, and close to a million were injured. Most experts agree that death and casualty rates that low were miraculous.

The city was in ruins, having taken most of the major damage. Because the outer burroughs suffered less, they were used for evacuation and treatment. It was a freak of nature that the only Manhattan building of any size that didn't collapse was the Empire State Building. Sure it was damaged, but a little re-strengthening was all it needed.

What does a city do when something like this happens?

Nail up a "Condemned" sign and leave it be?

Pave it over and try again?

### THE PRICE

After the disaster, the facts of life were hard. No way could the federal government (then still the U.S.A.) afford to rebuild New York. The *Shiawase* decision of 2001 had already eroded much of the tax base, and the billions in aid to the Middle East following the Israel/Libya "shotgun war" had put a huge dent in the national bank account. Facing an already staggering national debt, a legacy of the "faith healing" economic policies of the 80s and 90s, the government announced it could offer no more than basic disaster aid to NYC.

Well, it takes business to know business, and the next move was the corps'. NY had become an economic hub for very definite geographical reasons and the corps saw this as their chance to rebuild that center in their own image. A consortium of aspiring multinationals volunteered to pitch in and help rebuild the city. The catch? Deregulation.

Now, realize that back then the ole U.S.A. still hadn't fallen to ruin. The *Shiawase* decision was still young, and no one had really taken that long, hard look down the tracks to see what was coming. By agreeing to help rebuild the NY infrastructure and pump billions into the local economy in the process, the consortium, or Manhattan Inc. as it was sometimes known, would be helping to maintain the stability of the region, and therefore, the county. What they would ultimately be doing, however, is breaking the back of government.

In exchange for the billions in corporate aid, Congress passed legislation deregulating most industries, restructured the corporate tax base and regulations, shifted the balance of fees, tariffs, and duties, and generally gave the corps a free ride. It's true they planned to impose some temporal limitations. Once NY and the local/national economy were again on firmer ground, Congress would revoke the privileges granted the corps. They miscalculated seriously, however. To name a few:

•The Awakening (Hey, who coulda guessed?)

•The Treaty of Denver (Ooops, lost most of the West...)

•The CAS and CFS secession (Ooops, lost most of everything else...)

•Corporate intrusion in government (Here lies the real blame…)

By the time NY was back on its feet, and the Northeast with it, the corps were running the show. The economy of the country (now the UCAS) was drek and the corps were the only thing holding it together. They rebuilt New York, and bought themselves a country.

## CURRENT SITUATION

### GOVERNMENT

The government of the City of New York uses the trappings of old New York City but little of the reality. At the top of the bureaucratic totem pole is the Mayor of New York, currently one Andrew T. Small. (Small, a vacillating Democrat with one finger in the air to test the political winds and another up his butt, is a veteran of the corporate machine. A former Marketing VP for Trés Chic Cosmetics, Small knows as little about city government as he does about personal hygiene.)

Below the Mayor, downwind as they say, and ignoring all the various Mayoral Assistants, is the City Council. In the old days, each of the five boroughs elected representatives to the City Council, which had the job of trying to bully the Mayor into doing what they wanted. Nowadays, each of the Precincts (an apt term) of NY elects (hah) representatives to the City Council, which has the job of publicly supporting the Mayor on as many trideo programs as they can manage a day.

In NY it's the Corporate Advisory Board who calls the shots, though its ostensible role is as advisor to the Mayor on city business matters. Since everything is business these days in NY, they generate paperwork that he signs. Every member of Manhattan Inc. has a seat on the Advisory Board, which meets once every two to three weeks to lunch, blather, and advise. A simple majority is required before an advisement paper can be forwarded to the Mayor.

Currently, the membership of the Manhattan Inc. Consortium is roughly as follows. (I say roughly because they keep the exact membership quiet.) In a moment, I'll tell you why:

Ares Macrotechnology
Aztechnology
Eastern Financial
Fuchi Industrial Electronics
IIS (International Information Systems)
The Kesai & Wilhelm Group
Netlink Telecommunications
Prometheus Engineering
Saeder-Krupp Heavy Industries
Sony Dataworks
Trans-Orbital
UCAS Data Systems
Villiers International

The consortium can only have, and must have, 13 members to exist. However, the members of the consortium can remove one of its members by a unanimous vote. This was alleged to have happened about six years ago when Mitsuhama got bounced and UCAS Data Systems was installed in their place. You can bet your best pair of mirrorshades that the Yaks were none too happy about that.

The consortium likes to keep its membership quiet for defensive reasons: anybody connected with them is fair game in NY. In some circles, anti-megacorp terrorism is almost a sport.

The most powerful members of the consortium are undoubtedly the big three—Ares Macrotech, Fuchi, and Aztechnology—though Saeder-Krupp has been trying to muscle up with its latest series of acquisitions. Of them all, Ares is probably in the strongest position because of its place in the NY law-enforcement triad. More on than later.

Just because Ares seems to be in the best position doesn't mean it's king of the hill. Because of the one-corp, one-vote structure, Ares often is out-voted in the consortium meetings. You can also bet your best pair of mirrorshades the megacorps wish they hadn't written that in, because now all the smaller members can block any efforts to get the provision changed.

## PASSES

In the UCAS, if you don't have a SIN, you're nobody, as far as the government is concerned. In NY, if you don't have a pass, you're less than nobody. You're an *Illegal*.

Earlier I mentioned the different types of passes and their functions. More info follows.

### Resident Passes

Resident passes are white and come in two variations—solid white for full-time residents and green-striped for part-time residents. The difference? Paperwork.

Both are reserved nearly exclusively for the social elite. If you call NY home, and therefore dump most of your taxes there, you get a solid white pass. If you have residences other than NY, you get a white pass with a green stripe.

What does this mean?

Unlimited access to even the most restricted of shopping centers. Special deals at various financial institutions. Unlimited vehicle access to the island of Manhattan. Automatic subscription to either DocWagon or MediVac services. And so on.

It also means preferential treatment by some of the police forces, depending on who they are and who the corporate sponsor is. Oh, did I mention that? All white passes are corporate-sponsored. The only way to get one is if a corp backs your application. Just another perk in old NY.

The white residence pass is reviewed once every five years or if an officiating body (read corp) requests it.

### Work Passes

Work passes are for wage slaves. They're blue and have a white stripe for residents of NY who work within its borders, or a red stripe for those who live in NY but work in one of the Counties, or god forbid, Jersey.

The blue pass doesn't entitle even NY residents to own in-city transportation, so they have to walk it or take mass transit.

The blue work passes are reviewed yearly or at the request of an officiating or law enforcement body. (Did you notice that the law enforcement agencies can't request a review of a white pass?)

### Temporary Passes

For those who work in New York, but don't live there (which is 75 percent of the workforce), there is a red temporary access pass. You're barely anybody, but you've got a card.

If it's a solid red, you get reviewed every six months, at nearly anybody's request.

If it's red with a gray stripe, it's basically a "guest" card. You get reviewed once a month, hell, high-water, or Ghost Dance, and you better have a damn good reason why you haven't applied for an upgrade. Corps, if they like, can get "special guests" a gray "special guest" card. If it's solid gray, it's the equivalent of a white card as far as perks are concerned, but it gets reviewed every six months (or so) and the bearer is the responsibility of the sponsoring corp. If the gray card has a red stripe, it's a monthly pass and the rough equivalent of a blue pass.

## RESTRICTED PASSES

The fun ones. Restricted passes, shiny black suckers, are issued to felons. That's right, if you are convicted of a crime, you get to carry a black pass.

If it has a white stripe, you are a resident criminal.

If it has a blue stripe, you are a working-class criminal.

If it has a red stripe, you are a temporary criminal. (Yes, laugh! I swear they have such a thing.)

And, presumably, if a corp sponsors it, you can get a black pass with a gray stripe for their "special criminal guests." They should be issuing a lot more of those than they do.

Anyone who commits any crime above a misdemeanor, or five misdemeanors within a five-year period, gets a black card. That's his or her ID for the next five years. If he or she has been a good boy or girl during those five years, the city gives him or her the old card back. Ain't they sweet?

What does a black card get you? Hassle city. You are *persona non grata* as far as anyone above drek-level is concerned. Everything you do is scrutinized. Some places won't let you near the door. Life is hell.

You can get away with a lot, with or without a pass, if no one scrutinizes you. If you're driving a van down Broadway and you're being real legal-like, odds are no one will bother to ask for your papers. After all, no cop wants to stop, and thereby insult, someone important.

Like the book says, if you look the part and act the part, you may as well be the part as far as everybody else is concerned. Oh, and if you're going to try a fake white pass, lose the mohawk, the mirrorshades, the flak jacket, and the Uzi. Just a suggestion, chummer.

## PASSES, PASSES, WHO'S GOT THE PASSES?

The problem of passes in NY is compounded because the pass acts as a credstick as well as bearer of all ID information. Most of the card checkers in the city are connected to BIDVS (Bearer-Identity Verification System) run by UCAS Data Systems (which, no doubt, explains their inclusion in the consortium a few years back).

The pass card, as I said above, acts as a credstick. White passes are either Platinum or Gold equivalents, blue or red are either Silver or Standard, and gray runs the range from Standard to Platinum, depending on the wishes of the sponsoring corp. Blacks are always Standard. A colored dot on the card indicates the credstick equivalency rating.

NY pass cards are harder to forge and easier to spot than standard credsticks because of the improved encoding and the limited database the BIDVS needs to access. Forgeries cost five times the regular shadow-market value for a particular rating, double the cost for a blue pass, and double it again for a white pass.

## LAW ENFORCEMENT

Let's face it, law enforcement in New York is wacky. Three security companies hold the contracts: Knight-Errant (hence Ares' clout in the consortium), Winter

Systems, and the NYPD Inc. (taken over by the union and incorporated a few years after the big quake). NY has been divided into Zones, also known as Precincts, each of which is patrolled and under the jurisdiction of two of the three members of the law triad.

The plan was to reduce corruption by having each of the corps looking over the other's shoulder. You know, the spirit of competition. The problem was that the consortium built into the triad system the provision that the consortium could remove a member from the triad at the request of one of the other members. Now, this can't happen unless the requesting triad member has sufficient evidence of blatant wrongdoing, as Knight-Errant had of Warren Security back in 2041. Seems Warren had been systematically butchering squatter-residents of various buildings owned by Warren Habitats, their parent company.

The result of all this is lots of cross-agency suspicion, bad blood, paranoia, competition, investigation sabotage, evidence suppression, and generally even more corruption than normal, but of a different nature, of course.

Within the Precinct, the multi-corporation structure works like this. Within each department, a cop and his partner are members of the same corp, other partner-teams are of the same or another corporation. An effort is made to keep the number of enforcement teams balanced. Overseeing the department is an executive officer appointed by a tri-corporate, precinct-based advisory board.

With all this, the politics in one Precinct house rivals that of the whole UCAS.

There's also an added twist: the Port Authority. Controlled, amazingly, by New York State, the Port Authority's primary role is controlling New York Harbor and the surrounding waterways. They also have airspace jurisdiction over the entire Manhattan Island, which means all of New York City. If that weren't enough to drive the corps nuts, the PA controls the Terminal precinct, Grand Central Station, and the bridge and road accessways to the city. If something gets you into or out of Manhattan, the Port Authority covers it. As you can imagine, this make for fun jurisdictional problems.

## CRIME

Ah, crime. Well, officially, there's barely any, so all of this is theoretical, you understand.

The standard big three are present; the Mafia, the Yaks, and the Seoulpa Rings, in that order. The Mafia controls trucking and construction, leaving the petty street drek to the other two syndicates. The Yaks handle the illegal gambling, prostitution, and BTL peddling for the city. That leaves the Seoulpa Rings anything else they can get their hands on.

They compete with the Yaks for control of the black market, though not very successfully. Sometimes a Ring will give you a better deal for single items, but if you need it in bulk, the Yaks are your guys. Just don't tell them you also deal with the Rings. The Yaks are already mad enough at the way the Seoulpa have been undercutting their street-level BTL sales.

Almost every precinct has its own Yak clan controlling the area, and depending on the size of the area, one or more Rings. The Mafia work city-wide.

And the shadowrunners? As in most urban areas, NY's shadow underground operates as one big network. Many runners work in set groups, very much like Seoulpa Rings (and sometimes operating as one), that overlap with other groups, informally exchanging members based on who needs what where and when. The city has only a handful of real runner groups, no matter what fictions you hear about dozens on every street corner and coming out of holes in the wall. I can count all the *real* runners I know on all my fingers and toes (plus one for the big toe I lost last week). You can't fire your gun and not hit a wannabee or poser, though.

## STREET LIFE

If you had to pick one word, a socially acceptable one, to define New York these days, dynamic would have to be it. NY has always been the town that never sleeps and it has never been truer. Walk the streets at four in the morning (in certain areas at least) and you'll probably see more people than you would on most Saturday afternoons. Now, these people might not be anyone you'd want to call chummer, but that's beside the point.

Some people complain of the city's distinct odor, which can only be the collective scent of the single organism that is New York. Every member, from the highest white card to the lowest black card, is part of that organism. They are the very fiber of Manhattan's being, which moves and breathes, lives and dies with them.

The energy level of a city so many millions strong is real and palpable. Apathy may attack the denizens of various other sprawls around the globe, but apathy won't get you far on these mean streets. In Manhattan, the human animal does not survive long by being sluggish, unaware, or naive.

The night itself in New York is wired. Walk the streets, catch the breeze when it comes, and let your body's clock warn you that soon the nightly acid rain will fall. Catch the eye of a fellow pedestrian and give him a nod and tight smile. Share the energy. All it takes is the edge.

## NEIGHBORHOODS

Working south, they are:

### INWOOD, WASHINGTON HEIGHTS, AND NEWTOWN

|  | Security Rating |
|---|---|
| **Inwood** | |
| NYPD Inc. and Winter Systems | **C-B** |
| **Washington Heights** | |
| Knight-Errant and Winter Systems | **B** |
| **Newtown** | |
| NYPD Inc. and Knight-Errant | **B-A** |

Of these primarily residential neighborhoods, only Newtown shows signs of corporate presence. Residential buildings are usually less than eight stories, though some as high as twelve stories do exist, especially in the higher-rent areas along the Hudson. Most residents barely consider these areas part of Manhattan, so far removed do they seem.

Newtown is named for the fact that nearly 80 percent of the buildings were rebuilt or refurbished following the earthquake. This occurred more out of a desire to wipe the slate clean than out of structural necessity. The consortium apparently decided that New York was better off forgetting the crime-ridden neighborhood of Harlem that once occupied this area. What they forgot was the cultural and historical wealth of those streets. With the consortium making such decisions, it's a wonder the city survived at all. (Some genius, however, had the sense to maintain the historic Apollo Theater on 125th Street between 7th and 8th.)

This area offers few places of real interest, beyond a few neighborhood slam palaces and a shadow bar or two (strictly small-time). The one major exception is The Cloisters. Set on a hilltop near the northernmost tip of Manhattan Island, the Cloisters is a series of authentic and representational medieval buildings that formerly housed the Metropolitan Museum of Art's medieval collection. These days, much of the collection remains, but the ownership has changed.

An order of Hermetic mages working under the name The Children of the New Crusade acquired the Cloisters from the financially foundering Met in 2036. (Sounds like a policlub, but then, all those mage groups sound that way to me). The order, apparently incorporated, took control, keeping much of it open to the public while maintaining the rest as living and working quarters. The only other thing I know about the Children of the New Crusade is that it's best not to mess with them. The other bit of news are the repeated sightings of what seems to be a young Eastern dracoform at the site, apparently under the care of the order.

Newtown also has Columbia University, at Broadway and 116th, along the precinct border with Riverside. Much of the grounds are very old (it having been founded as King's College in 1754) and somehow survived the quake. Before that, part of the area was the Bloomingdale Insane Asylum (which now sits south a bit and across the park), and some say shades of its former inhabitants appear on the darkest, quietest nights. Today the university is noted for primarily its Liberal Arts, Pre-Business Law, and Mystic Studies/Parapsychology Departments.

### RIVERSIDE AND EAST RIVERSIDE

|  | Security Rating |
|---|---|
| **Riverside** | |
| NYPD Inc. and Winter Systems | **A-AA** |
| **East Riverside** | |
| NYPD Inc. and Knight-Errant | **B-A** |

These two are also primarily residential areas, with some corporate structure overflow from Midtown. Many middle-management corp-types live in East Riverside, so much of the available entertainment is appropriate to that style of life. Across the river is Randall's Island, the location of the city's minimum and moderate-security prisons.

### MIDTOWN (AA-AAA)
Winter Systems and Knight-Errant

The glory that is Manhattan. Bright and shining skyscrapers and even taller skyrakers command the area, ringing Central Park. An especially good view is from one of the giant towers at either end or from the northern end of the Central Park reservoir.

All the buildings in Midtown are gigantic, and are either new or were erected within the last half-century. There are probably more square meters of glass, chrome, and stonework here than in any other similar-sized area in the world. Many years back, one of the Middle Eastern madmen called New York "Satan's Seat of Judgement." Well, I can't vouch for that one way or the other, but someone sure didn't skimp on the upholstery.

The corporate heart of NY, Midtown is where most of New York's corporate buildings and complexes are located. At the north edge of Central Park, is the IIS Tower (Lenox and West 115th) and Sony Dataworks (Fifth and East 106th). Heading south on either side, one finds Netlink

(East 96th and Park), UCAS Data Systems (Park and West 99th), Villiers International (East 86th and Park), and Saeder-Krupp (Third and East 72nd).

At the end of the park are Ares Macrotech (West 63rd and Eighth Avenue), Aztechnology (Fifth and East 52nd), Eastern Financial (Lexington and East 60th), Kesai & Wilhelm (West 61st and Columbus Avenue), and Trans-Orbital (East 55th and Sixth).

Also scattered throughout the area are the offices of Renraku, Mitsuhama, and most of the other multinational and domestic giants.

Midtown is so clean it squeaks. Winter Systems and Knight-Errant ride the area hard, keeping the street-drek away and the taxpayers safe. At any time of day or night, at least one aircraft, whether law-enforcement or otherwise is in the area, probably heading to one of the many rooftop VTOL-pads.

Also located here is Lincoln Center (Columbus and West 63rd), the haute-cultural institute that attracts herds of limousines almost every night. The Metropolitan Opera is in Lincoln Center, but these days, it alternates with the Japanese-backed Kobo Playhouse.

At the southeast corner of the park (Fifth and East 60th) is the Manhattan Club, a ritzy and members-only club. If a person is one of the powers-that-be in NY, you can bet he or she's a member here.

## WESTSIDE AND UPPER EASTSIDE

|  | Security Rating |
|---|---|
| **Westside** | |
| NYPD Inc. and Winter Systems | AA (AAA) |
| **Upper Eastside** | |
| NYPD Inc. and Knight-Errant | A-B |

Both Westside and Upper Eastside are primarily residential, with a few towers overflowing from Midtown. Westside is definitely corptown, while Upper Eastside begins to look more residential. The homes along Riverside Drive and overlooking the river are among the most expensive pieces of residential property in the city.

The southernmost section of Westside, at the site of the old 16th Street Conrail Terminal, is the massive spire of Prometheus Engineering. An architectural impossibility, the 100-story building mimics a DNA spiral twisting in on itself. Hundred-stories or no, remarkably few wage slaves work above the 40th floor. Those employees who do are most likely to be those who also reside in one of the building's many living-quarters floors. They're also likely to be the most tight-lipped about what goes on there. Prometheus does R&D in everything from macrotechnoloy, nanotechnology, and telemechanics to cybernetics and bionetics.

The most notable site on the Upper Eastside is Gracie Mansion (East 86th and the river), the long-standing residence of the Mayor of New York. It's easily recognizable by the barricades and platoons of armed guards all around.

## CENTRAL PARK EAST AND WEST

|  | Security Rating |
|---|---|
| **Central Park East** | |
| NYPD Inc. and Knight-Errant | AAA |
| **Central Park West** | |
| NYPD Inc. and Winter Systems | AAA |

Here is where anybody who is anybody in New York lives. When the city was being redesigned, the planners set aside these two great strips on both sides of the park for residential buildings. The strips run from 86th to 60th Street and are a city-block wide. The views are tremendous. Bet on it.

No big surprise that cops are everywhere.

## LOWER WESTSIDE AND EASTSIDE

|  | Security Rating |
|---|---|
| **Lower Westside** | |
| NYPD Inc. and Winter Systems | C |
| **Eastside** | |
| NYPD Inc. and Knight-Errant | A-B |

Now we're starting to get down to my part of town. The Lower Westside descends quickly from the splendors of Midtown and Westside, ending in near-squalor against the walls of Terminal. It's primarily a lower-middle-class/poor residential, wage-slave zone. A few street gangs roam the area, the most powerful being the Blood Monkeys, who expanded their turf into Downtown and Southside. The river-edge portion of the Lower Westside also contains some port and cargo-handling facilities.

The Eastside is the Land of Lower Managers, and nervous ones at that. Ya see, across the river from Eastside is Roosevelt Island, now more commonly known as Penitentiary Island, where the city maintains moderate-, maximum-, and ultra-maximum security prisons. Even with help from Warren Security, they can't prevent at least three riots and a dozen attempted prison breaks every year. No one knows how many make it off the island and live to reach the shore, but I can tell you for a fact that some do.

## TIMES SQUARE AND NEON CITY

|  | Security Rating |
|---|---|
| **Times Square** | |
| NYPD Inc. and Knight-Errant | AAA |
| **Neon City** | |
| NYPD Inc. and Winter Systems | AA-A |

Times Square is where those who have the nuyen go for a dose of high culture. That is, when they're not absorbing the Modern Kabuki at Lincoln Center. Most of Manhattan's old theater district got crammed into this area during the rebuilding. It now has about half a dozen full-size theaters and maybe double that number in smaller venues. The turn-over in shows is rapid-fire as this season's giant flop goes down in flames and another rises in its place. Of course, one show makes it to blockbuster status every season. This year it's *Bloody Buzz-Bombs*, a musical, simsense-augmented version of the story of London during the World War II blitz.

Neon City is where the elite go to pretend they're slumming. Designed to look like an authentic red-light district where decadent pleasures of the flesh, intellect, and spirit lurk behind every door, it's one of the few zones in NY where the rich and everyone else rub shoulders and occasionally butt heads. The area is patrolled fairly heavily, but the cops stay back as long as everyone seems to be having fun and the fun isn't getting too illegal.

A series of interconnected, mall-like structures, the buildings of Neon City are linked by glass-enclosed crosswalks that rise high above the traffic. There are many open-air spaces, some dozens of floors above the street, where fun-folk can meet and look down on the city.

Neon City is also a focal point for heavy criminal activity. You name the scam or the scrag and someone's bound to be at it in Neon City, but only if you know where to look and who to ask. Remember, this is a heavily patrolled area, obvious as well as undercover, so don't jander down the street with too many of your intentions hanging out. Playing the part is always at least half of the show.

### TERMINAL (Security Rating C-E, occasional bursts of Z)

Knight-Errant and Winter Systems

The name says it all, for Terminal is a kind of huge drainage ditch for the rest of the city. Most of the cheap transportation coming into New York City unloads here, either at the Port Authority Transit Terminal (mostly buses) or Penn Station (PATH and/or Conrail or LIRR trains connecting to the seedier outlying Connecticut or Long Island areas.)

Except for choke points at 42nd and 10th, 7th and 42nd, 7th and 38th, and 7th and 34th, Terminal is sealed off from the rest of the city. Security posts keep a constant eye on the flow of street drek, and the guards will card anybody who looks even remotely suspicious. During some of the wage-slave shift changes, the wait to get through can be as long as half an hour.

Anybody with the money and status to avoid the place uses Grand Central Station (on the border of Neon City and Eastside) or any of the intermediary stations. The Terminal is for the rest of the huddled masses.

Terminal is also where you'll find most of the city's cheapest crash-houses and coffin hotels. The residents of these are a good 75 percent pushers, pimps, or black marketeers. No blue- or white-pass holders on these blocks, chummers. The passes around here are blood red (with some shiny black ones thrown in for spice.) Winter and Knight try to maintain some semblance of order in the zone, but it's a losing battle. You could almost set your watch by the nightly street brawls.

The Zone is nearly void of vehicles; the only ones permitted are delivery trucks during certain times of the day. Occasionally, a go-gang will barrel in through one of the choke points, raising a brief bit of hell, then scramming before the heavy security comes down. As a show of force, one of the enforcement agencies flies a combat chopper low overhead every hour or so.

### DOWNTOWN (Security Rating B-A)
NYPD Inc. and Knight-Errant

Downtown is pretty much what New York was a century ago, before the arrival of the multinational megacorps and the 300-story skyrakers. The zone starts at the old Empire State Building, the only edifice of more than 20 stories to survive the quake undamaged. The building is currently privately owned, but nobody knows by who. Most of the floors are leased out as office space, with the exception of the top 30 floors, which are either empty, quake-damaged, or used by the mysterious owner, depending on who you talk to. The only thing for certain is that those top floors are protected (according to my magician friends) by a powerful ward that no one has ever been known to penetrate. I've even heard that a couple of megacorps gave it a try with no success.

The skyscrapers and smaller buildings of Downtown are filled with a mix of businesses and residences, but not much industrial space because of the high rent.

Downtown does have a gang problem. Few are local, rolling in from other areas. On occasion, you'll spot the Ancients here, drifting over from the elven areas of Southside or The Pit. The Blood Monkeys cruise through, too, often clashing with the Ancients or a local street gang called The Wrathchildes.

### SOUTHSIDE AND STUYVESANT

|  | Security Rating |
|---|---|
| **Southside** | |
| NYPD Inc. and Winter Systems | B |
| **Stuyvesant** | |
| Knight-Errant and Winter Systems | AAA |

Southside is similar to Downtown, a mix of businesses and residences, but tending slightly toward the business side. The buildings tend to be lower, with few skyscrapers, and the region along the river contains most of Manhattan Island's port and cargo-handling facilities.

A heavy elven community exists in the northern area of Southside, very near Terminal. This section is a little more depressed than the rest of the area and usually only gets C-Rating enforcement.

The Ancients hold the most power in this area, but have lately been getting a serious challenge from an ork/troll gang calling themselves The Axemen.

Stuyvesant has neither gang problems nor any other kind, thanks to the area's level of security. You'd be hard-pressed to find any building over five stories in this neighborhood of residences of the rich and ultra-rich. Most, amazingly enough, are single-family.

### THE VILLAGE AND SOHO

|                                          | Security Rating |
| ---------------------------------------- | --------------- |
| **The Village**                          |                 |
| NYPD Inc. and Knight-Errant              | A               |
| **Soho**                                 |                 |
| NYPD Inc. and Winter Systems             | B               |

The Village has the name, and so it's gotta be wiz, right? Wrongo. No matter how cool they tell you the Village is, it's all PR. What it does have is plenty of *faux culture*, most of which would benefit from a good bath by a flamethrower.

Oh, sure, the area is full of art galleries, book-nooks, poetry spots, loft apartments at hideous prices, and more moody-looking, leather-clad children of the night than you can catch with a tac-nuke. Group-style is in round these parts, so expect to see a dozen Van Cliber-clad women at any of the nightly parties. Of course, since you can buy Van Cliber at the local boutique, do you really care?

Soho is where the people with a little more style—and sense—tend to lurk. Here's where you might actually hear people say real things in conversation and in their art. Many Soho residents are eccentric. Some are even dangerous, having crossed the knife edge beyond reality, be it from too much BTL, life in general, or occasionally magic-burn. There's a quiet power on these streets, and you'll find more than a few magical orders meeting behind the shuttered windows.

### LOWER EAST SIDE, "THE PIT" ( Security Rating Z, occasional E, rare AAA)

All/None

Compared to The Pit, Terminal is paradise. The enforcement agencies haven't yet given up on Terminal, but The Pit they leave to the animals. It's probably as close to true anarchy as you're going to find in NY, which is why I live here.

Streetlife is the only life there is, and you live and die by its codes. Dozens of street gangs fill the area, and their nightly clashes get higher local ratings than the Urban Brawl World Cup, or even *Shadowrun*, the white-hot trideo program about runners (which is, unintentionally, hysterically funny.) On these streets, you'll find the likes of the Ancients, Blood Monkeys, Axemen, Duelists, Merlyn's Pride, The Sisters Sinister, Night-Spawn, and the psychotic thrill-kill gang known as the Billyboys.

But alas, it's not true anarchy because some people are still calling the shots. Who are they? Why, you and I, chummers. You and I.

### FUCHI-TOWN, CITY CENTER, AND CHINATOWN

|                                           | Security Rating |
| ----------------------------------------- | --------------- |
| **Fuchi-Town**                            |                 |
| Fuchi Corporate Security                  | AAA             |
| **City Center**                           |                 |
| Knight-Errant and Winter Systems          | A               |
| **Chinatown**                             |                 |
| NYPD Inc. and Knight-Errant               | B-C             |

Fuchi-Town was built on the ruins of the old World Trade Center. In its place, Fuchi raised a triad of buildings, each 200 stories tall and as black as the heart of one of the Billyboys. Technically, the buildings rise 250 stories because all grow out of a wider, 50-story high, octagonal-shaped structure that acts as a base. Radiating outward are interconnected buildings that contain residences, shopping, and such for Fuchi employees.

Fuchi owns the entire area, which is under exclusive jurisdiction of Fuchi Corporate Security, who are contractually prevented from ever smiling.

City Center is where are gathered City Hall, the criminal courts, and various other government-like buildings. You'll also find UCAS government buildings and a foreign consulate or two, though any of real interest are probably either in Westside or Midtown.

Chinatown is still the same as its name. Most of the buildings retain much of their character, having survived the quake more or less intact or else been rebuilt by the locals, using time-honored construction techniques. To date, area residents have resisted the efforts of corporations to drive them or buy them out. Perhaps for that reason, Chinatown is insular, and the locals keep a close watch on unfamiliar faces. Youth gangs are common in the area, as is gang-related violence, which often sloshes over from The Pit.

### BATTERY CITY (Security Rating C-D)

NYPD Inc. and Winter Systems

Battery City isn't the nicest place in the world, but it could be worse. Formerly the Battery Park area, it now contains primarily large, multi-story housing tenements in varying states of decay and occupancy. Most families in the area are poor and lower-middle-class (not much difference these days) wage slaves.

Battery City is the southernmost tip of Manhattan Island, from which you can still look southwest across the bay at the Statue of Liberty (Or, if you are so inclined, at the Governors Island/Port Authority Complex. Jack up the optical magnifiers enough, and you'll spot the gleaming rows of combat choppers.) The area is still park, but unquestioningly the turf of the Battery Boys, a local street youth gang. The Boys control the streets of Battery City and some say the remains of the old Brooklyn-Battery Tunnel.

# ATTENTION SHADOWRUNNERS!

It's a big sprawl out there and no one can see it all. Look closely at one thing and you're turning your back on something else. That's just the way it is.

We need your help. NewsNet is looking for short news articles (50 words or less) telling us what is happening as a consequence of your runs. We don't want names, we don't want events. We want only the results. Be careful, chummer, these are still shadowruns.

These articles should *not* deal with any shadowruns described in published adventures. Follow the format found in the pages of the Seattle News-Intelligencer at the back of several Shadowrun™ books.

We will publish your articles with your name in the byline in exchange for any and all rights to future use of the material. Send your articles to:

FASA Corporation
P.O. Box 6930
Chicago, IL  60680
Attn: Newsnet

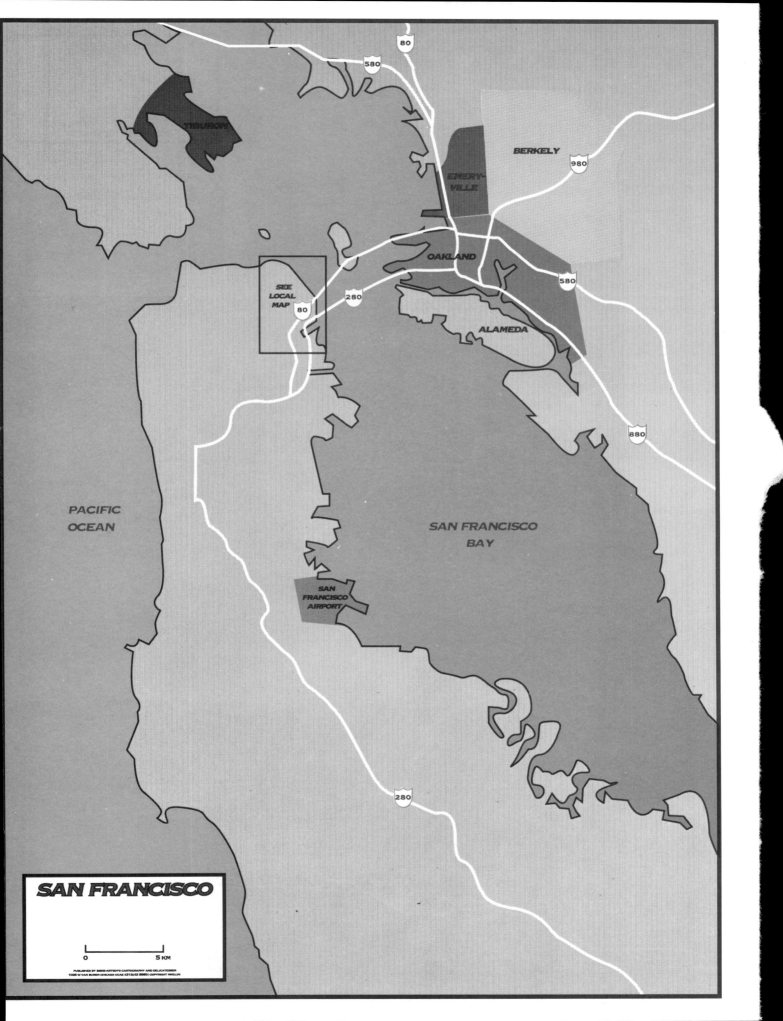

TIBURON

BERKELY

EMERY-
VILLE

OAKLAND

ALAMEDA

PACIFIC
OCEAN

SAN FRANCISCO
BAY

SEE
LOCAL
MAP

SAN
FRANCISCO
AIRPORT

**SAN FRANCISCO**

0      5 KM

PUBLISHED BY BONE-ARTBOYS CARTOGRAPHY AND DELICATESSEN
1025 W VAN BUREN CHICAGO UCAS (312)43 9990) COPYRIGHT NIKOLUN

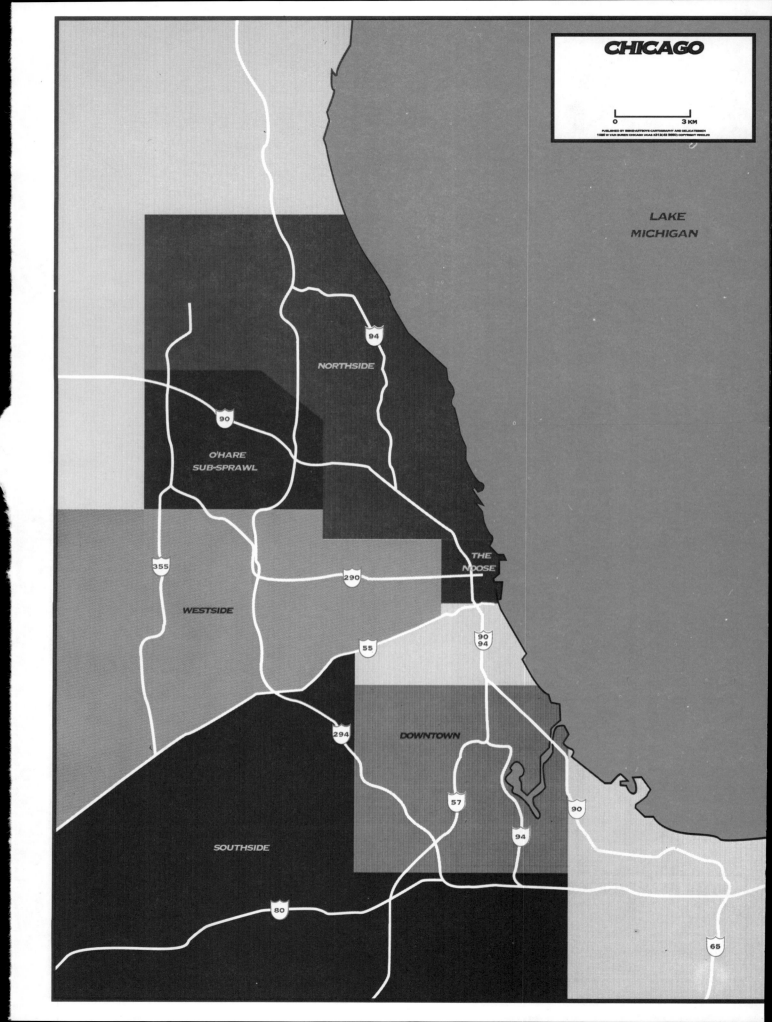

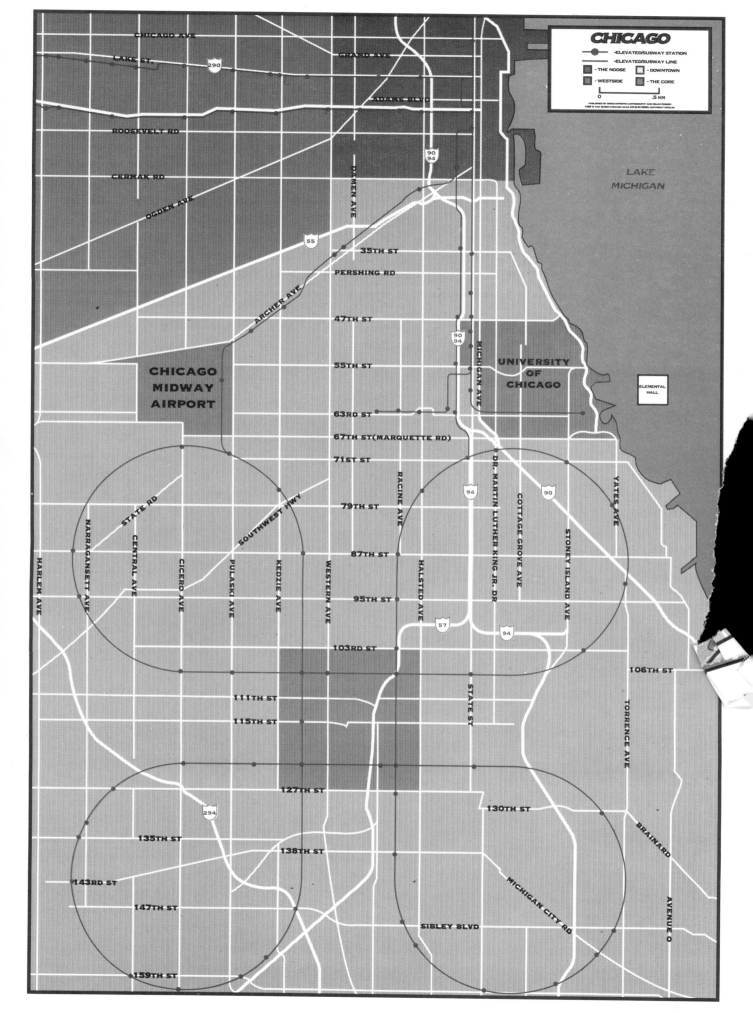

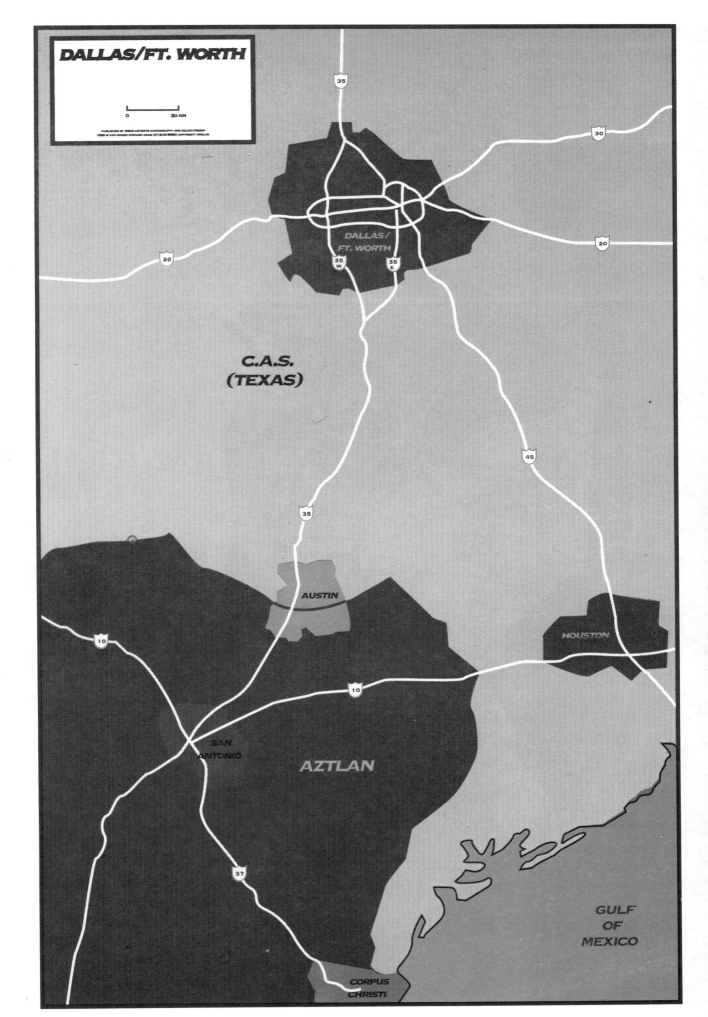

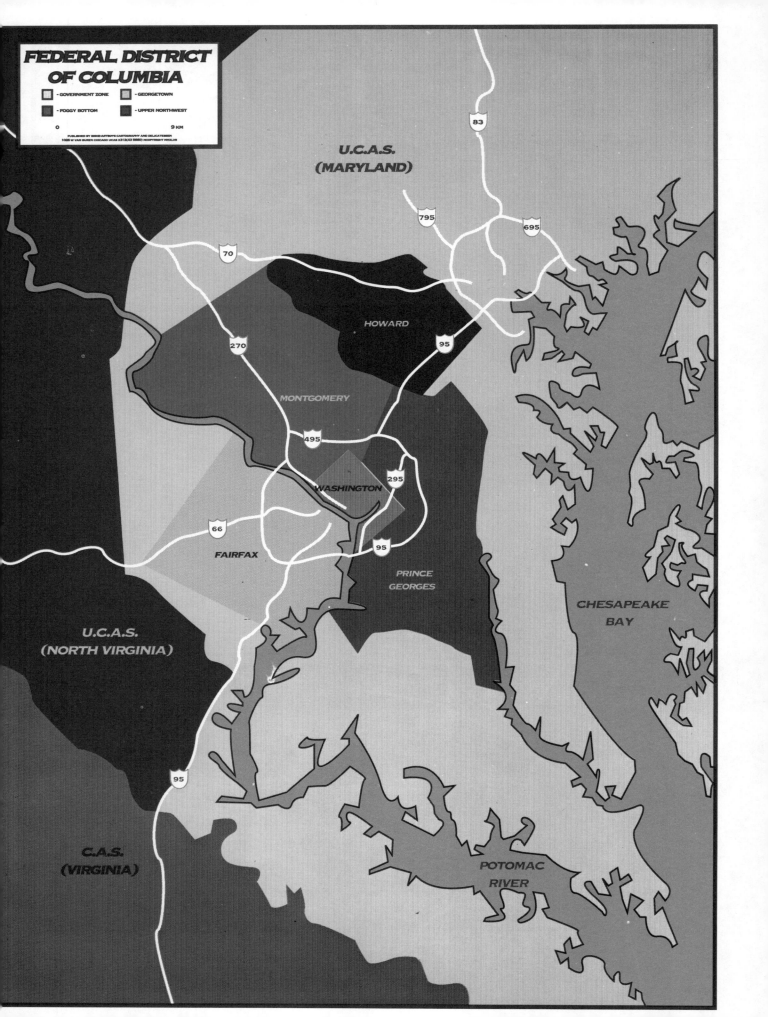

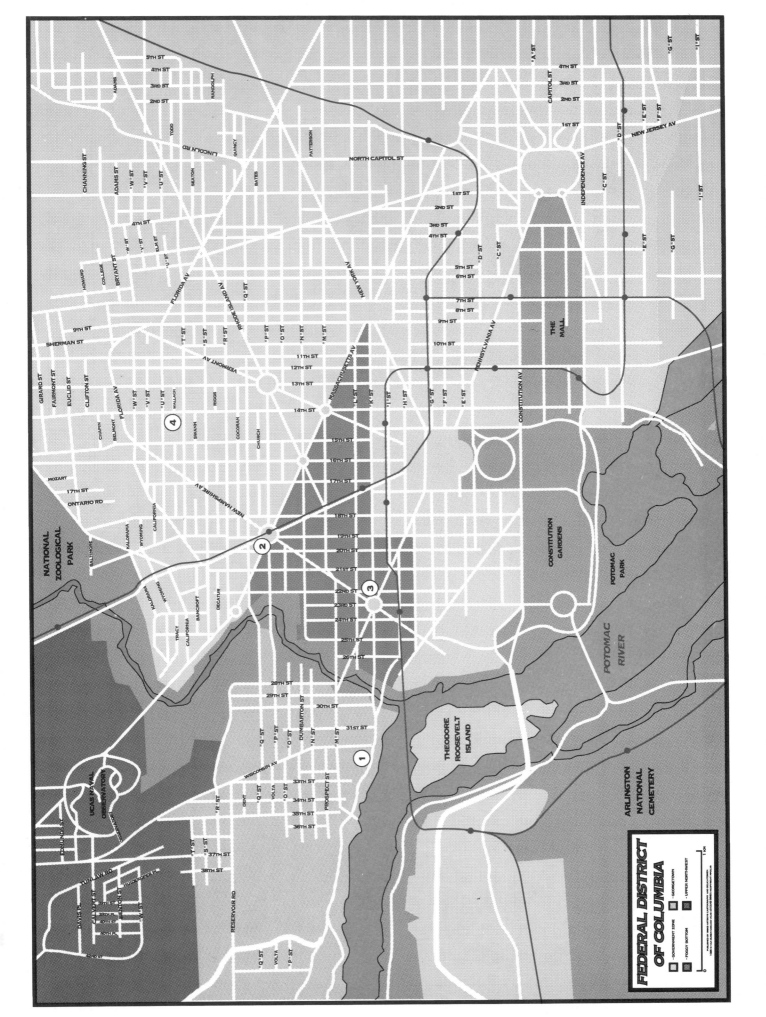

FEDERAL DISTRICT
OF COLUMBIA

NATIONAL ZOOLOGICAL PARK

U.S. NAVAL OBSERVATORY

THEODORE ROOSEVELT ISLAND

CONSTITUTION GARDENS

POTOMAC PARK

POTOMAC RIVER

ARLINGTON NATIONAL CEMETERY

THE MALL

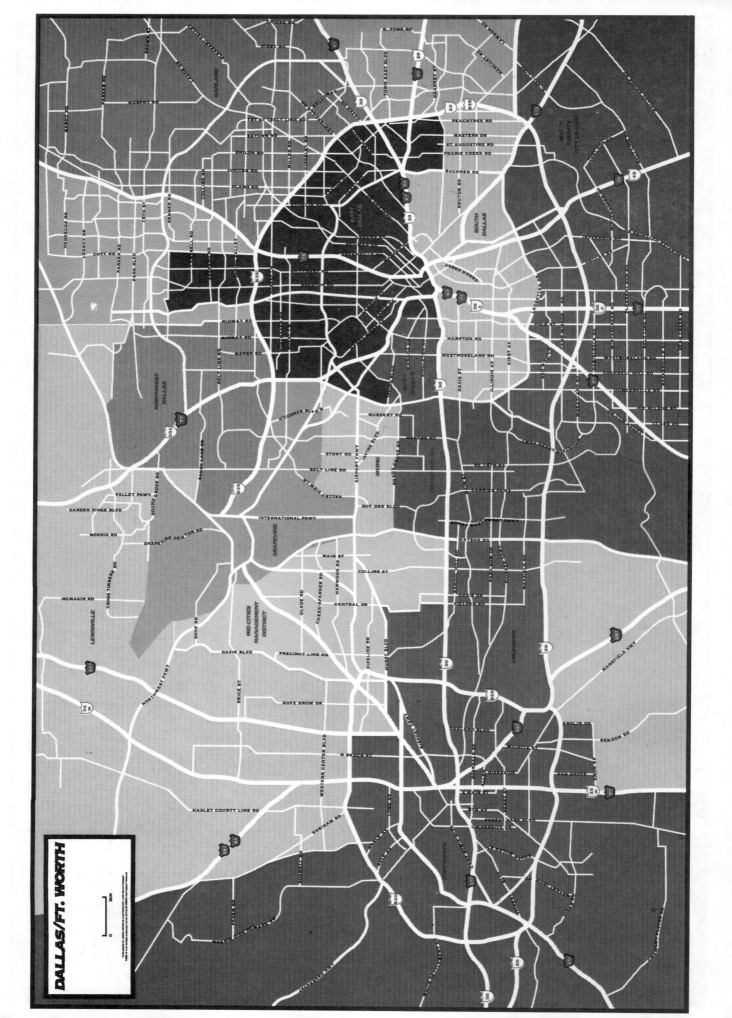

DALLAS/FT. WORTH

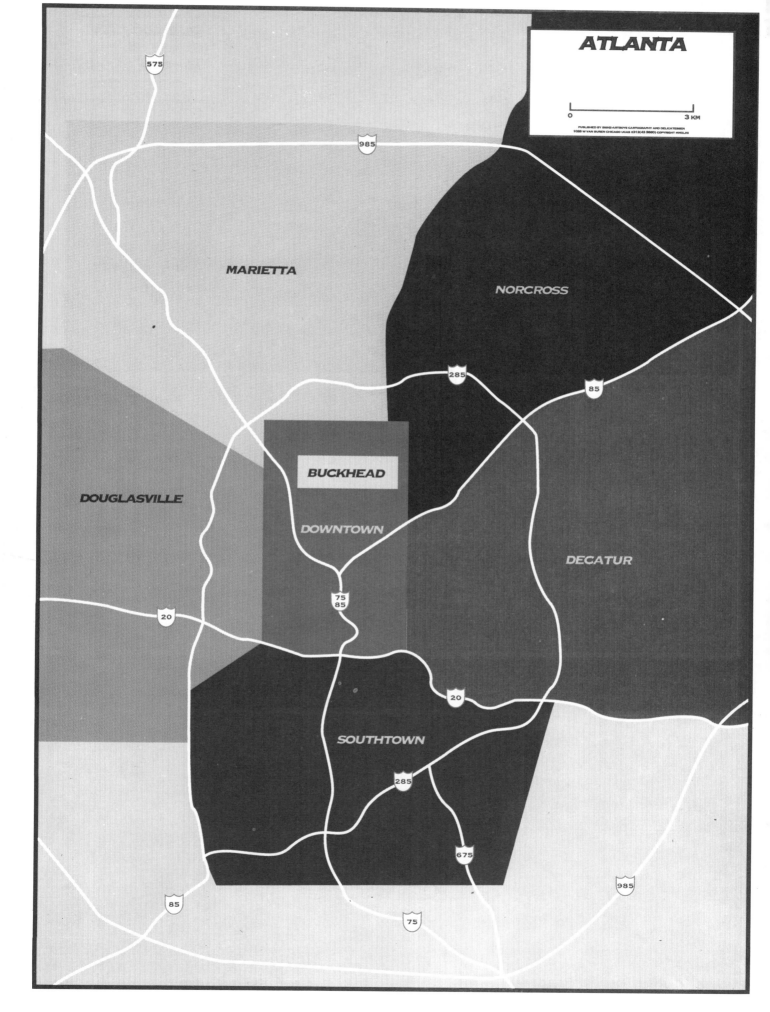

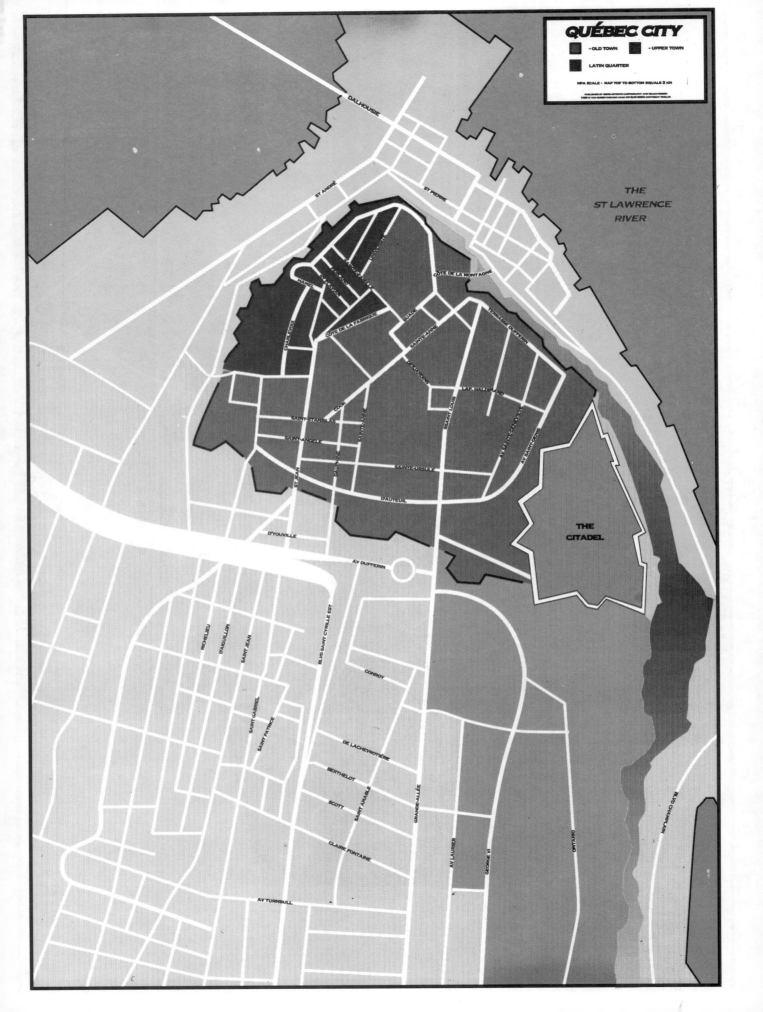

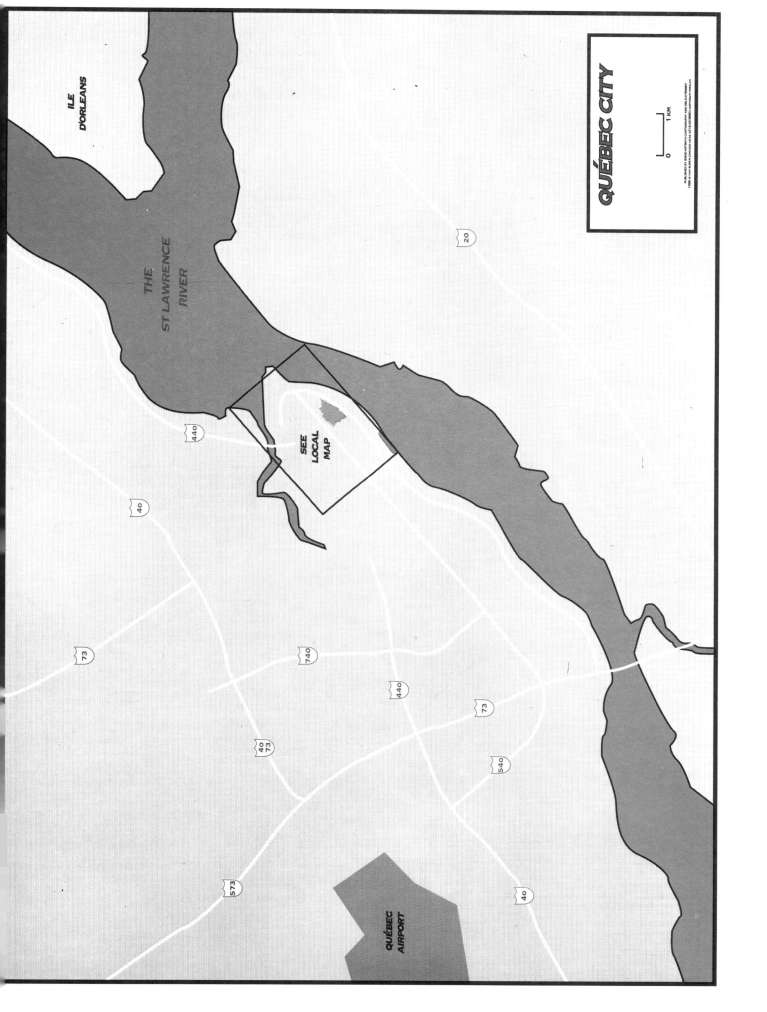

# QUÉBEC CITY

ILE D'ORLEANS

THE ST LAWRENCE RIVER

SEE LOCAL MAP

QUÉBEC AIRPORT

20

440

40

73

740

440

73

540

40 73

573

40

0 — 1 KM

PUBLISHED BY BØKE-ARTØN'S CARTOGRAPHY AND DELKATIESEN.
1038 W VAN BUREN CHICAGO UDAS ILS (342 5950) COPYRIGHT PHKLIN

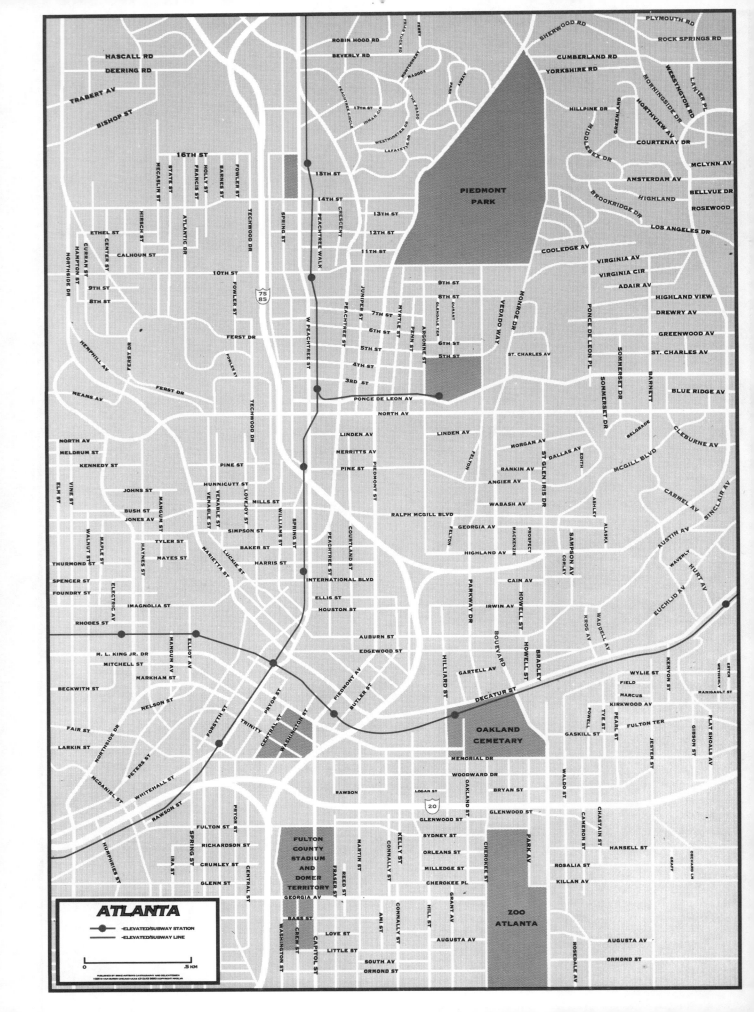

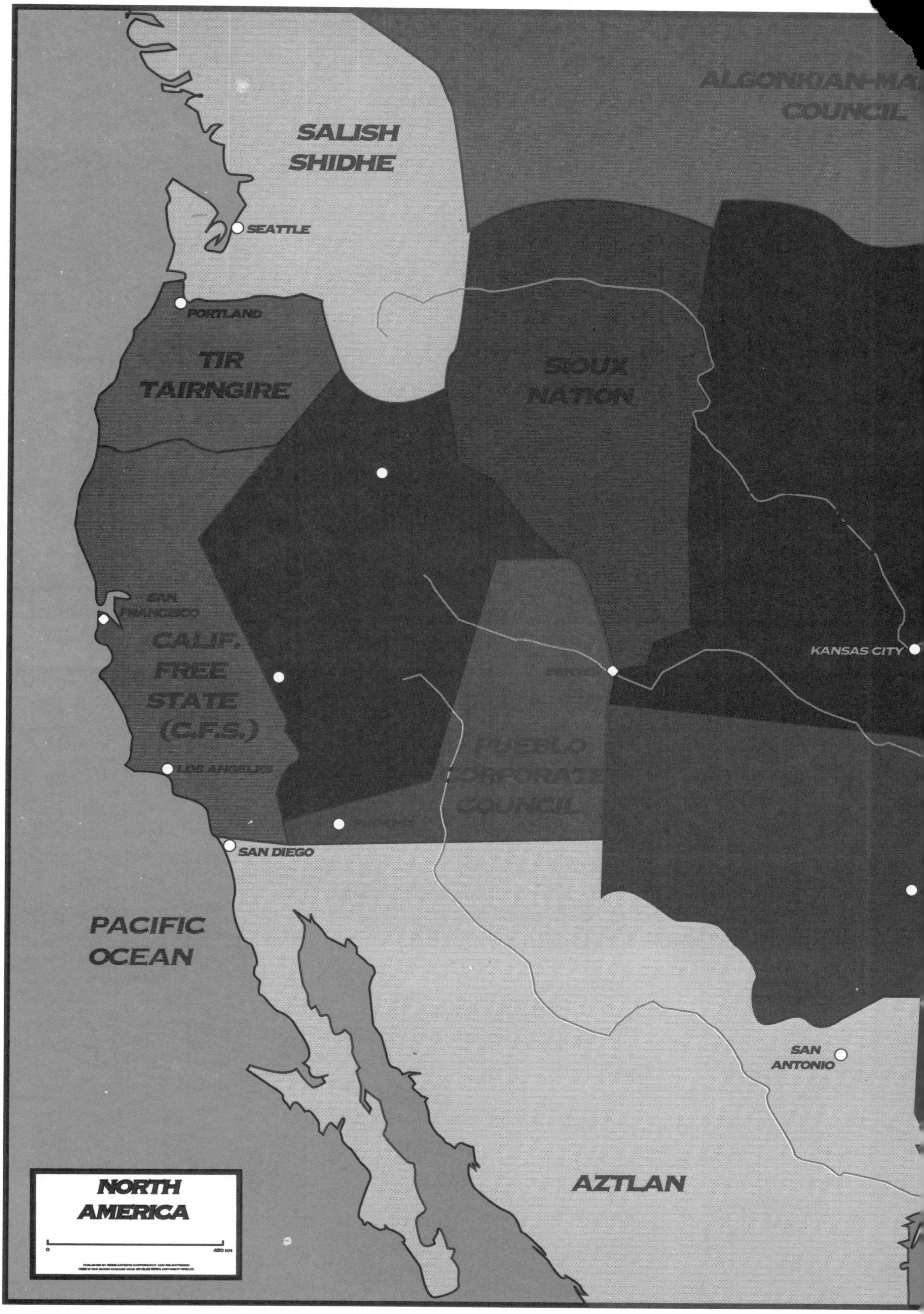

# SALISH SHIDHE

● SEATTLE

● PORTLAND

## TIR TAIRNGIRE

### ALGONKIAN-MA
### COUNCIL

## SIOUX NATION

SAN
FRANCISCO

## CALIF.
## FREE
## STATE
## (C.F.S.)

● LOS ANGELES

● SAN DIEGO

DENVER

KANSAS CITY ●

## PUEBLO
## CORPORATE
## COUNCIL

## PACIFIC
## OCEAN

SAN ○
ANTONIO

## AZTLAN

**NORTH AMERICA**

0                                      450 KM

PUBLISHED BY SEREB-ASTARA CARTOGRAPHY AND DELINEATIONS
1488 W VAN BUREN CHICAGO UCAS XE13-49 55501 COPYRIGHT PRESLER

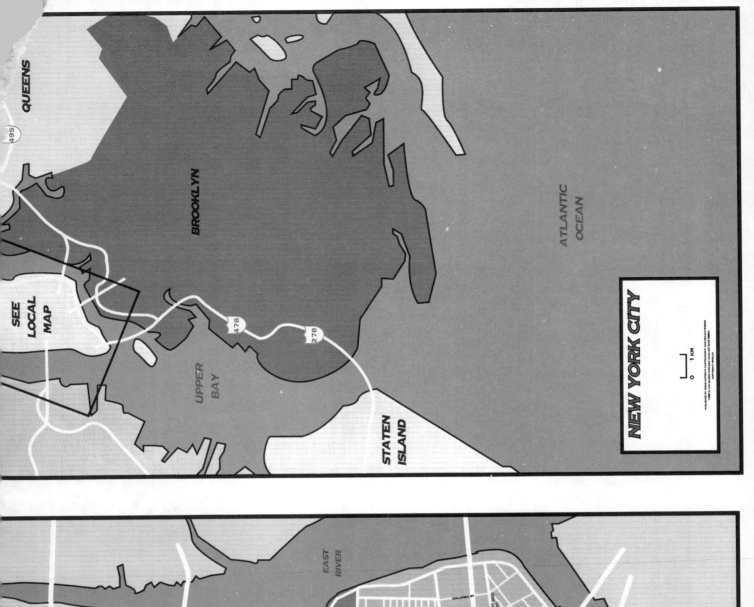

QUEENS

495

BROOKLYN

SEE
LOCAL
MAP

UPPER
BAY

478

278

STATEN
ISLAND

ATLANTIC
OCEAN

## NEW YORK CITY

0    1 KM

PUBLISHED BY RAND ARTISTS CARTOGRAPHY AND DELICATESSEN
1098 N VAN BUREN CHICAGO DEAR 537-3463 58450
COPYRIGHT PABLUN

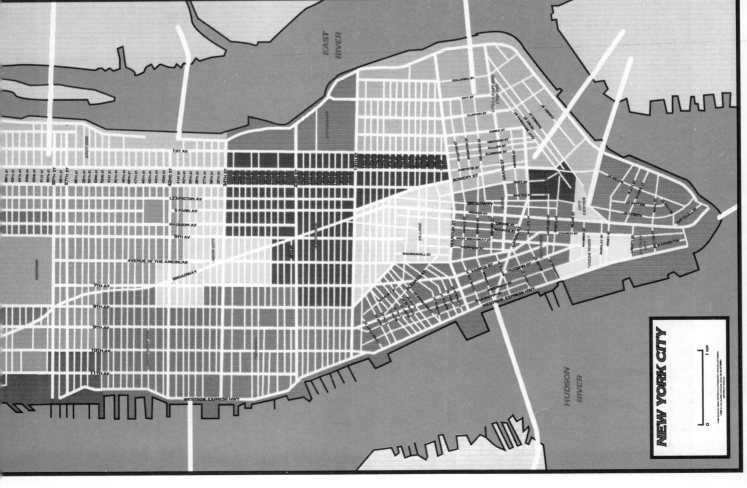

EAST
RIVER

COLUMBIA ST

PITT ST

CLINTON ST

STUYVESANT

BOWERY ST

1ST AV

LEXINGTON AV

S PARK AV

MADISON AV

5TH AV

AVENUE OF THE AMERICAS

BROADWAY

7TH AV

8TH AV

9TH AV

10TH AV

11TH AV

MACDOUGALL ST

CITY
CENTER

BROADWAY

MERCER ST

WEST BROADWAY ST

THOMPSON ST

VARICK ST

HUDSON ST

CHURCH ST

WESTSIDE EXPRESS HWY

WESTSIDE EXPRESS HWY

HUDSON
RIVER

## NEW YORK CITY

0    1 KM

PUBLISHED BY RAND ARTISTS CARTOGRAPHY AND DELICATESSEN
1098 N VAN BUREN CHICAGO DEAR 537-3463 58450
COPYRIGHT PABLUN

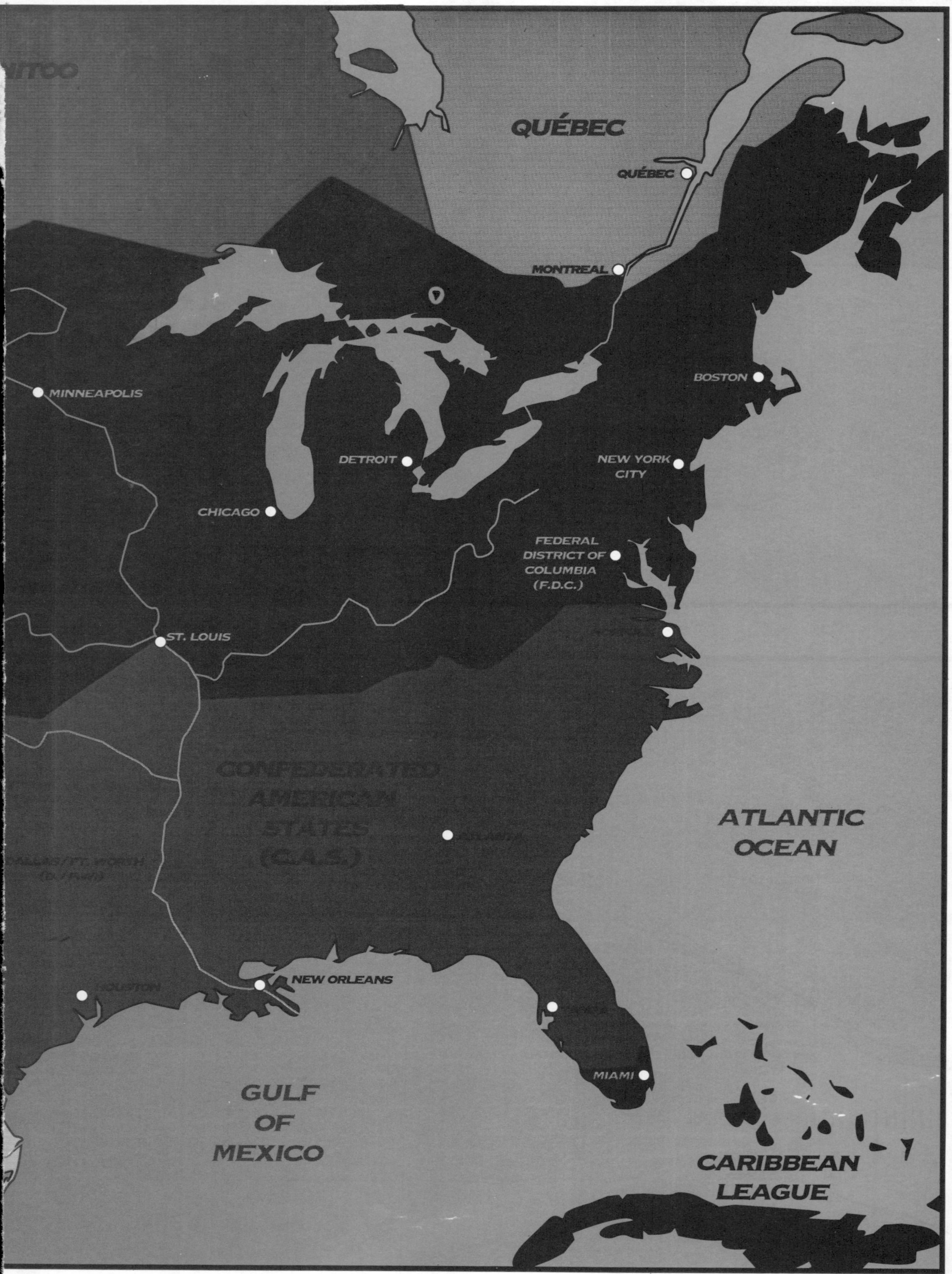

QUÉBEC
QUÉBEC
MONTREAL
BOSTON
MINNEAPOLIS
DETROIT
NEW YORK CITY
CHICAGO
FEDERAL DISTRICT OF COLUMBIA (F.D.C.)
ST. LOUIS
CONFEDERATED AMERICAN STATES (C.A.S.)
ATLANTIC OCEAN
NEW ORLEANS
MIAMI
GULF OF MEXICO
CARIBBEAN LEAGUE